MSP430 Microcontroller Essentials

Architecture, Programming and Applications

Miroslav Cina

elektor
design > share > sell

an Elektor Publication

This is an Elektor Publication. Elektor is the media brand of
Elektor International Media B.V.
78 York Street
London W1H 1DP, UK
Phone: (+44) (0)20 7692 8344

First published in the United Kingdom 2022

British Library Cataloguing in Publication Data
Catalogue record for this book is available from the British Library

978-3-89576-492-9

978-3-89576-493-6 (E-book)

Prepress production: DMC ¦ dave@daverid.com
Printed in the Netherlands by Ipskamp

Table of Contents

Chapter 1 • Introduction

In this book, I would like to talk about a very interesting family of microcontrollers from a major semiconductor manufacturer - Texas Instruments. The microcontroller family is the MSP430.

We will aquire some information on the MSP430 family in this chapter and get to know the architecture of the microcontrollers.

In later examples, we will work with the MSP430G2553 microcontroller and will see some examples with the smaller MSP430F2001 and MSP430F2012.

I can already say that we will not dig deep inside the hardware of microcontrollers. We will use the C-language to walk through our exercises and will not go down to the assembler level. The kind-of advantage of higher-level languages is, that usually, besides the functionality and communication possibilities, we only need to know the basics of the microcontroller itself, and do not need to discover the "internal parts", e.g. the definition of register sets, etc.

Let's have a short look at the Embedded Processing Portfolio from Texas Instruments. More or less, the variety of different microcontrollers is described in the following picture:

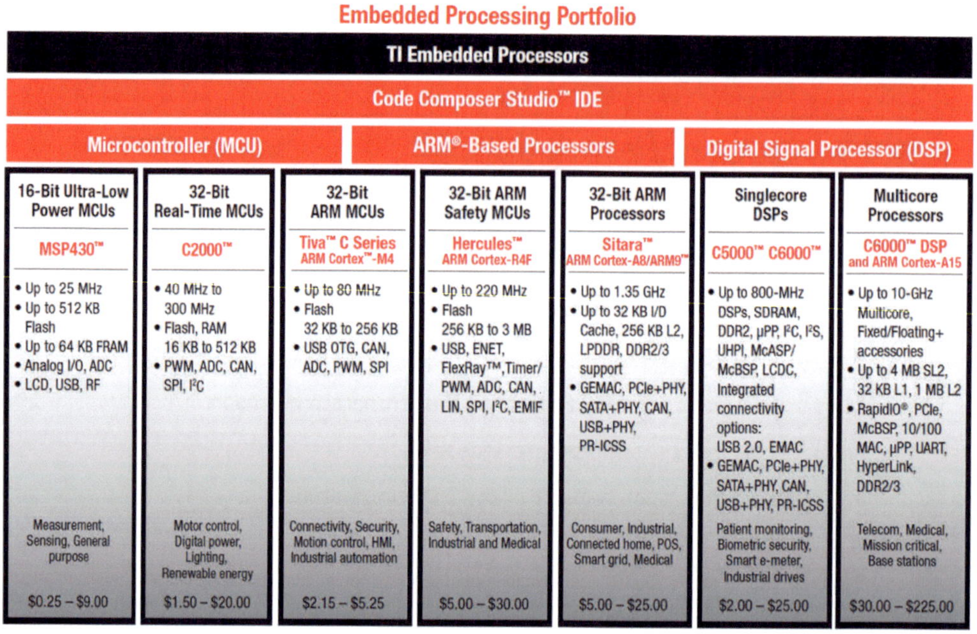

The portfolio of Texas Instruments microcontrollers and processors is quite wide. Even these are not very widely available to the amateur community. At least not so widespread as PIC and AVR microcontrollers from Microchip (and formerly Atmel).

In this book we will stay to the left of the image: talking about and working with 16-bit ultra-low-power MCUs - microcontroller family MSP430.

1.1 • MSP430

MSP430 microcontrollers are 16-bit RISC-based processors designed for ultra-low power applications. The microcontrollers contain a set of different peripherals. From "simple" GPIO (General Purpose Input Output Ports), through ADC modules and communication modules to for example an LCD-driver module.

The MSP430 offers a couple of multiple low-power modes inclusive of a standby mode where power consumptions drop below 500nA. But even in this mode, a lot of different functionalities are still available, e.g. updating an LCD, taking ADC samples, etc.

What I especially like about these microcontrollers is, that they are still produced in amateur-friendly packages - P-DIP. And all the microcontrollers we will use will be either P-DIP14 or P-DIP20. Just to make sure it is clear, what I'm talking about: P-DIP is the abbreviation of "Plastic Dual In-line Package", where the distance between pins is 2.54mm.

Here we can see the dimensions of the P-DIP14 package:

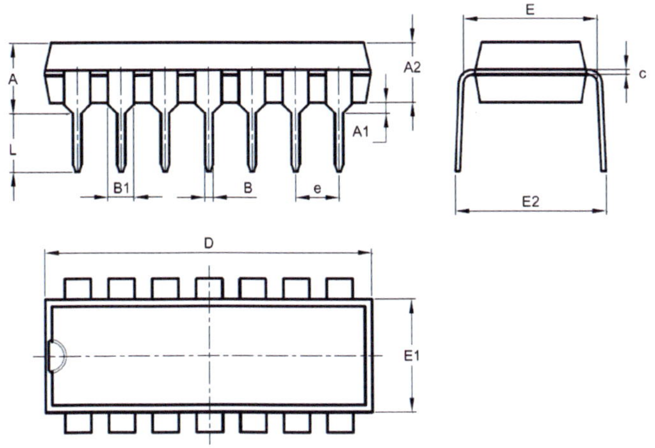

PDIP-14		
Dim	Min	Max
A	3.710	4.310
A1	0.510	-
A2	3.200	3.600
B	0.380	0.570
B1	1.524 (BSC)	
c	0.204	0.360
D	18.800	19.200
E	6.200	6.600
E1	7.320	7.920
E2	8.400	9.000
e	2.540 (BSC)	
L	3.000	3.600
All Dimensions in mm		

1.1.1 • Family Overview

Currently (Spring 2021) there are 572 members of the MSP430-family available. What I especially like is, that some of them (exactly 46) are available in "prototyping-friendly" packages: DIP14 (15 of them) or DIP20 (31). These will be the focus of the book. We will see how easy it is to undertake the first steps and realise our first circuits.

Let's have first a short look at the part numbers of the MCU from TI. We will carry out a short depiction based on one of the microcontrollers we are going to use: the MSP430F2012IN. I do not want to explain all the parts, just some of them, which are of interest.

1.1.2 • Part Numbers

The first part is called "Processor Family" - in our example (MSP430F2012IN) it is MSP = Mixed Signal Processor.

The next part (MSP430F2012IN) is 430 - what is the "MCU Platform" - 430 is the code for Texas Instruments Low Power Microcontroller Platform.

The next letter (MSP430F2012IN) defines the type of the program memory used: G = Flash memory (and additionally stays for "value line microcontroller); F = Flash memory, FR = FRAM, C= ROM, L = no nonvolatile memory, etc.

Then we will always see the first number (**MSP**430F2012IN), which defines "the series" - actually the maximum clock frequency and some additional information of the MCU: 1 = up to 8 MHz, 2 = up to 16 MHz, 3 = legacy OTP, 4 = up to 16 MHz with LCD driver, etc.

The next three digits (MSP**430**F2012IN) describe the "feature set".

The next letter (MSP430F**2012**IN) says something about the temperature range: S = 0°C to 50°C, C = 0°C to 70°C, I = -40°C to 85°C and finally T = -40°C to +105°C.

The last letter in our example part defines the package (MSP430F2012**IN**); it can be more letters or a combination of letters and numbers; where N = P-DIP package.

In the examples, we will use three of the family members: we will mainly work with the biggest of the smallest: the MSP430G2553, but we will see a simple example with the smallest of smallest: the MSP430F2001, and additionally the MSP430F2012.

1.1.3 • Flash, EEPROM, RAM, FRAM, or even ROM?

I would like to touch on this kind of basic topic at the beginning - just to make sure it is clear what the differences between these kinds of memories are - as sometimes we will touch on them either in descriptions or exercises. I know - it is nothing new and nothing specific for MSP430-microcontrollers, I guess it is just important.

I'll not go to the depth on the different technologies, - I'll just try to make clear what is what.

All of the mentioned memories - except for RAM are nonvolatile memories. This means the data is still in memory even if the power supply is switched off.

We can now have a look at the different types of memories.

1.1.3.1 • ROM

ROM stays for Read-Only Memory. These kinds of memories are used very stable pieces of software or data, which shall never be changed. These type of chips are manufactured directly with content. It is not possible to save anything to the chips. Once the chip leaves production, it is already with content. Therefore it is not possible to make content on this kind of chip for hobby electro-fanatics.

1.1.3.2 • RAM

With RAM we describe fast internal/external memory for data storage during the firmware execution. Data is stored, which is important for the program execution. After power off, the data is gone. After power-up, the content of the RAM is usually undefined. RAM stands for "Random Access Memory", which has historically grown and is quite market driven. Why market driven? Because the description "random access memory" makes clear the difference, for example, in tapes, where we can access data only sequentially - to read exactly what is at the moment available or we need to rewind the tape to another place... etc. Random Access in opposite means - by providing an address, we can get any data in the whole addressable space within the same time. It doesn't matter if we want to read from address 0000h or 1F89h or FE47h - we just provide the address and can access the data. But this is true for ROM memory, EPROM, and any other type of memory using addressing of the cells in the chip. Therefore there was a very short time where this type of memory was described as RWM = Read / Write Memory. As the read and write operations, they are handled in the same way, and the execution time of the read and write operation is also the same. For the fastest chips, only around 50ns. But "RWM" does not sound as nice as RAM. Just try to say RWM... and try to say RAM. Therefore the decision was to use the abbreviation RAM - because it sounds good, even though the technical background doesn't fit...

In general, we differentiate between two different types of RAM: SRAM and DRAM. SRAM means Static RAM, and DRAM is dynamic RAM. DRAM is much cheaper and easier to manufacture than SRAM - we can roughly say, that for 1-bit of SRAM storage we need ~5 transistors, and for 1-bit of DRAM only 1 transistor and 1 capacitor... but the DRAM needs to be refreshed periodically, as the data is stored on the capacitor. If the DRAM is not refreshed, the content will get lost after a few milliseconds.

Within microcontrollers, SRAM is always used. Data can be stored on the SRAM and later obtained without the need for any kind of refreshing.

Data from SRAM / DRAM is lost once a power supply is interrupted.

1.1.3.3 • PROM and EPROM

Once upon a time, there was EPROM memory. These were very nice chips in CerDIP (Ceramic DIP) packages with a small clean window.

At that time there were PROM memories in place as well. Without a window and usually in typical P-DIP, meaning plastic DIP package.

But what is it? PROM means Programmable Read-Only Memory. Today we will call it OTP; OTP = One Time Programmable. This kind of memory is empty when it is new and typically contains all address places to the value FFh (if we are talking about 8-bit wide memory). It is possible to change the value of memory cells from only 1 to 0 (never back). This change is typically completed by applying a special programming procedure with programming voltage - usually +12V to the chip. This change is not reversible. It means in practice, it is possible to write the information to the PROM (or OTP) memory exactly once. It is not possible to erase the memory later and it is not possible to rewrite the data anymore.

The chips with a window can be erased. Therefore they are called EPROM - Erasable Programmable Read-Only Memory. With this memory, it is possible to program electrically - very similar to PROM types of chips, but it is possible to erase the content later and program the chip again. Nevertheless, it is not possible to erase the chip electrically - this is done using ultraviolet light which is the reason, for the windows on the chip. Of course - it is nice to see the structure of the silicon stuff inside, but the reason for the window is the need to apply ultraviolet light to the chip if we want to erase programmed content. UV light has to be applied for a couple of minutes to erase the chip.

Today this kind of chip is not frequently used as working with them is cumbersome. Also, production is quite expensive. A chip with a window is a luxury today.

Read-access to this kind of chip is very fast. If we are talking about parallel memories (e.g. 8-bit memory), the access time to get the required byte is around 50ns - 120ns (depending on the type of chip).

Write access is of course very slow, as programming is a complex procedure. But this is not the important point, as the chips were typically programmed only (even EPROM) once.

1.1.3.4 • EEPROM

EEPROM is more-less EPROM, which can be erased electronically - no UV-light needed. No window in the package of the chip. EEPROM means Electrically Erasable Programmable Read-Only Memory. What I like about EEPROM is, that the memory does not need to be erased before reprogramming. We can just rewrite already used cells. Just write, and write and write... nice. But - there are two important points to be considered - one is performance. Writing to EEPROM is very slow to compare to read. We need to calculate in milliseconds instead of nanoseconds. Another important point is endurance. Depending on the manufacturer and the type of the EEPROM, it is possible to rewrite the same cell from roughly 10.000 times up to 1.000.000 times. The latter figure includes the most durable chips.

At the moment we can find a lot of parallel and serial EEPROM memories. Parallel ones are typically used to store code to be executed by a microcontroller, the serial to store data.

1.1.3.5 • Flash

Flash is in some ways similar to EEPROM memory, but there are some important differences. Flash allows quite fast write operations to compared to EEPROM - usually 1000 times faster. It means instead of milliseconds we are talking about microseconds regarding writes. The Flash memories typically have more on-chip capacity compared to EEPROM. This is the main advantage when compared to EEPROM. There is a disadvantage as well - flash memory can be written, but not re-written. This is not possible. If we want to rewrite already used cells of flash - we need to erase them before, which means we can write to flash several times on the same position always different information, but we need to erase the position before each new write. But, even worse, typically the whole capacity of flash is divided into "sectors" - and it is not possible to erase a specific cell only (e.g. a specific byte) - always the whole sector needs to be erased, meaning if we have a sector of 128 bytes, and we want to re-write a single byte within the sector, we need to erase the whole 128 bytes first, and then write them back again with the changed byte we wanted to adjust.

Flash memory is very often used in microcontrollers as program memory.

1.1.3.6 • FRAM

We can say, that FRAM (= ferroelectric random access memory) combines the advantages of SRAM and EEPROM. FRAM is a nonvolatile memory. Write performance is nearly the same as read operation and the endurance is very high - 10^{15} write cycles endurance. To reach 10^{15} writes is nearly impossible, meaning endurance from a practical point of view is boundaryless.

Newer MSP430 microcontrollers from Texas Instruments use FRAM as a memory for firmware and customer data (instead of flash memory). These microcontrollers are easily recognisable - the part number starts always with MSP430FR.

1.1.4 • MSP430x2xx architecture

I would like to show a generic architecture picture describing the architectural building blocks of all microcontrollers we will touch upon here. Independent of fact if we are working with "F" (e.g. MSP430F2012) or "G" (e.g. MSP430G2553) devices, the basic architecture is always the same and can be described with the following picture of the MSP430x2xx architecture:

MSP430x2xx architecture:

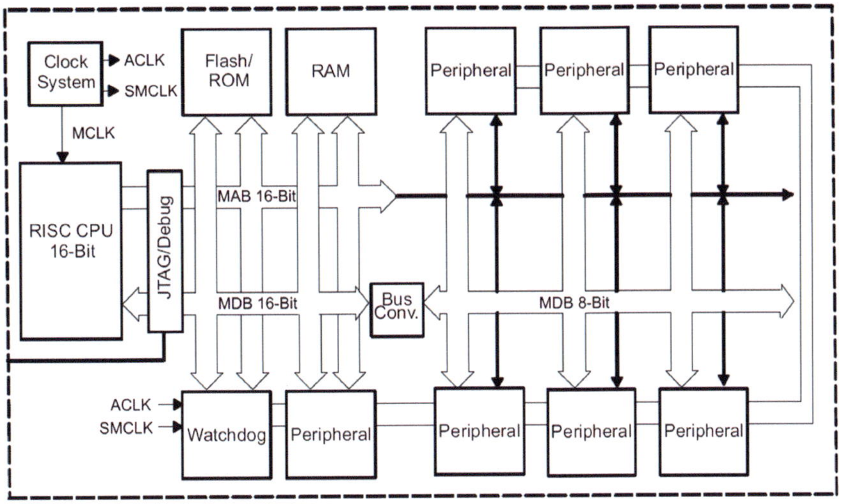

As we can see, the heart of all the microcontrollers is a 16-bit RISC CPU. Besides that, we can see the flash memory (to store the firmware), RAM for usage by the firmware, a clock system, Debugging and Watch-Dog system, and a couple of peripherals. The size of the memories and available peripherals depends on the type of the microcontroller.

Some of the MSP430 microcontrollers contain ROM memory with built-in code. This could be communication routines, LCD drivers, etc. MSP430-family members provide a JTAG/ Debug component allowing debugging of the code.

We will touch upon a couple of peripherals during our experiments - we will see the first list soon in the overview about MSP430G2553.

Let's mention now, that all peripherals are available through the memory addressing space - on addresses 0000h to 01FFh. Using these address places, it is possible to read and write special peripheral registers, etc.

1.1.5 • POR vs. PUC

I was struggling with the system reset and initialisation - POR and PUC; especially with the understanding of the difference between these two functionalities - POR vs PUC.

First of all: POR = Power-on Reset and PUC = Power-up Clear. Well, at least for me not completely self-explanatory. Especially, if the two terms are "coexist".

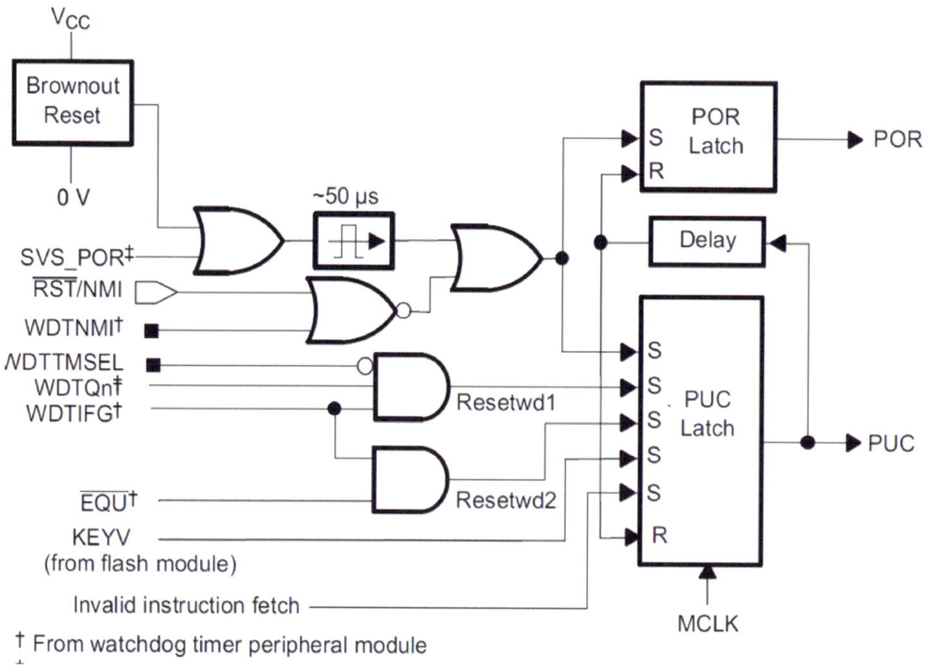

Just to mention - some of the MSP430-family members include an SVS-module (SVS = Supply Voltage Supervisor). This module can trigger a POR in case of instability of the power supply.

But just come back to POR vs. PUC. Let's make it very short: POR is more than PUC. **POR** is generated in only three different situations:

- powering up the device
- activation of RESET signal (low signal on RST pin)
- SVS initiates a system reset if the SVS module is incorporated and PORON-bit of configuration of the device allowed this trigger

PUC is always triggered when POR has been triggered (but not the other way around). PUC is triggered by the following conditions:

- POR has been triggered (as just mentioned)
- Watchdog timer expiration when working in watchdog mode only
- Watchdog timer security key violation
- Flash memory security key violation
- A CPU instruction fetch from the peripheral address range 0000h to 01FFh

1.1.6 • MSP430G2553

Let's take a short look at the "strongest-one". In the following picture we can see the "building blocks" - the architecture of the MSP430G2553 microcontroller:

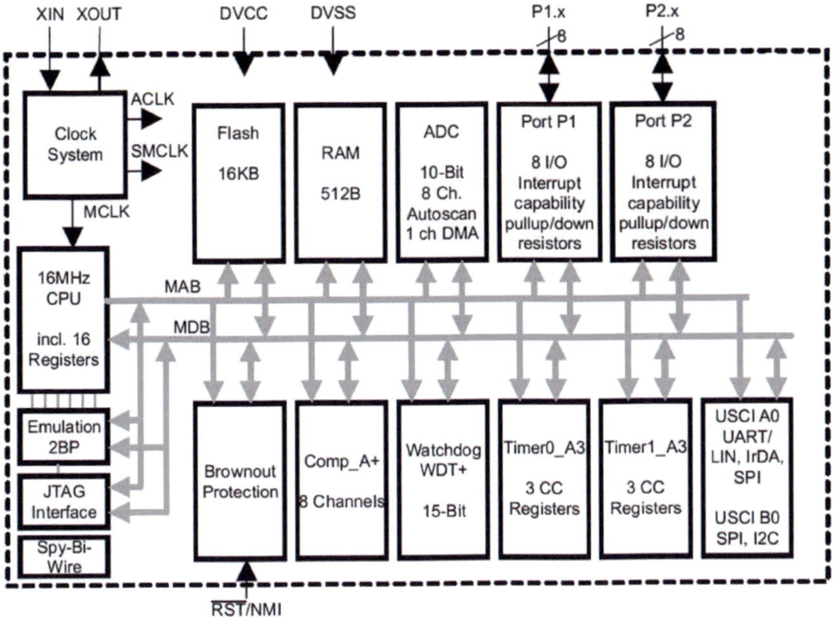

The structure of the picture is of course the same as the general architecture of the MSP430-family we saw earlier. But here we can see, what is really in the MSP430G2553 chip inside. We see the following peripherals:

Periphery	Short characteristic
Port P1	General Purpose Input / Output ports. P1 is an 8-bit port
Port P2	General Purpose Input / Output ports. P2 is an 8-bit port
ADC	Analog to Digital Converter - 10-bit 8 channel ADC
Comparator	Comparator_A+ module - 8 channel
Timer 0 / 1	2 x 16-bit timer
USCI	Universal Serial Communication Interface allowing UART, SPI, and I²C communication and providing an IrDA encoder and decoder
Watchdog	Watchdog Timer

Every member of our MSP430-Family has a 64kB addressable memory space. Within this memory space, we will find registers, SRAM, Flash, peripherals - actually everything we can use.

The memory map of the MSP430G2553 is defined like this:

Type of memory	Memory size	Address from	Address to
Special Function Registers (SFR, 8-bit)	16 B	0000h	000Fh
8-bits Peripheries	240 B	0010h	00FFh
16-bit Peripheries	256 B	0100h	01FFh
SRAM	512 B	0200h	03FFh
Unused address space		0400h	0FFFh
Information memory / flash	256 B	1000h	10FFh
Unused address space		1100h	0BFFh
Code memory / flash	16 kB	C000h	FFBFh
Interrupt Vectors / flash		FFC0h	FFFFh

From the table, we can find out which addresses within the whole memory space we can find what. Just to make it clear - we will not need this information when working with Energia or CCS environments in C-language.

Now let's take a short look at the different peripherals.

1.1.6.1 • Digital Ports

Family members of the MSP430 provide up to 8 digital I/O ports (each port with 8 bits). Our focus members provide maximal 2 ports - exactly as the MSP430G2553. We have P1 and P2 available - always with 8 bits - P1.0, P1.1, ... P1.7 and P2.0, P2.1, ... P2.7.

Every I/O can be configured as digital input, digital output, or configured for usage with a periphery (e.g. as an analog input for ADC module). If the port is used as digital input, a pull-up or pull-down resistor can always be activated. Change of P1 or P2 can trigger an interrupt, nevertheless, we will not touch the interrupt functionalities in the context of our beginners-book.

All digital ports have an input and output data register.

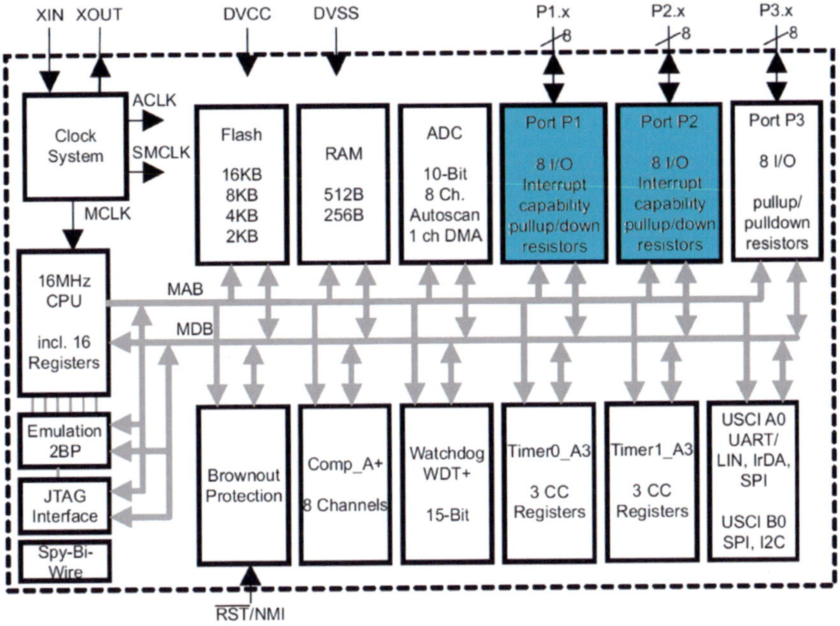

I guess we can use this chapter to show the pin-connections of the MSP430G2553 microcontroller in the P-DIP20 package. The pins are connected as we can see here:

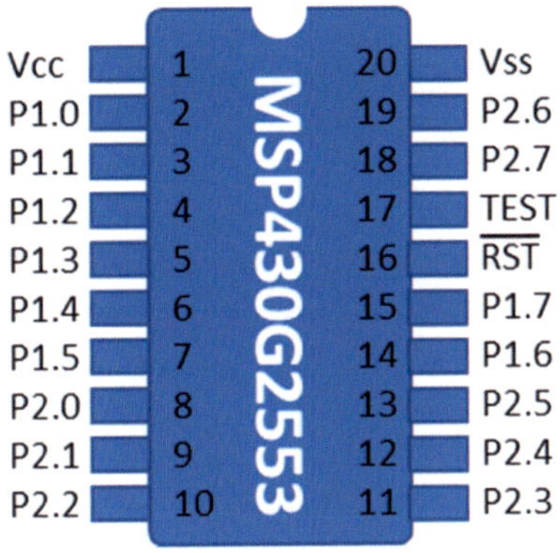

Pin	Description	Usage
1	V_{cc}	Positive power supply: 1,8V - 3,6V
2	P1.0	Digital I/O P1.0 or A0 or CA0 (analog input A0 for ADC10 module / comparator A input CA0)
3	P1.1	Digital I/O P1.1 or A1 or CA1 (analog input A1 for ADC10 module / comparator A input CA1)
4	P1.2	Digital I/O P1.2 or A2 or CA2 (analog input A2 for ADC10 module / comparator A input CA2)

5	P1.3	Digital I/O P1.3 or A3 or CA3 (analog input A3 for ADC10 module / comparator A input CA3)
6	P1.4	Digital I/O P1.4 or A4 or CA4 (analog input A4 for ADC10 module / comparator A input CA4)
7	P1.5	Digital I/O P1.5 or A5 or CA5 (analog input A5 for ADC10 module / comparator A input CA5)
8	P2.0	Digital I/O P2.0
9	P2.1	Digital I/O P2.1
10	P2.2	Digital I/O P2.2
11	P2.3	Digital I/O P2.3
12	P2.4	Digital I/O P2.4
13	P2.5	Digital I/O P2.5
14	P1.6	Digital I/O P1.6 or A4 or CA6 (analog input A6 for ADC10 module / comparator A input CA6)
15	P1.7	Digital I/O P1.7 or A4 or CA7 (analog input A7 for ADC10 module / comparator A input CA7)
16	RST	Reset Input - active in 0; when this pin is put to zero, the POR situation is triggered. Shall be put on V_{cc} for normal operation.
17	TEST	Activation of Test mode for JTAG. We will not use this functionality.
18	P2.7	Digital I/O P2.7
19	P2.6	Digital I/O P2.6
20	V_{ss}	Power supply: ground

Just to mention, the pins can be used in other (not mentioned) configurations.

1.1.6.2 • ADC

The analog to digital converter module integrated within the MSP430G2553 chip has a 10-bit resolution. 8 different sources can be used as an input for conversion. The maximum conversion rate is 200-kbps (200.000 samples per second).

8 different external sources can be selected as input for the ADC, besides that an internal temperature sensor or 0.5 x power supply (V_{cc}). As a reference, we can use V_{cc}, GND or a precise on-chip voltage reference 1,5V or 2,5V.

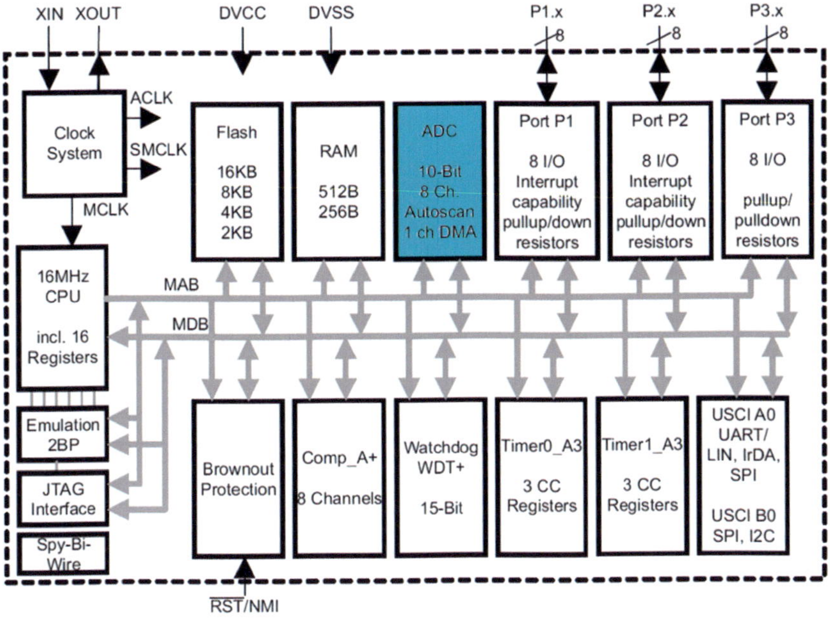

As we can see on the block diagram, there is a lot of functionality behind the ADC10 module:

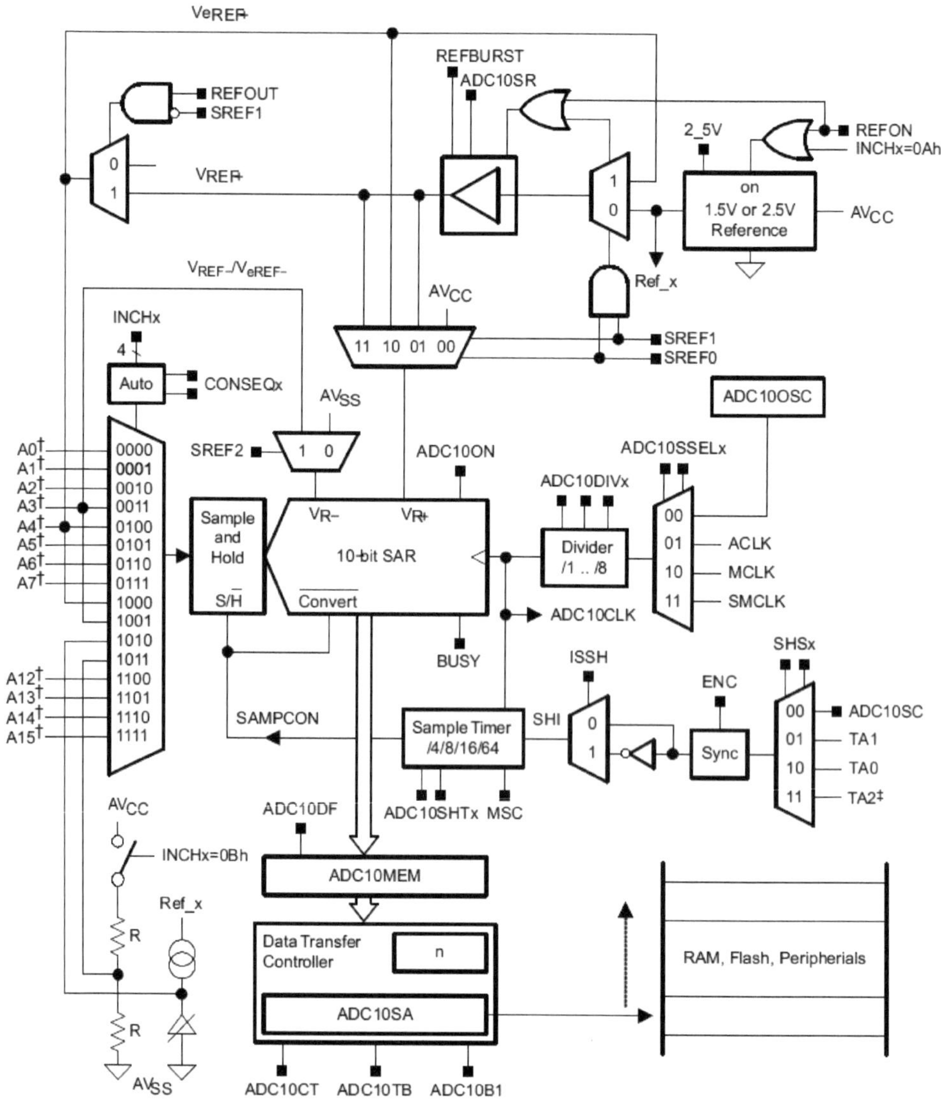
VeREF+
REFBURST
ADC10SR
REFOUT
SREF1
2_5V
REFON
INCHx=0Ah
VREF+
on
1.5V or 2.5V
Reference
AVCC
VREF-/VeREF-
Ref_x
AVCC
11 10 01 00
SREF1
SREF0
INCHx
4
Auto
CONSEQx
AVSS
ADC10OSC
A0†
A1†
A2†
A3†
A4†
A5†
A6†
A7†
A12†
A13†
A14†
A15†
SREF2
ADC10ON
ADC10SSELx
ADC10DIVx
Sample and Hold
S/H
VR-
VR+
10-bit SAR
Convert
Divider /1 .. /8
ACLK
MCLK
SMCLK
ADC10CLK
BUSY
ISSH
ENC
SHSx
SAMPCON
Sample Timer /4/8/16/64
SHI
Sync
ADC10SC
TA1
TA0
TA2‡
AVCC
ADC10DF
ADC10SHTx
MSC
INCHx=0Bh
ADC10MEM
Ref_x
R
Data Transfer Controller
n
RAM, Flash, Peripherials
ADC10SA
R
AVSS
ADC10CT
ADC10TB
ADC10B1

1.1.6.3 • WDT+

As we know (I assume at least) the watchdog module is used in the microcontrollers as the "last line of defense" - in case something went wrong with the coding execution and the firmware is not doing any more expected tasks, the watchdog module will restart the microcontroller. Unexpected behaviour can be sometimes triggered by a real bug in the firmware. It can also be provoked by external noises in power lines etc. Therefore, especially for 24/7 applications, it always makes sense to configure a watchdog (even we will not do it in our simple applications) to make sure the device does not become "frozen", or if it is, that it can "come back to track" without the need of any external (human) interaction. The Watchdog module in MSP430-Family members can be used differently. If watchdog functionality itself is not required, the watchdog module can be configured as an interval timer and can trigger interrupts in predefined time intervals.

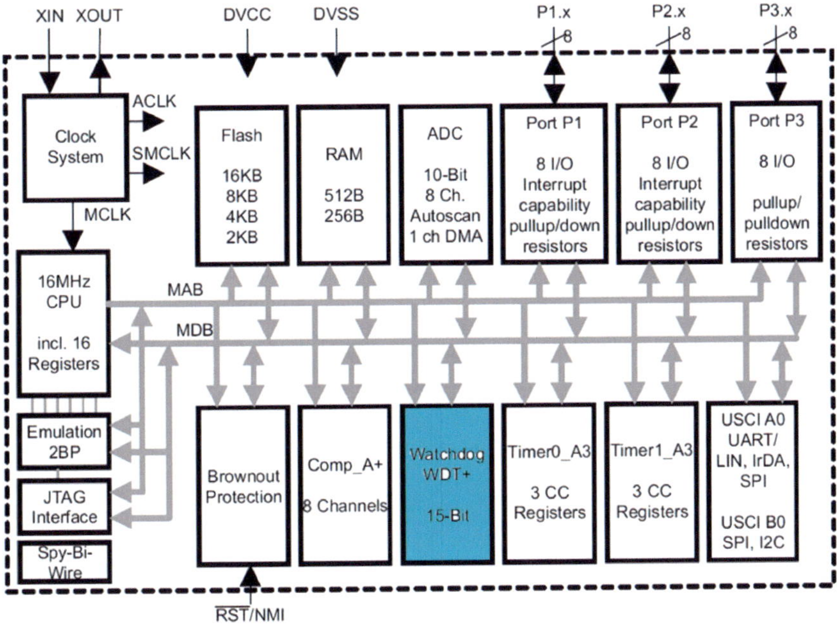

Particular to the MSP430 family, access to the watchdog is protected by a password. I've never seen this kind of watchdog protection for example with PIC or Atmel microcontrollers. We can see the functional block diagram of the watchdog module here:

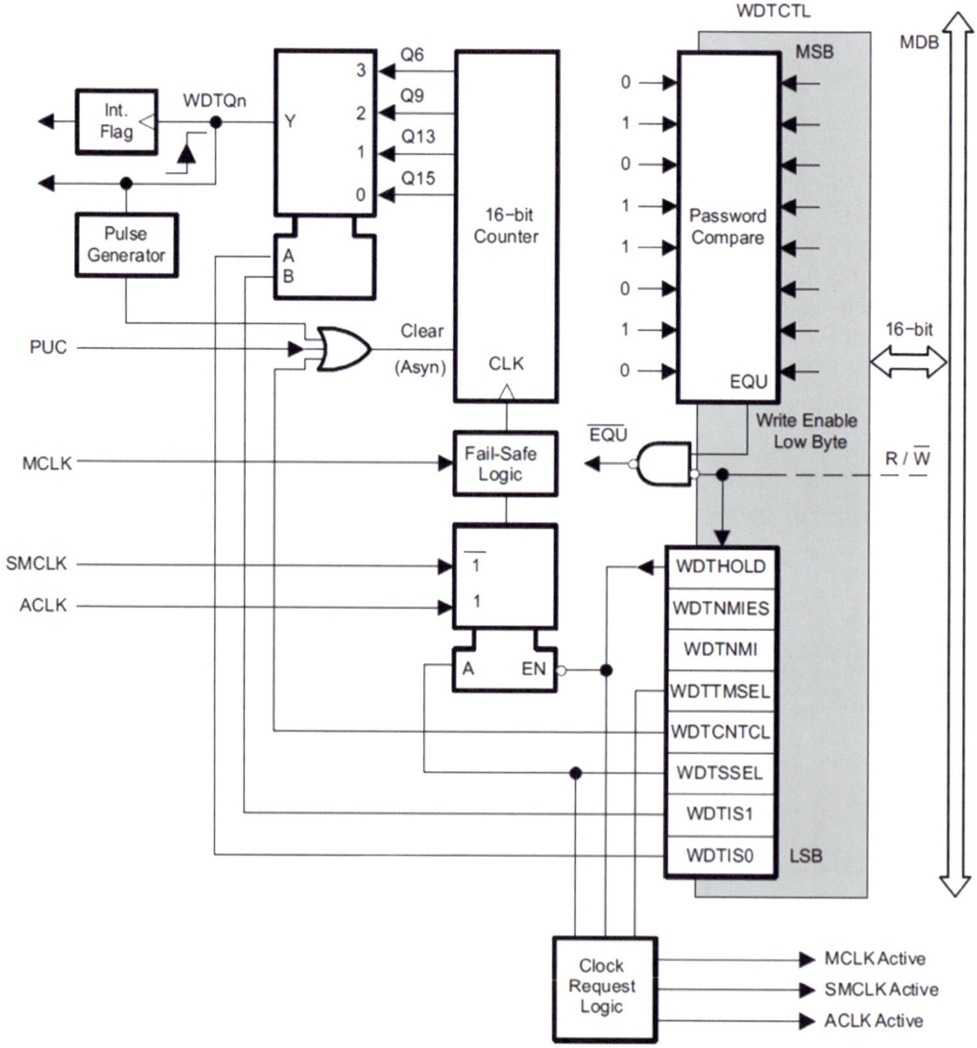

1.1.6.4 • Comparator A

The comparator module of the microcontroller allows us to check external analog signals, and even supervise the power supply. An RC filter is available which can be enabled or disabled by the software. The output of the comparator can be connected (by software) directly to Timer_A capture input.

8 different inputs can be selected for MSP430G2553 as sources for the comparison, and of course, internal voltage references can be utilised as well.

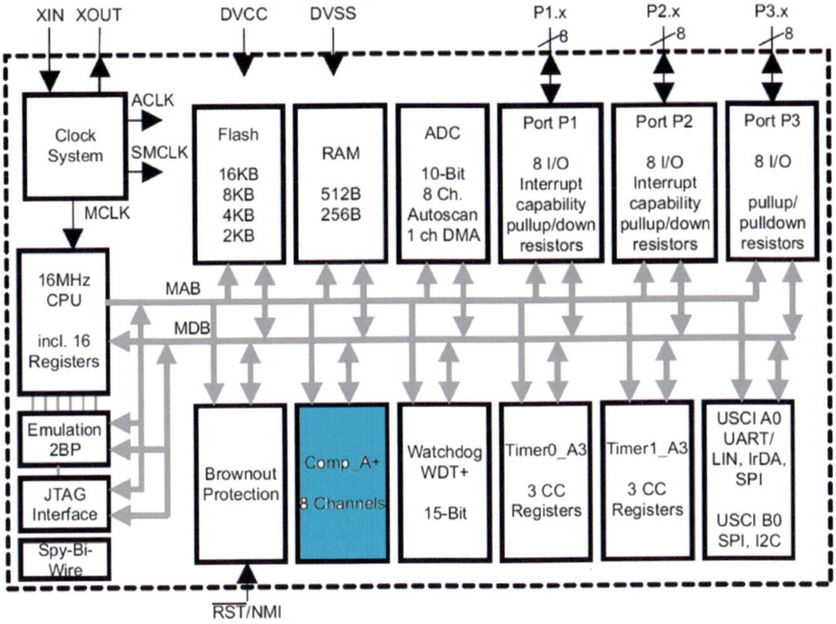

The external signal can be connected (by configuration) to + or - terminal of the comparator itself.

The comparator module is capable to trigger interrupts.

The Block diagram of functionality looks like this:

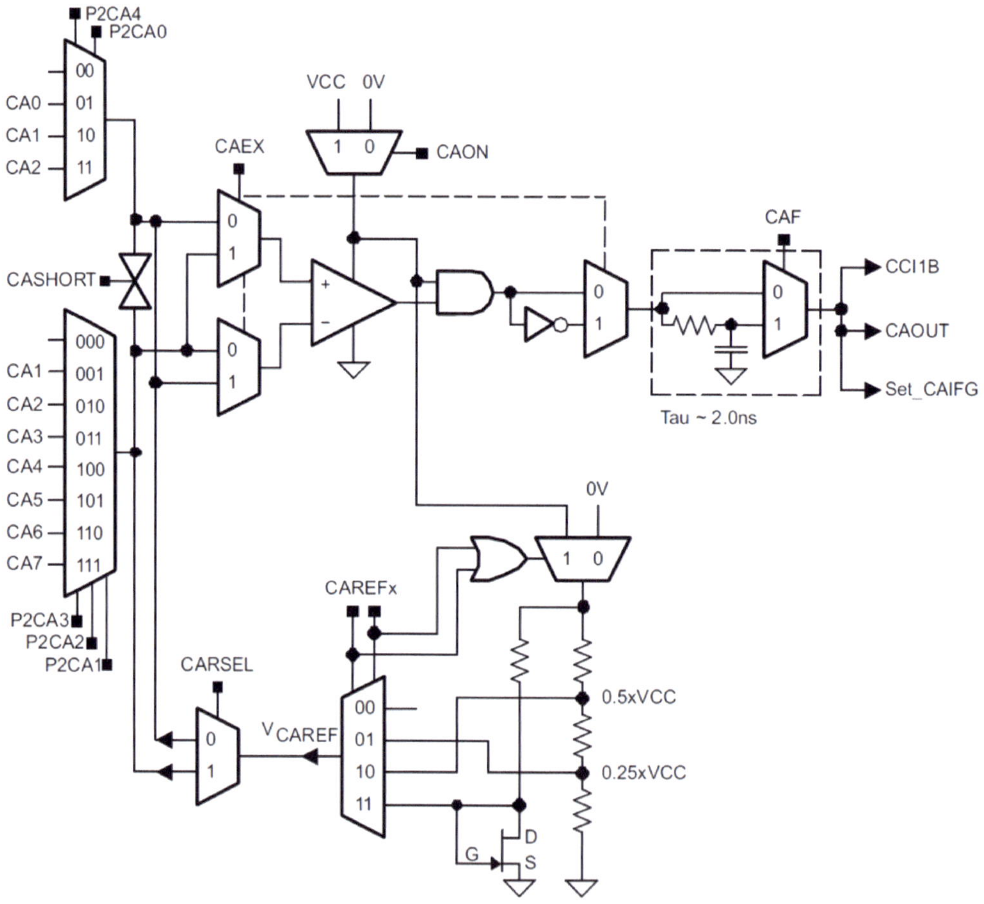

The Comparator module is used many applications to measure resistive elements.

1.1.6.5 • Timer_A

The Microcontroller provides two 16-bit Timer_A blocks with three capture/compare registers. The timer module can be configured as a simple synchronous 16-bit timer count up or down. An initial value of the counter can be provided by software. Of course, a timer can raise an interrupt by overflow.

The Clock divider can be configured to change "the speed" of counting. The timer can be used in different modes, like continuous mode (counting forever) or to just count up to a predefined value, etc.

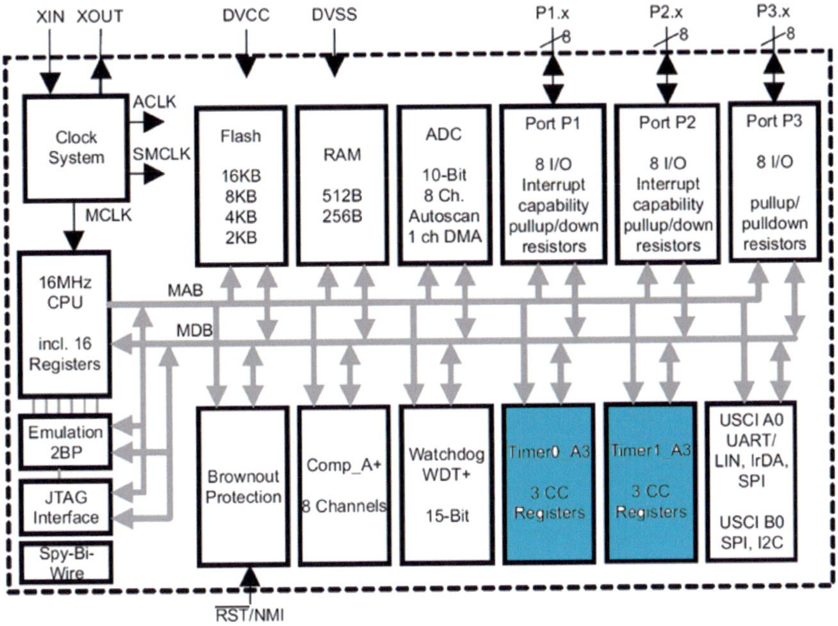

The timer module can be used to capture events as well, in different modes.

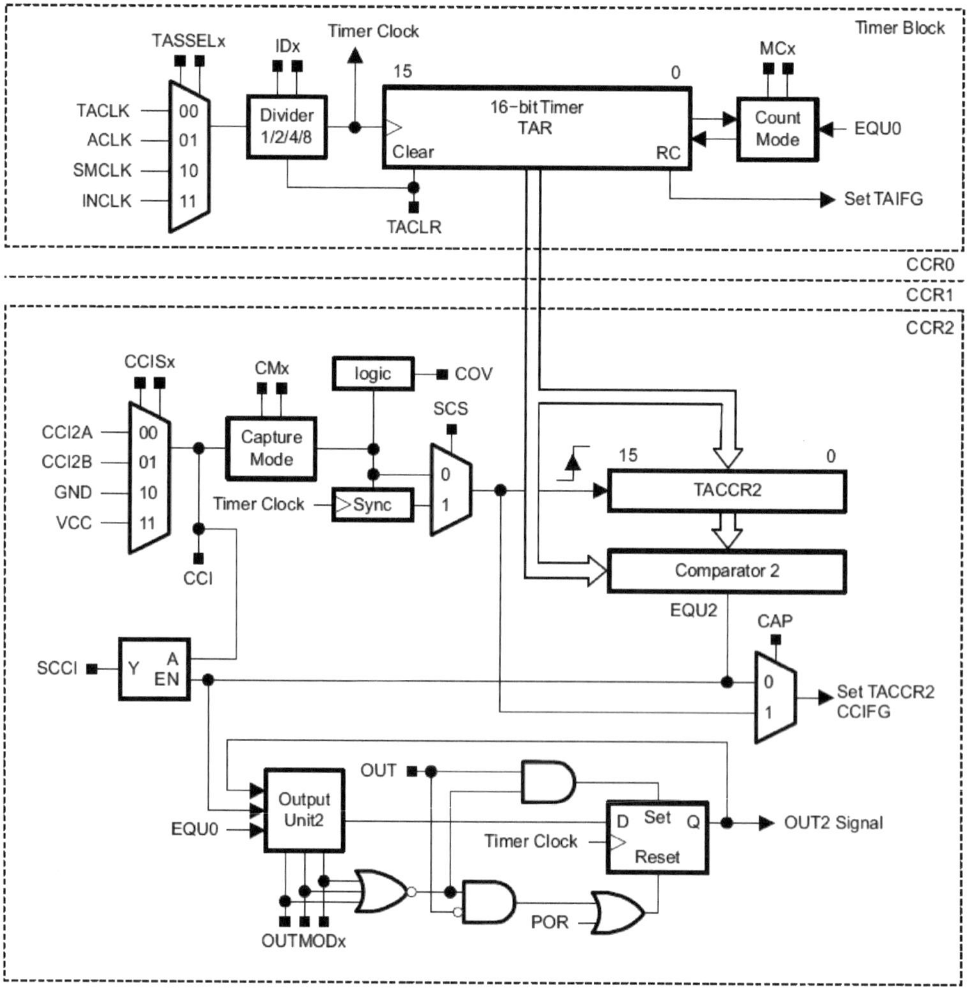
Timer Block
TASSELx
IDx
Timer Clock
MCx
15
0
16-bit Timer
TAR
TACLK
00
ACLK
01
SMCLK
10
INCLK
11
Divider
1/2/4/8
Clear
RC
Count
Mode
EQU0
Set TAIFG
TACLR
CCR0
CCR1
CCR2
CCISx
CMx
logic
COV
SCS
CCI2A
CCI2B
GND
VCC
Capture
Mode
Timer Clock
Sync
0
1
15
0
TACCR2
Comparator 2
CCI
EQU2
CAP
SCCI
Y
A
EN
Set TACCR2
CCIFG
OUT
Output
Unit2
EQU0
D
Set
Q
Timer Clock
Reset
OUT2 Signal
POR
OUTMODx

1.1.6.6 • USCI

Universal Serial Communication Interface (USCI) modules provide the possibility to set up easily with hardware support different serial communication protocols - using different modes:

- UART mode (incl. IrDA communication encoder and decoder)
- SPI mode
- I^2C mode
- automatic baud rate detection for LIN communications

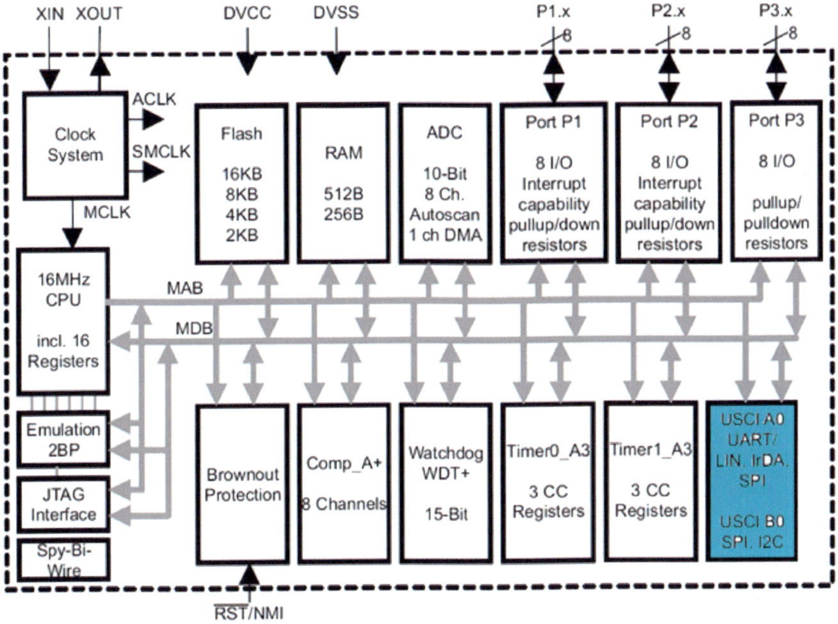

Let's take a short look at some of the functionalities and possibilities of the USCI module in different modes.

In UART mode, 7 or 8-bit data with odd, even or non-parity transfer can be used. The module provides independent transmit and receive shift registers and separate transmit and receive buffers. LSb-first or MSb-first transfer can be configured. Independent interrupts can be raised for receive and transmit cycles.

In SPI mode, several communication options are available as well. For this mode, a 7 or 8-bit data length can be selected, LSb-first or MSb-first transfer and receive can be configured. SPI master and as well SPI slave modes are supported. Similar to UART, for SPI mode independent transmit and receive registers and buffers are available. For SPI mode, clock and phase polarity can be selected as well, meaning different SPI communication protocols can be configured.

I^2C mode is quite flexible. For this, we can use master, multi-master and slave modes. We can configure the module for the usage of 7 or 10 bit I^2C addressing on the bus. The transfer rate is supports standard mode (up to 100kbps) and fast mode (up to 400kbps). I^2C general call is also supported.

1.1.7 • MSP430F2001

This microcontroller is one of the "smallest" in the MSP430 family. We will use it later in some exercises. Let's have a short look at the pin connection in the P-DIP14 package:

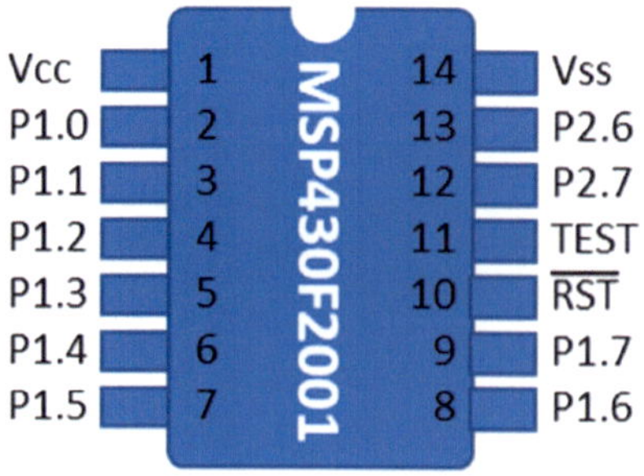

Pin	Description	Usage
1	V_{cc}	Positive power supply: 1,8V - 3,6V
2	P1.0	Digital I/O P1.0 or CA0 (comparator A input CA0)
3	P1.1	Digital I/O P1.1 or CA1 (comparator A input CA1)
4	P1.2	Digital I/O P1.2 or CA2 (comparator A input CA2)
5	P1.3	Digital I/O P1.3 or CA3 (comparator A input CA3)
6	P1.4	Digital I/O P1.4 or CA4 (comparator A input CA4)
7	P1.5	Digital I/O P1.5 or CA5 (comparator A input CA5)
8	P1.6	Digital I/O P1.6 or CA6 (comparator A input CA6)
9	P1.7	Digital I/O P1.7 or CA7 (comparator A input CA7)
10	RST	Reset Input - active in 0; when this pin is put to zero, the POR situation is triggered. Shall be put on V_{cc} for normal operation.
11	TEST	Activation of Test mode for JTAG. We will not use this functionality.
12	P2.7	Digital I/O P2.7
13	P2.6	Digital I/O P2.6
14	V_{ss}	Power supply: ground

As we can see on the architecture drawing, we only have the basic modules integrated into this chip:

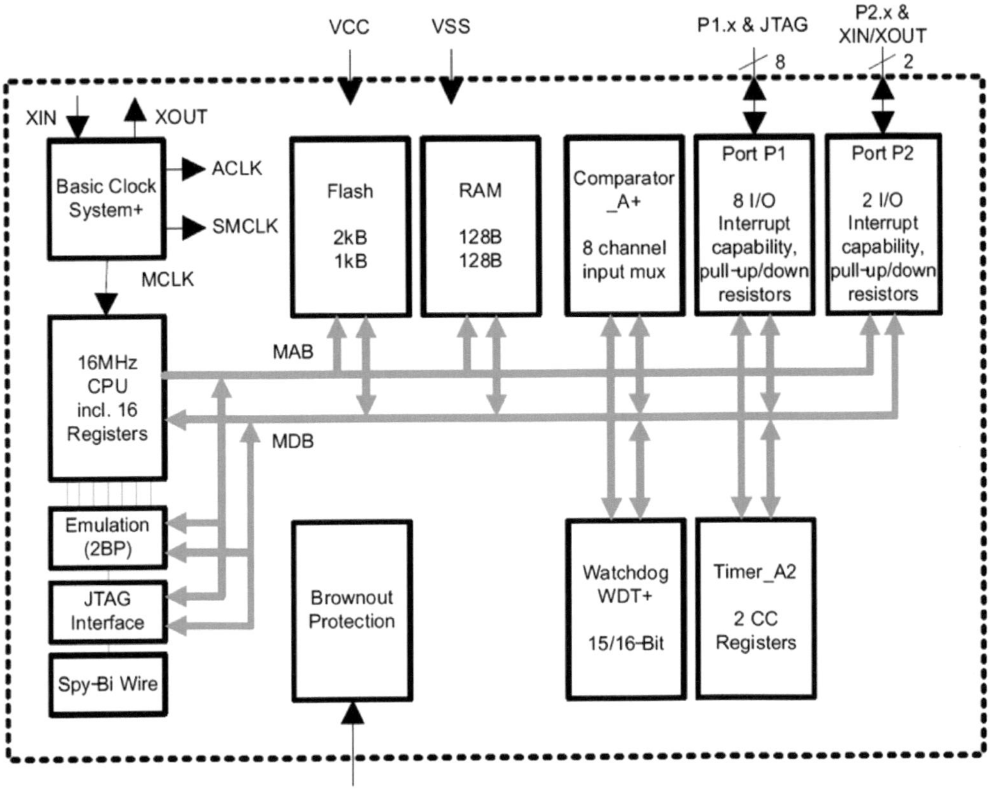

From "additional" modules only the Comparator_A module is available.

In general, the memory map of the MSP430F2001 looks exactly like the memory map for MSP430G2553, just that different memory blocks are smaller.

Type of memory	Memory size	Address from	Address to
Special Function Registers (SFR, 8-bit)	16 B	0000h	000Fh
8-bits Peripheries	240 B	0010h	00FFh
16-bit Peripheries	256 B	0100h	01FFh
SRAM	128 B	0200h	027Fh
Unused address space		0280h	0FFFh
Information memory / flash	256 B	1000h	10FFh
Unused address space		1100h	FDFFh
Code memory / flash	512 B	FE00h	FFBFh
Interrupt Vectors / flash		FFC0h	FFFFh

1.1.8 ● MSP430F2012

The last MCU we will use in the examples is only a bit "bigger" than MSP430F2001. The major difference is that the MSP430F2021 contains an ADC10 module (instead of the Comparator_A module).

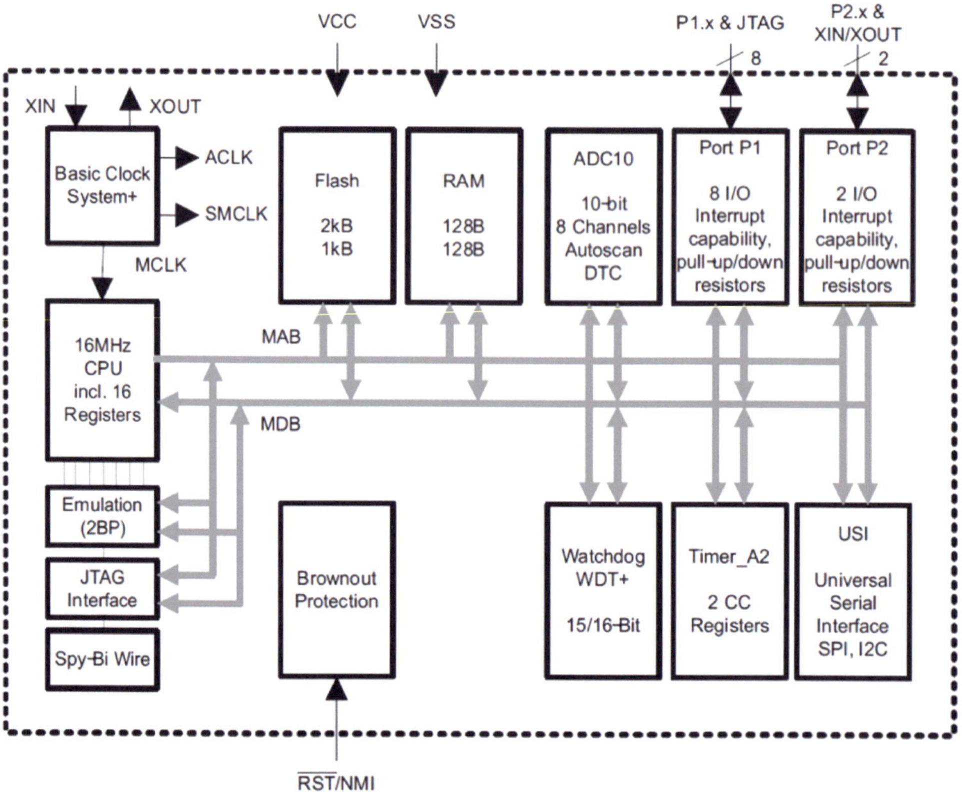

The memory map is again similar to other family members:

Type of memory	Memory size	Address from	Address to
Special Function Registers (SFR, 8-bit)	16 B	0000h	000Fh
8-bits Peripheries	240 B	0010h	00FFh
16-bit Peripheries	256 B	0100h	01FFh
SRAM	128 B	0200h	027Fh
Unused address space		0280h	0FFFh
Information memory / flash	256 B	1000h	10FFh
Unused address space		1100h	FDFFh
Code memory / flash	2 kB	F800h	FFBFh
Interrupt Vectors / flash		FFC0h	FFFFh

This MCU is available in the P-DIP14 package and the pin connection is the same (looking at digital I/O) as for MSP430F2001:

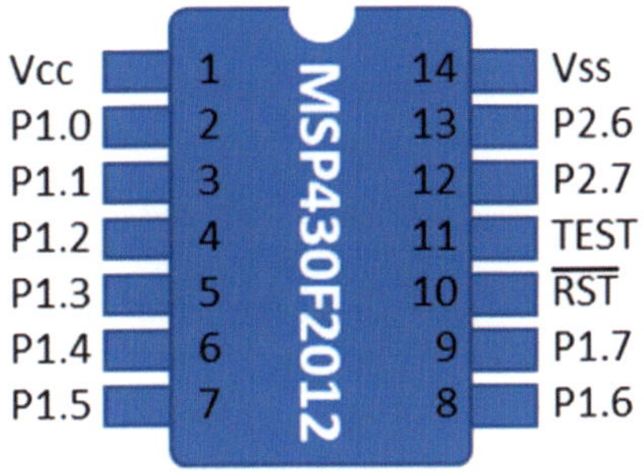

Pin	Description	Usage
1	V_{cc}	Positive power supply: 1,8V - 3,6V
2	P1.0	Digital I/O P1.0 or A0 (analog input A0 for ADC10 module)
3	P1.1	Digital I/O P1.1 or A1 (analog input A1 for ADC10 module)
4	P1.2	Digital I/O P1.2 or A2 (analog input A2 for ADC10 module)
5	P1.3	Digital I/O P1.3 or A3 (analog input A3 for ADC10 module)
6	P1.4	Digital I/O P1.4 or A4 (analog input A4 for ADC10 module)
7	P1.5	Digital I/O P1.5 or A5 (analog input A5 for ADC10 module)
8	P1.6	Digital I/O P1.6 or A4 (analog input A6 for ADC10 module)
9	P1.7	Digital I/O P1.7 or A4 (analog input A7 for ADC10 module)
10	RST	Reset Input - active in 0; when this pin is put to zero, the POR situation is triggered. Shall be put on V_{cc} for normal operation.
11	TEST	Activation of Test mode for JTAG. We will not use this functionality.
12	P2.7	Digital I/O P2.7
13	P2.6	Digital I/O P2.6
14	V_{ss}	Power supply: ground

1.2 • Texas Instruments LaunchPads

There are many LaunchPad boards from Texas Instruments.

I would like to mention some of them here, to see, that there are a lot of possibilities for how to start with your projects or learning path.

TI LaunchPads are not expensive at all. Some of them can be purchased for ~10,- €. Typical hardware extensions for LaunchPads are so-called BoosterPack(s). These provide additional functionality and can be easily connected to LaunchPads.

The concept of LaunchPads and BoosterPacks enables a fast and easy way to prototype with TI-microcontrollers.

1.2.1 • LP-MSP430FR2476

This LaunchPad contains the MSP430FR2476 microcontroller running at 16MHz. The MCU contains 64kB FRAM and 8kB RAM.

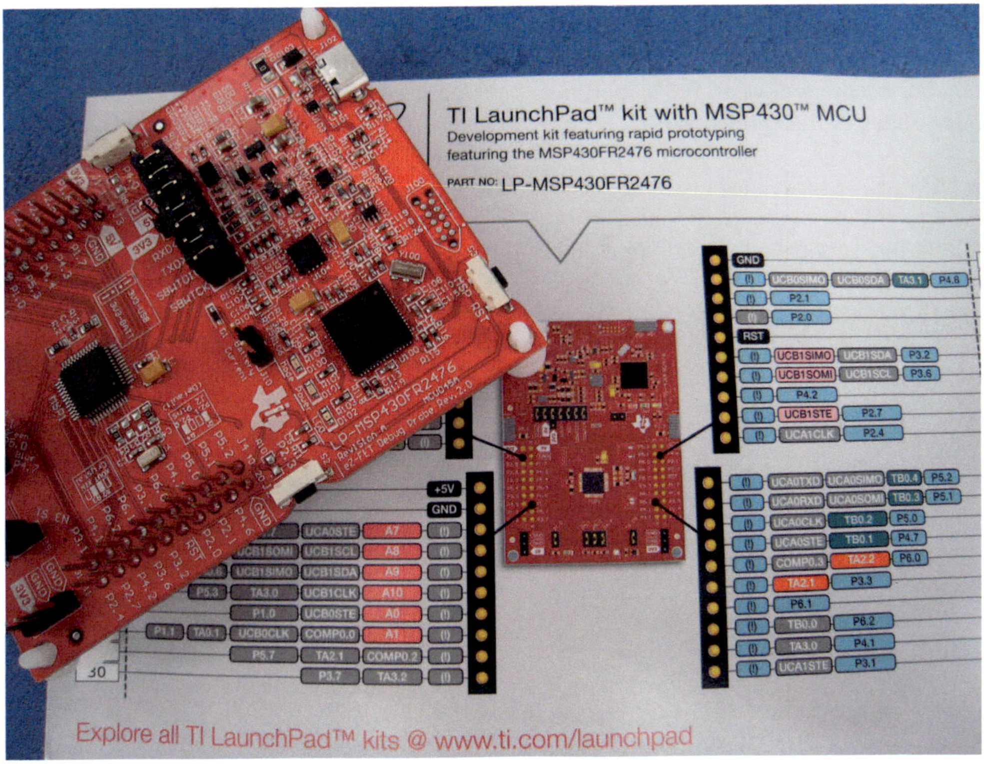

The device can be shortly described like this:

Operation power supply can be between 1.8V and 3.6V. The MCU architecture is 16-bit RISC and is running with a clock up to 16MHz. The total memory includes 64kB FRAM for firmware and data storage, additionally 512 bytes of information FRAM and 8kB of RAM.

The MCU includes a lot of peripheries as well: 12-channel 12-bit ADC, enhanced comparator with integrated 6-bit DAC for reference voltage, many different 16-bit timers, and integrated 16-bit CRC module. Besides this, there are 43 GPIO for general usage.

The board contains 2 buttons and 2 LEDs (1 RGB-LED) for direct user interaction, meaning it is possible to start directly with simple coding without the need to add any additional hardware to the board.

The microcontroller on the board is pre-loaded with demo software showing the possibilities of the integrated ADC of the MSP430FR2476 to measure the output voltage of an analog temperature sensor. The measured temperature is indicated on the RGB LED, where the green color means "ambient temperature", red means hot, and blue means cold. The onboard used external temperature sensor is the TMP235 from Texas Instruments. This is an analog temperature sensor with an operating supply voltage of 2.3V to 5.5V, measuring temperature from -40°C to +150°C.

This LaunchPad (as nearly all of them) provides a 40-pin extension connector to connect BoosterPack(s) from TI or the community (ecosystem). BoosterPacks can include sensors, human interface devices (LCD, buttons, ...), etc. to extend the hardware and software possibilities of the LaunchPad.

1.2.2 • MSP-EXP430FR4133

Within this LaunchPad, we can find one of the FRAM MCU's: MSP430FR4133.

The power supply voltage can be between 1.8V and 3.6V. The MCU is working with a clock up to 16MHz. On chip, we can find 16kB FRAM for firmware and application data and 2kB SRAM.

The peripherals integrated on-chip are IR modulation logic, 10-channel 10-bit differential ADC, RTC, CRC-module, and a direct LCD driver.

On the LaunchPad we can find an LCD, which is driven directly from this quite small microcontroller.

The LCD used has the following design:

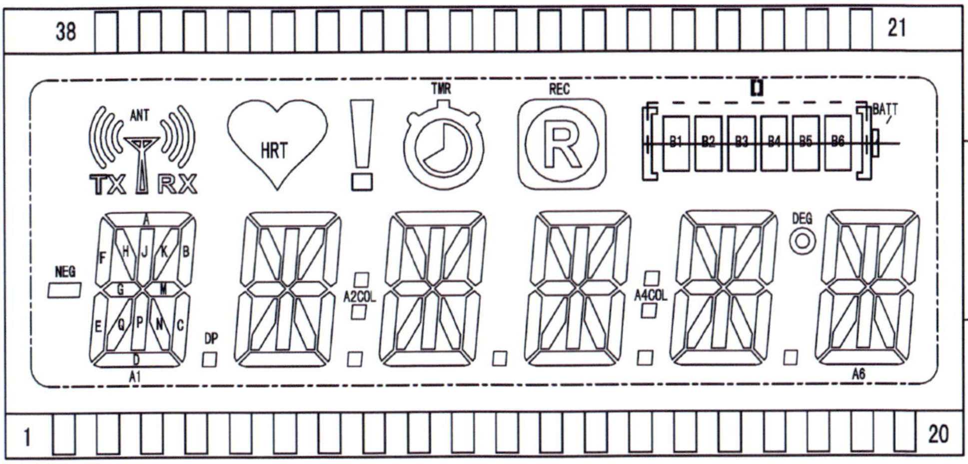

All segments of the LCD can be used for purposes fitting to the requirements of our construction.

And of course, in our applications "outside", the LaunchPad we can use another LCD fitting to the possibilities of the MCU.

We will find a good out-of-the-box example implemented in the new LaunchPad - it is a firmware providing two different functionalities: a stopwatch and thermometer. Besides that, we can see different "flashing" special signs on the LCD.

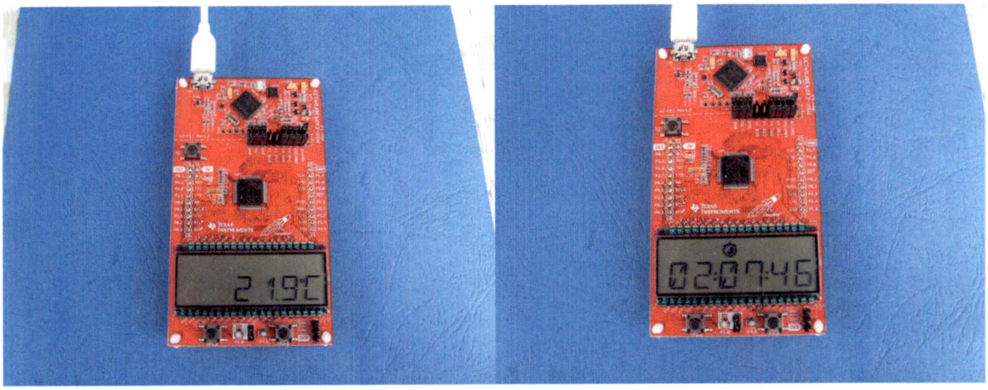

The low-power LCD module supports up to 4x36 or 8x32 segment LCD configurations. Each LCD pin can be configured as SEG or COM by software. Contrast control is provided from 2.6V to 3.5V configurable in 0.06 V steps.

1.2.3 ● MSP-EXP430FR2355

To get a feeling and build our first applications with the MSP430FR2355 MCU we can pick up this LaunchPad.

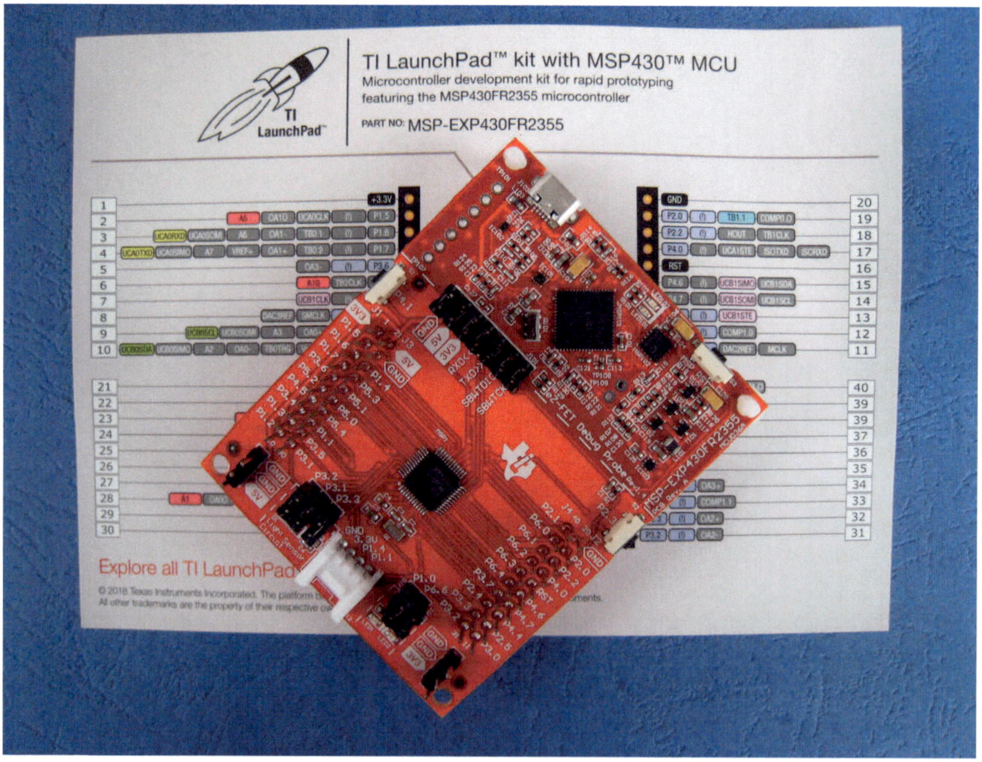

The microcontroller used works from 1.8V to 3.6V and contains 32kB FRAM and 4kB SRAM. In addition, there is 20kB of ROM memory containing different driver and FFT libraries. This can be used directly in CCS (Code Composer Studio) to get faster execution of code and saving space in FRAM for another application coding.

This 16-bit RISC microcontroller run at 24MHz and contains some - let's say - unusual peripherals, like smart analog combo (SAC-L3) providing a general-purpose operational amplifier, rail-to-rail input and output, configurable high-power and low-power modes. We got configurable PGA mode supporting noninverting mode: x1, x2, x3, x5, x9, x17, x26 and x33 and inverting mode: x1, x2, x4, x8, x16, x25 and x32.

And we will find a couple of "intelligent digital peripherals", like timers, RTC, CRC-module, 32-bit hardware multiplier, and some more.

On the board, we of course have the obligatory 2 user buttons and LEDs which can be used by first experiences and exercises. In addition, we can find a photodiode on board. This one is used in the out-of-the-box demo implemented in the microcontroller once the LaunchPad is new.

The out of the box demo contains two different functionalities: one is utilising the photodiode, where the light intensity is indicated by LED1 and LED2 on the board.

The next functionality is a function generator mode. In this mode, the LaunchPad development kit starts to generate a 1-Hz inverted sine wave at 0.8-V amplitude on pin P1.5. This signal is a result of using one of the SAC 12-bit DACs to generate a sine wave and feeding it into a second SAC, which is configured as an inverting programmable gain amplifier (PGA).

1.2.4 • MSP-EXP432P401R

With this LaunchPad, we get a bit outside the MSP430-Family. Just to see, for other microcontroller families from TI, we can find appropriate LaunchPads as well.

As it is obvious from the name of the LaunchPad - within this board we will find the MCU MSP432P401R.

This MCU is a SimpleLink™ ultra-low-power 32-bit Arm Cortex-M4F MCU With Precision ADC, 256KB Flash, and 64KB RAM.

The microcontroller is working with a clock up to 48MHz.

In addition, it contains an MCU 32kB ROM with SimpleLink MSP432SDK libraries.

From the list of peripheries integrated directly into MSP432P401R, let's mention at least four 16-bit timers with capture, compare, or PWM, two 32-bit timers, and an RTC module. In addition, we can build up to eight serial communication channels - I²C, SPI, UART, and IrDA. And of course many analog peripheries.

LaunchPad provides a 40-pin connection to add BoosterPack plug-in modules - as we saw already with another LaunchPad for MSP430 microcontrollers.

1.2.5 • MSP-EXP430G2ET

This is ours. All experiments and examples within this book utilise this LaunchPad. This LaunchPad supports all 14 and 20-pin DIP MSP430 microcontrollers.

I like this board. It is the smallest, or weakest (if you like) of all here mentioned. It has a big advantage when compared to all others. As the MSP-EXP430G2ET LaunchPad uses 20 pin IC-socket supporting DIP-package microcontrollers, it is possible to write firmware to the flash of the microcontroller, then take the MCU out of the LaunchPad and put it in its own hardware. We can then just put the new MCU in the LaunchPad and write the same or other firmware to the new MCU, all the time using the same LaunchPad.

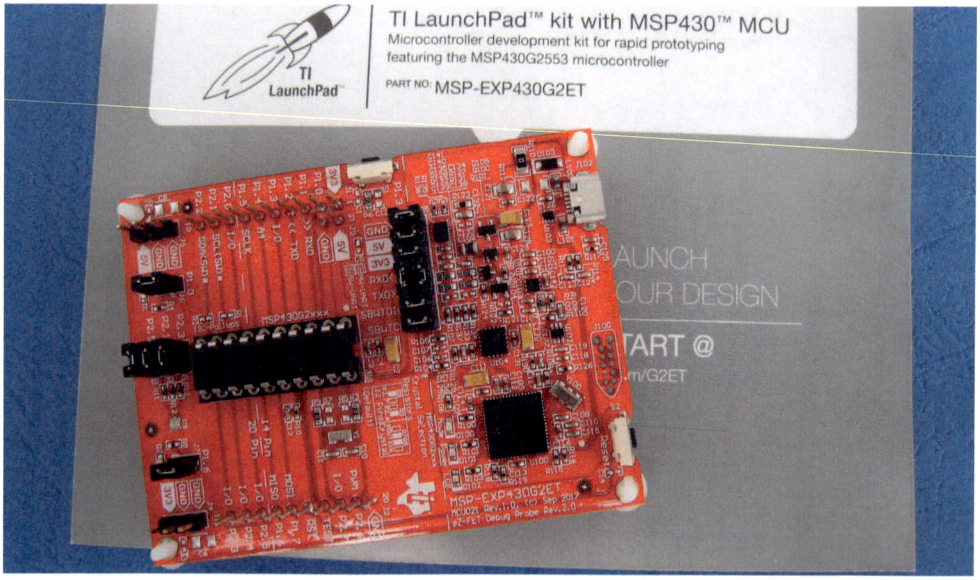

We already know approximately the possibilities and features of the MSP430G2553. To summarise: the supply voltage for this MCU can be between 1.8V and 3.6V. The architecture is a 16-bit RISC microcontroller working with a clock up to 16MHz. The microcontroller contains 16kB of flash memory and 512 byte RAM. Regarding peripheries, we have 8-channel 10-bit ADC, an 8-channel comparator, and two 16-bit timers available. Besides this, we have a USCI interface and 16 GPIOs. Regarding GPIO I can add that the MSP430G2553 in QFN or TSSOP package provides 24 GPIOs.

It is important to mention another advantage of this LaunchPad. Not only the "default" MCU is supported by this board.

Here is the list of devices supported by the LaunchPad:

Microcontroller	**Flash**	**RAM**	**Peripheries**
MSP430F2001	1 kB	128 B	Comparator
MSP430F2002	1 kB	128 B	10-bit SAR A/D, USI for SPI / I^2C
MSP430F2003	1 kB	128 B	16-bit Sigma-Delta A/D, USI for SPI / I^2C
MSP430F2011	2 kB	128 B	Comparator
MSP430F2012	2 kB	128 B	10-bit SAR A/D, USI for SPI / I^2C
MSP430F2013	2 kB	128 B	16-bit Sigma-Delta A/D, USI for SPI / I^2C
MSP430G2001	0,5 kB	128 B	-
MSP430G2101	1 kB	128 B	-
MSP430G2111	1 kB	128 B	Comparator
MSP430G2121	1 kB	128 B	USI for SPI / I^2C
MSP430G2131	1 kB	128 B	10-bit SAR A/D, USI for SPI / I^2C
MSP430G2201	2 kB	128 B	-
MSP430G2211	2 kB	128 B	Comparator
MSP430G2221	2 kB	128 B	USI for SPI / I^2C
MSP430G2231	2 kB	128 B	10-bit SAR A/D, USI for SPI / I^2C
MSP430G2102	1 kB	256 B	USI for SPI / I^2C
MSP430G2202	2 kB	256 B	USI for SPI / I^2C
MSP430G2302	4 kB	256 B	USI for SPI / I^2C
MSP430G2402	8 kB	256 B	USI for SPI / I^2C
MSP430G2112	1 kB	256 B	Comparator, USI for SPI / I^2C
MSP430G2212	2 kB	256 B	Comparator, USI for SPI / I^2C
MSP430G2312	4 kB	256 B	Comparator, USI for SPI / I^2C
MSP430G2412	8 kB	256 B	Comparator, USI for SPI / I^2C
MSP430G2132	1 kB	256 B	10-bit SAR A/D, USI for SPI / I^2C
MSP430G2232	2 kB	256 B	10-bit SAR A/D, USI for SPI / I^2C

MSP430G2332	4 kB	256 B	10-bit SAR A/D, USI for SPI / I^2C
MSP430G2432	8 kB	256 B	10-bit SAR A/D, USI for SPI / I^2C
MSP430G2152	1 kB	256 B	10-bit SAR A/D, Comparator, USI for SPI / I^2C
MSP430G2252	2 kB	256 B	10-bit SAR A/D, Comparator, USI for SPI / I^2C
MSP430G2352	4 kB	256 B	10-bit SAR A/D, Comparator, USI for SPI / I^2C
MSP430G2452	8 kB	256 B	10-bit SAR A/D, Comparator, USI for SPI / I^2C
MSP430G2153	1 kB	256 B	10-bit SAR A/D, Comparator, USCI for SPI / I^2C
MSP430G2203	2 kB	256 B	Comparator, USCI for SPI / I^2C / UART
MSP430G2313	2 kB	256 B	Comparator, USCI for SPI / I^2C / UART
MSP430G2333	2 kB	256 B	10-bit SAR A/D, Comparator, USCI for SPI / I^2C / UART
MSP430G2353	2 kB	256 B	10-bit SAR A/D, Comparator, USCI for SPI / I^2C / UART
MSP430G2403	8 kB	512 B	Comparator, USCI for SPI / I^2C / UART
MSP430G2413	8 kB	512 B	Comparator, USCI for SPI / I^2C / UART
MSP430G2433	8 kB	512 B	10-bit SAR A/D, Comparator, USCI for SPI / I^2C / UART
MSP430G2453	8 kB	512 B	10-bit SAR A/D, Comparator, USCI for SPI / I^2C / UART
MSP430G2513	16 kB	512 B	Comparator, USCI for SPI / I^2C / UART
MSP430G2533	16 kB	512 B	10-bit SAR A/D, Comparator, USCI for SPI / I^2C / UART
MSP430G2553	16 kB	512 B	10-bit SAR A/D, Comparator, USCI for SPI / I^2C / UART

We will find 43 devices on this list.

On this LaunchPad we can find one custom button, reset button, green LED, red LED and an RGB LED.

1.2.6 • BOOSTXL-EDUMKII

At the end of this first chapter let's take a short look at one of the generic BoosterPacks - extensions of LaunchPads.

This BoosterPack can be used with a couple of different LaunchPads, e.g. with the MSP-EXP432P401R, we mentioned earlier.

This booster pack contains a couple of sensors and input and output devices. We can find an OPT3001 light sensor and a TMP006 remote temperature sensor. We can see and utilise a servo motor driver, 3-axis accelerometer, RGB LED, and piezo buzzer.

In the central part of the board is a 128x128 TFT LCD. We can also find a microphone, 2-axis joystick, and some user buttons. It is a lot of different devices for playing on the board.

On the Texas Instruments website, we can find a lot of different software examples showing the possibilities of how to work with these different external peripherals.

Chapter 2 • Integrated Development Environment (IDE)

In this chapter, we will touch upon two different IDEs for Texas Instruments microcontrollers. They will be the Code Composer Studio (CCS) and an Arduino-Version from Texas Instruments called "Energia". We will see the basics of the IDEs - to be able to create a new project, compile the code and upload the result to the microcontroller. I'll keep this chapter quite slim, as the IDEs are regularly improved by their issuer and nearly all information on the most current release can be found easily on the internet.

We will look at the Code Composer Studio Version 10.1.1.00004 and Energia 1.8.7E21. In these IDEs all examples shown in this book are written and tested.
We will not do any fast training of C-language, just create a new project: step-by-step; and the rest - what we need, we will see later in examples.

2.1 • Code Composer Studio (CCS)

The current version of the Code Composer Studio can be downloaded free of charge from Texas Instruments. In the meantime again a new release of the CCS (10.3.0.00007) has been issued by TI - and currently the IDE itself and documentation for the IDE, assembler, C, etc. can be found here: https://www.ti.com/tool/CCSTUDIO

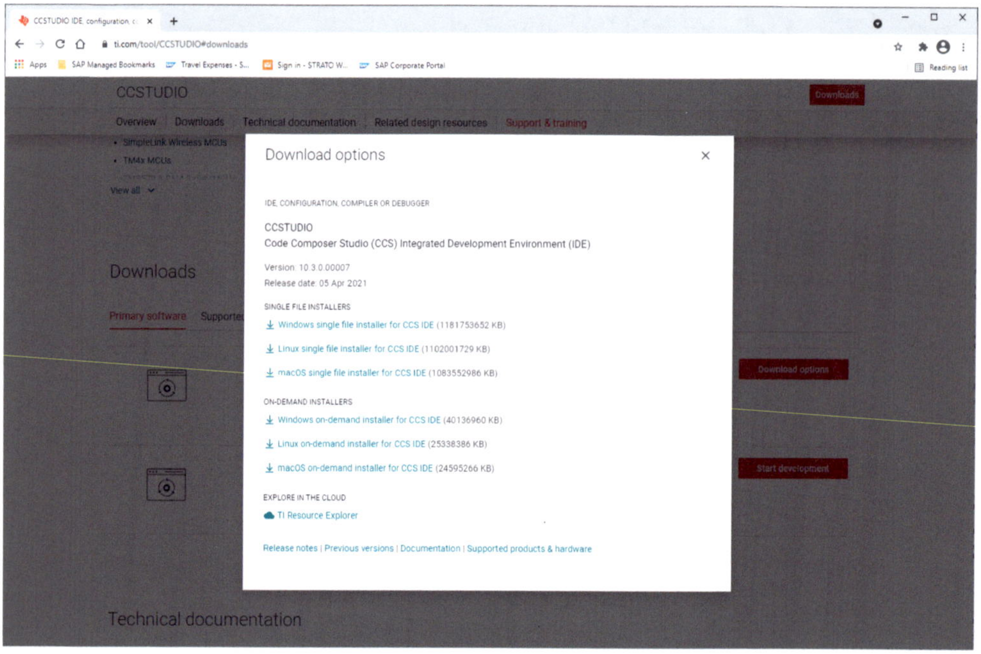

Once we pick up the download option we like and install the CCS, we can launch the IDE.

When starting, we will see the following startup screen:

Once the basics of the IDE are initialised, we have to select the so-called "workspace":

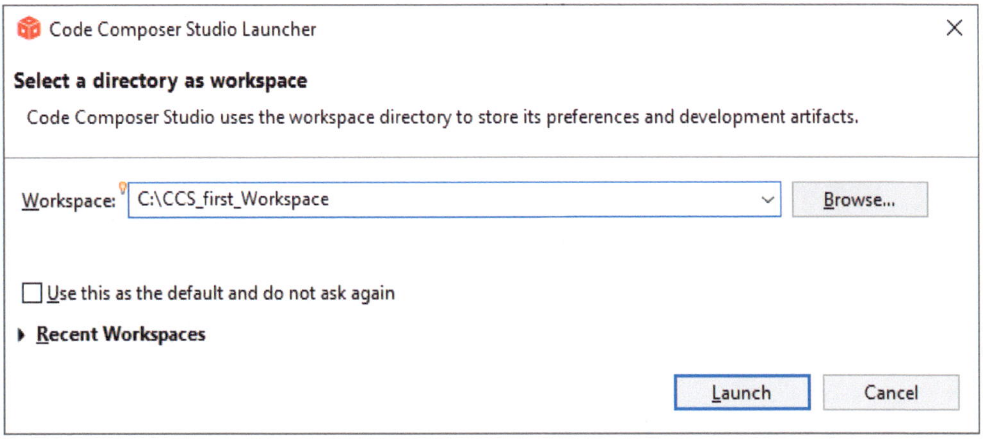

In the end, the workspace is a directory in the file system where all projects we are creating and using are / will be stored. Of course, we can maintain a lot of different workspaces. Typically we will store all projects in one workspace.

In this dialog box, we pick up the directory, which will be used (is used already) as a workspace.

After clicking "Launch", the CCS is started and we can create a "New Project":

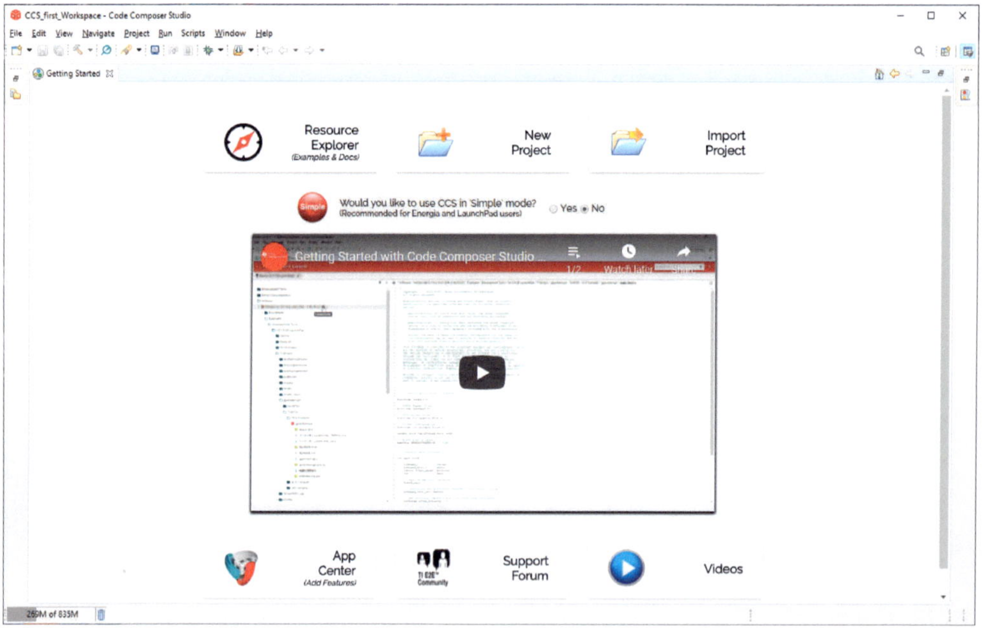

Once we press the button "New Project" we can set up basic parameters for the project we are about to create.

Alternatively to the button is menu path: Project -> New CCS Project:

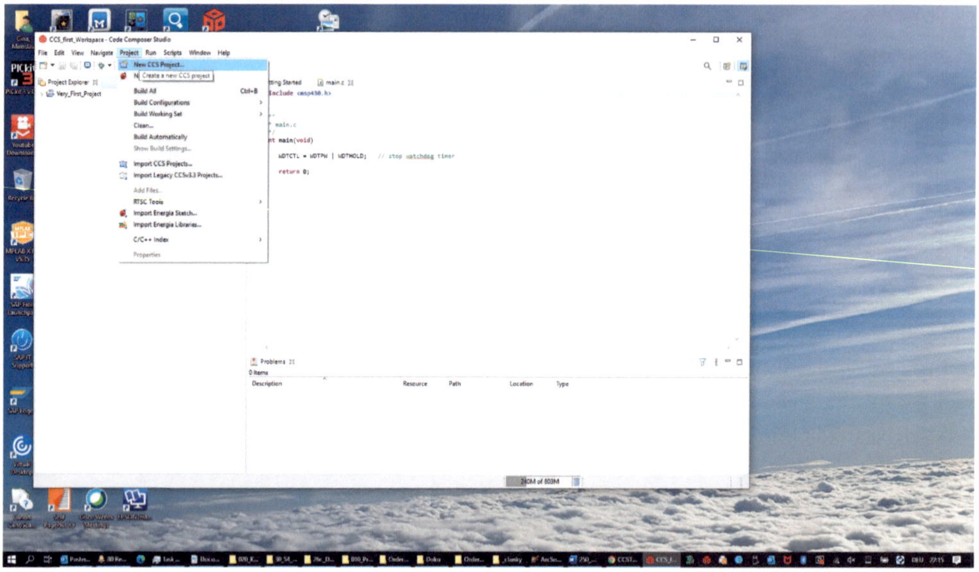

In the dialog box appearing after choosing the creation of a new project, we can see this dialog:

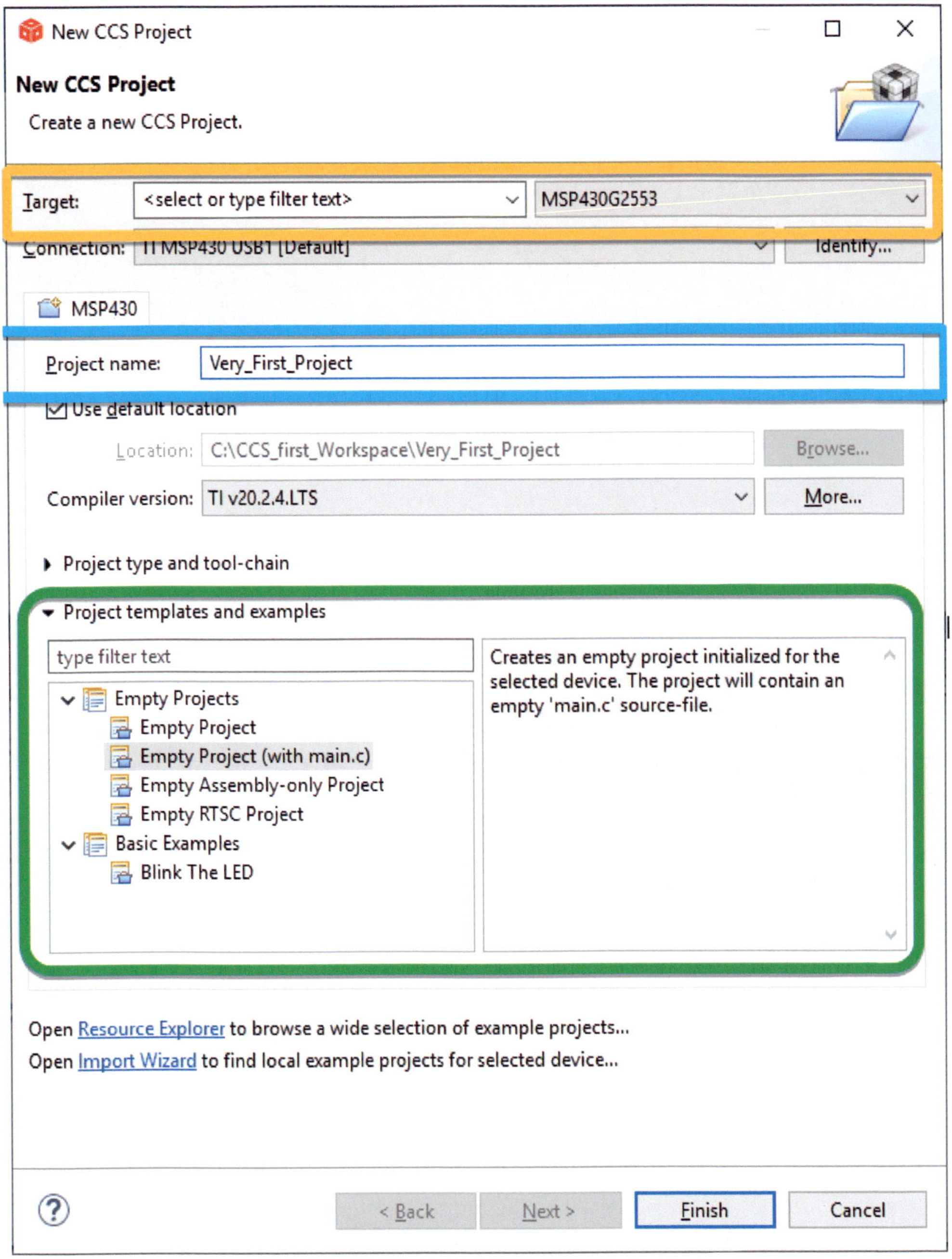

Here - in the orange marked box, we have to select the microcontroller we want to work with. In the example, we can see we selected the MSP430G2553. We will work with this microcontroller a lot. We shall type in the name of the future project to the blue marked field and select an "Empty Project (with main.c) from the list in the green marked box.

Once we maintain the required fields and hit "Finish", the project is created and the CCS navigates us directly to the main.c file of the newly created project:

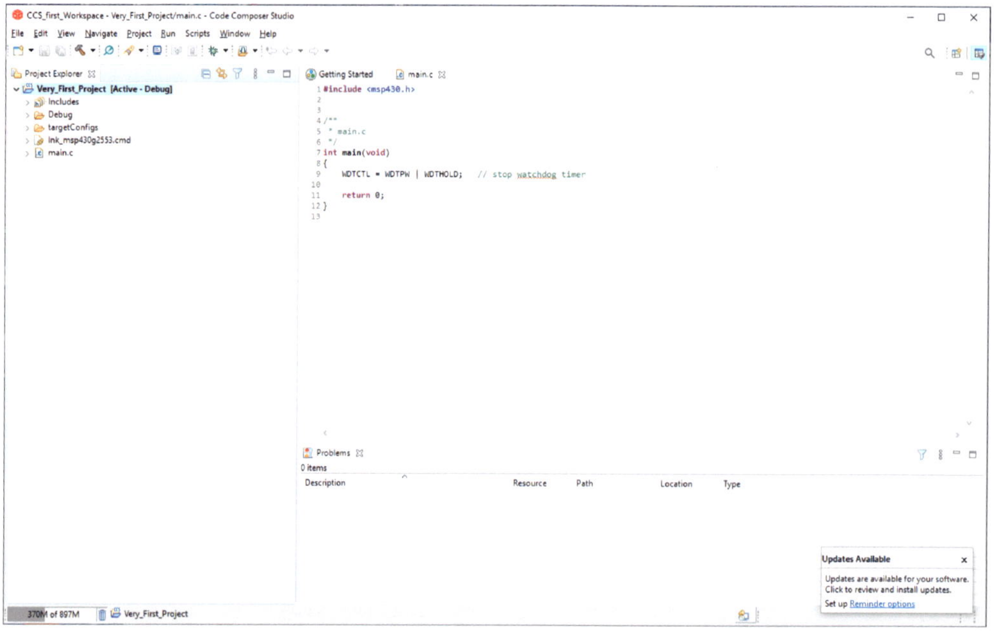

As we can see, we get a few prefilled lines of code already: the <msp430.h> library is included, the main() function predefined, and the line to stop the watch-dog timer is included as well.

Having looked into the filesystem, we can see the workspace as a directory created, and our project will be another directory within the workspace:

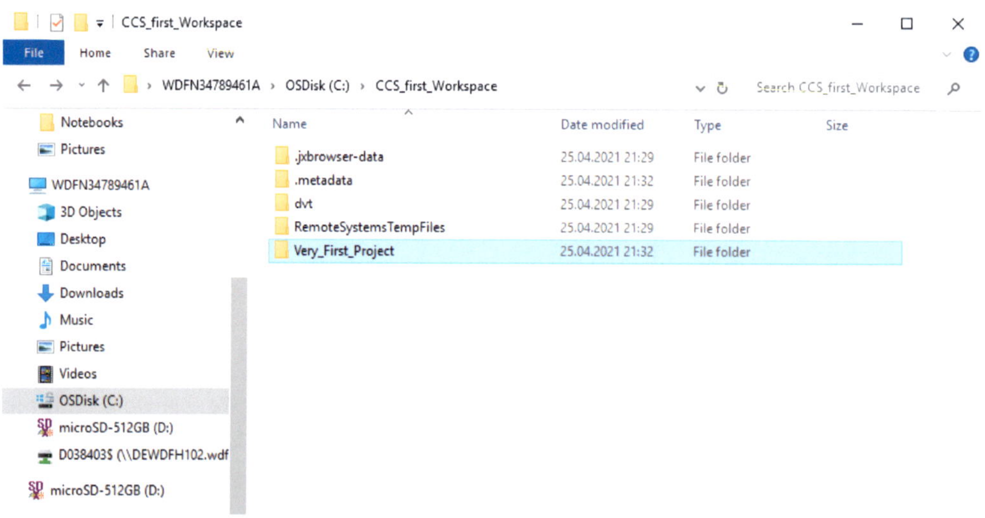

If we jump to the project directory, we will find - besides of lot of different files - one file called "main.c":

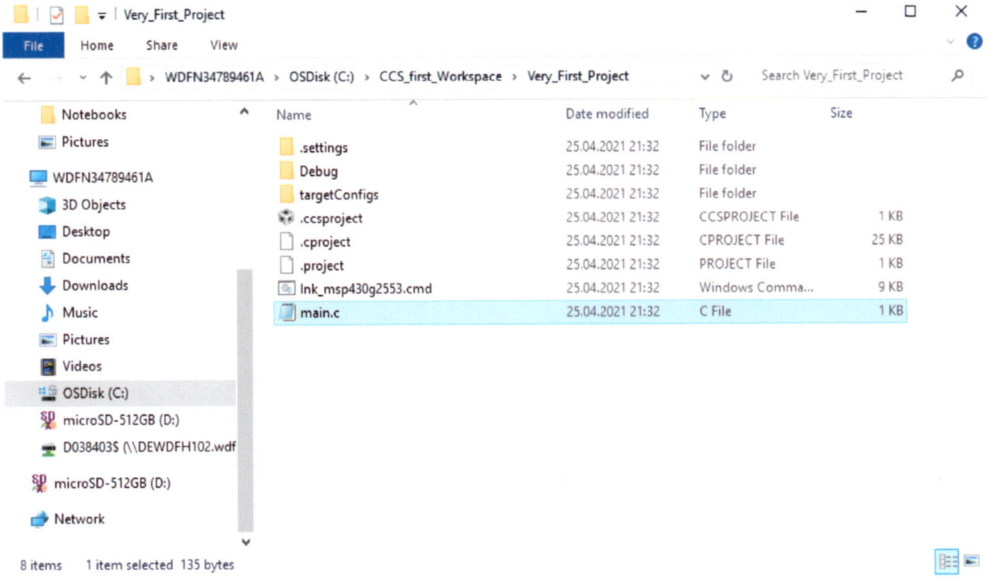

In this file we can see the coding, we will put to the main.c module of the project:

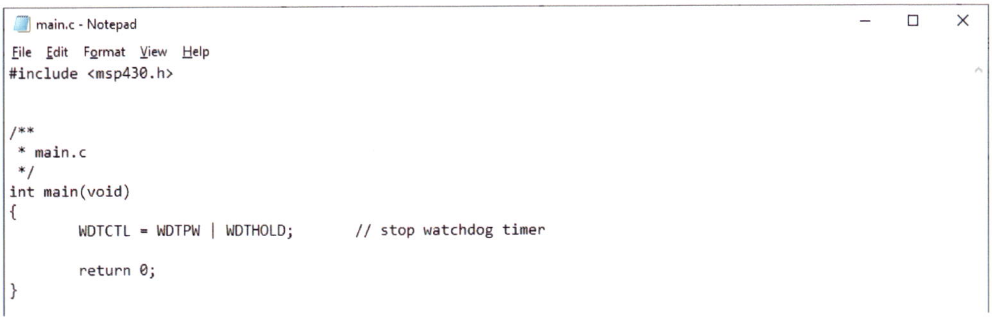


```
#include <msp430.h>


/**
 * main.c
 */
int main(void)
{
	WDTCTL = WDTPW | WDTHOLD;	// stop watchdog timer

	return 0;
}
```

At this moment everything is prepared, and we just need to write the code:

```
#include <msp430.h>                          //(1) include msp430 constants & declarations

void wait001(unsigned long int i_wt);        //(2) there will be "wait001" function
//------------------------------------------------------------------------
//------------------------------------------------------------------------
int main(void)                               //(3) main function starts here
{
    WDTCTL = WDTPW | WDTHOLD;                //(4) Stop watchdog timer
    P1DIR = 0xFF;                            //(5) Set P1.0 - P1.7 to I/O output

    for(;;)                                  //(6) endless loop
    {
    P1OUT = 0b00000001;                      //(7) switch on the LED on P1.0 (pin #2)
    wait001(8000);                           //(8) wait a while
    P1OUT = 0b00000000;                      //(9) switch off the LED on P1.0 (pin #2)
    wait001(8000);                           //(10) wait a while
    }
}
//------------------------------------------------------------------------
//------------------------------------------------------------------------
void wait001(unsigned long int i_wt)         //(11) delay routine
{
    volatile unsigned long int i;            //(12) volatile to prevent optimisation
    i = i_wt;                                //(13) SW delay
    do i--;                                  //(14) delay loop
    while(i != 0);                           //(15) delay loop

    return;                                  //(16) done
}
//------------------------------------------------------------------------
```

This is a very simple code, which will flash a LED connected to port P1.0 (pin #2) of the microcontroller. We will see this example later.

When we are done, and our code is at least syntax-errors free, it is the right time to upload the result of our work to the microcontroller. One possibility how to do that, is start a debugging session - by pressing F11 or following the path from menu: Run -> Debugging:

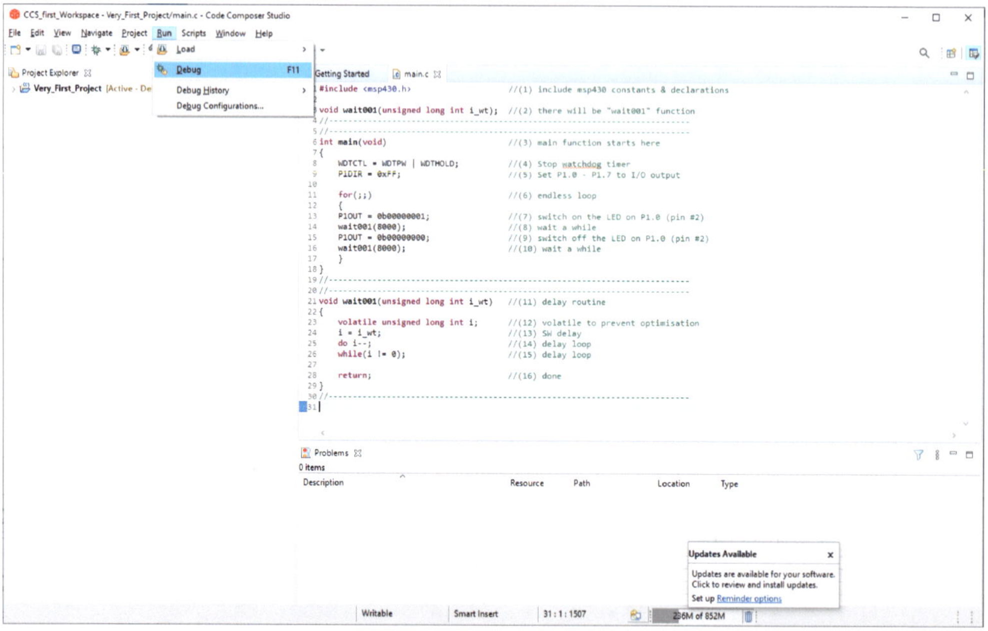

Doing this, the IDE will compile the code and write it to the microcontroller flash / program memory.

When the "flashing" is done, debugging is started and we can follow the code execution directly from IDE - starting with the first line of coding:

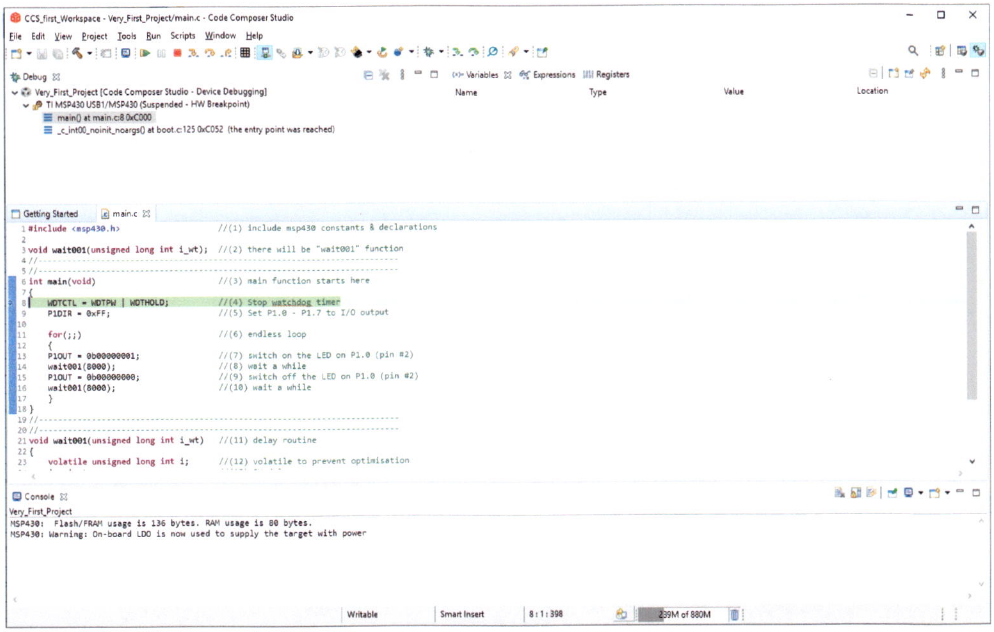

If we do not really want to debug, we can just let the code run by pressing "Resume" or the F8 button on the PC-keyboard:

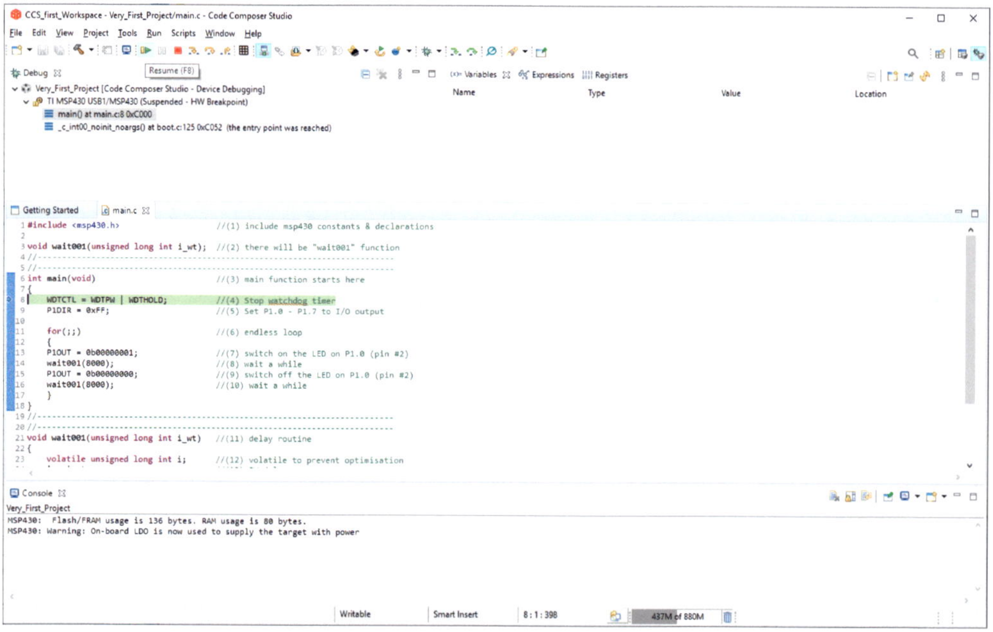

To leave the debugging session completely, we can just hit the "Terminate" button on the screen, or press Ctrl+F2:

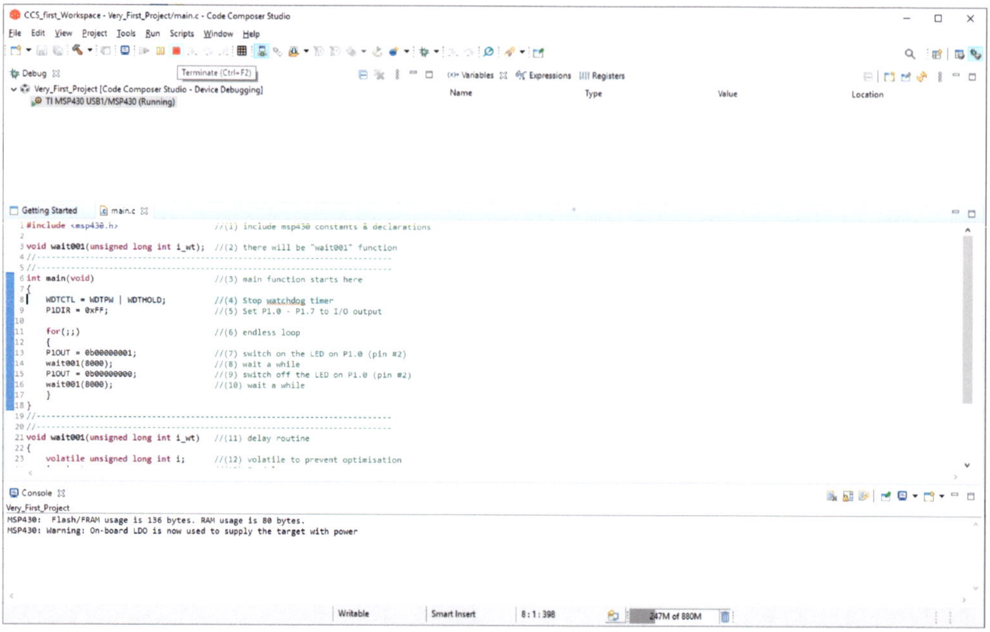

In that moment, debugging will be terminated, and the microcontroller will start to execute uploaded code autonomy - independent of the IDE-control... and the LED is flashing:

In this moment we can even close CCS; or disconnect the LaunchPad and put it just to a external 5V power supply, or even remove the microcontroller from the LaunchPad and put it to own application; after powering, the code uploaded earlier is executed.

2.2 • Energia (MSP430 Arduino)

Now it is the time to do the same exercise with Energia.

Therefore - second IDE we will have a short look on is the Energia. This IDE is able to work with couple of MSP430, some MSP432, Tiva C and CC3200 LaunchPad boards.

For us is of course interesting the support of the MSP430 LaunchPads. Nevertheless with the P-DIP based LaunchPads is only the MSP-EXP430G2ET with microcontroller MSP430G2553 supported. No other P-DIP microcontroller with this LaunchPad can be used with IDE Energia. There is an older version of the MSP-EXP430G2ET LaunchPad - with name MSP-EXP430G2. With this older version two more microcontrollers are supported (MSP430G2231 and MSP430G2452, both of them are kind of "less powerful" versions of the MSP430G2553). But this version of the LaunchPad is not manufactured anymore.

Energia is exactly the same environment as Arduino for the famous ATmega328P manufactured for years by Atmel; in the meantime by Microchip.

IDE Energia can be (at least currently: April 2021) downloaded from following internet site: https://energia.nu/. Like "the another" Arduino - Energia can be downloaded and used for free. At the moment the most current release is: Energia 23 aka Energia 1.8.10E23. Nevertheless our examples are written and tested with release 1.8.7E21. This release can be downloaded from the mention internet side as well.

Once we (download and install and) start Energia, we can straight start to write a code. After starting of IDE, we will see something like this:

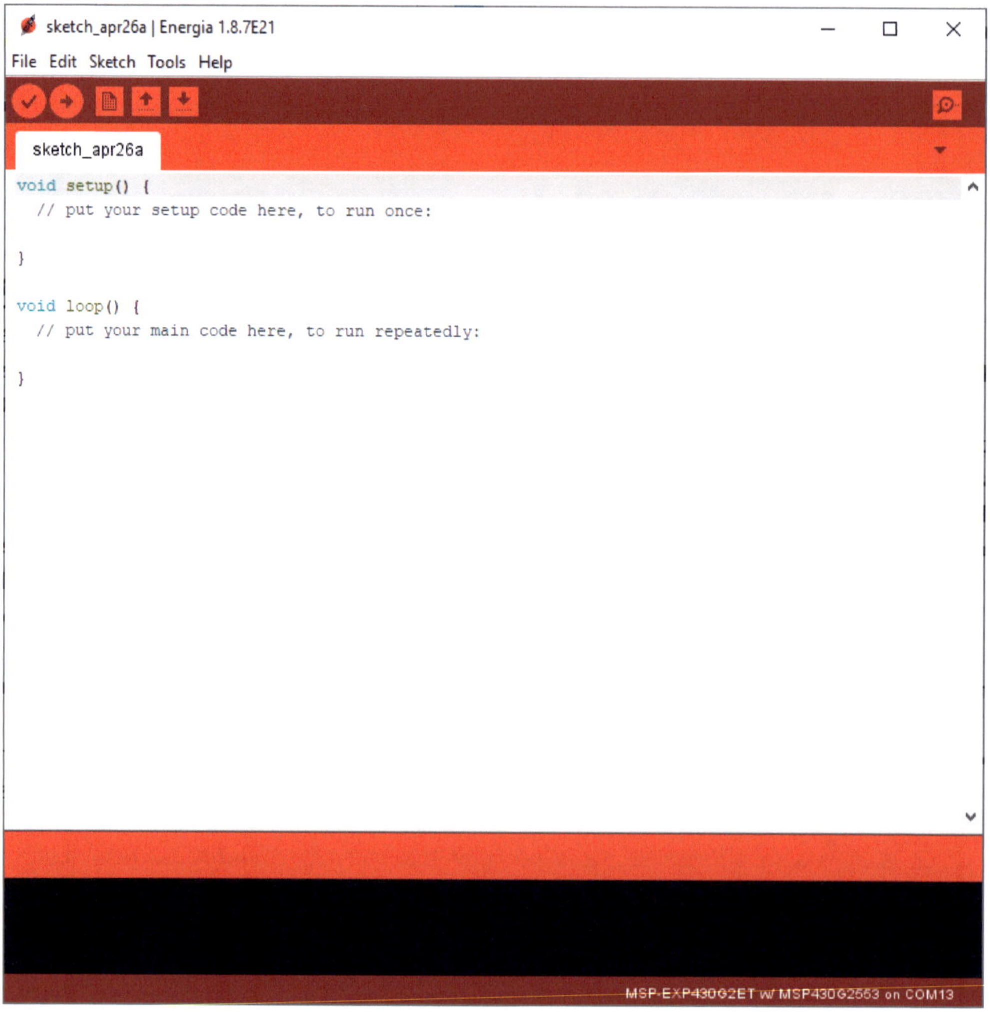

Energia will prepare for us two functions: setup() and loop() as it is usual from Arduino-IDEs. Function setup() is kind of initialization executed exactly once after reset. The loop()-function is then endless main loop of the firmware. All code written in the loop() function will be executed again and again...

For our exercises it is only important to pick-up the right board and port. Therefore from menu Tools -> Board we have to select "MSP-EXP430G2ET w/MSP430G2553":

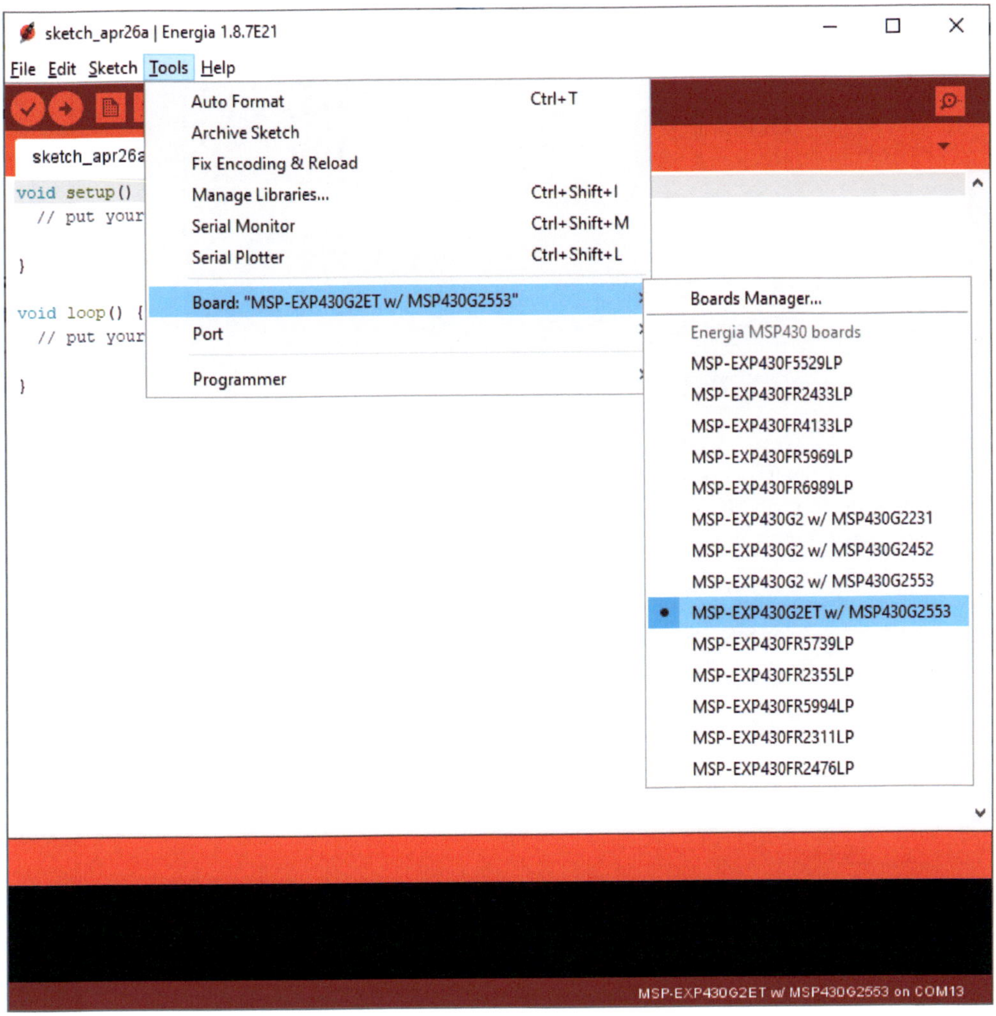

Then we have to select a port, where the board is connected:

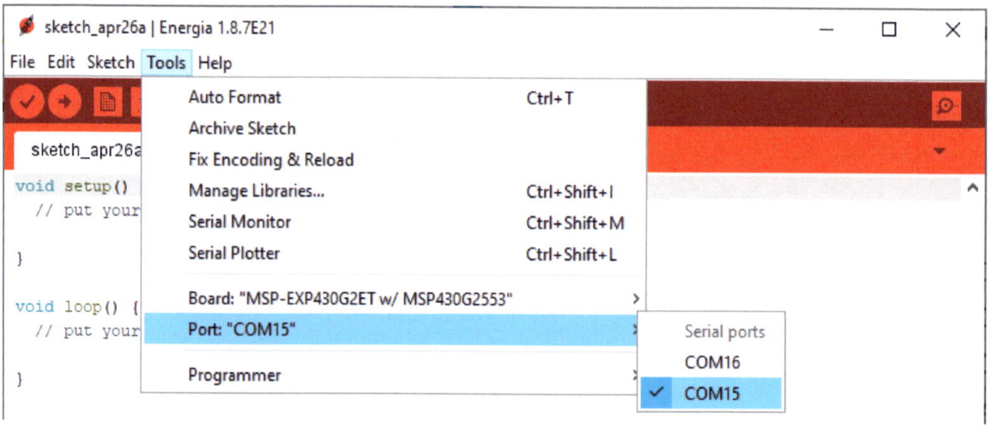

The list of ports available to select can be different every time when you connect your board to the USB slot on the PC. Therefore it is always good - when starting - to check, if the port selected "last time" is still valid.

Now it is good time to save the empty code somewhere (e.g. using Ctrl + S) or the menu path: File -> Save or File -> Save As:

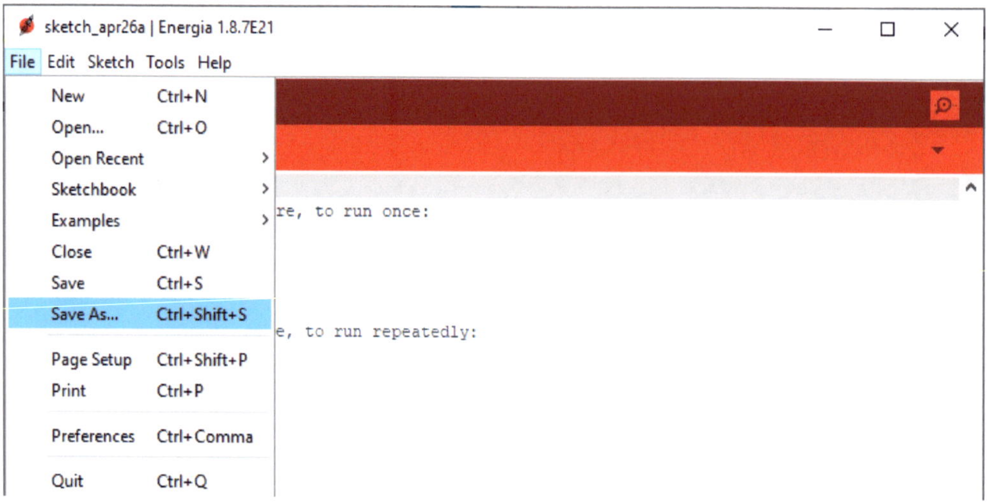

Now we can put the name of the project and our work will be saved:

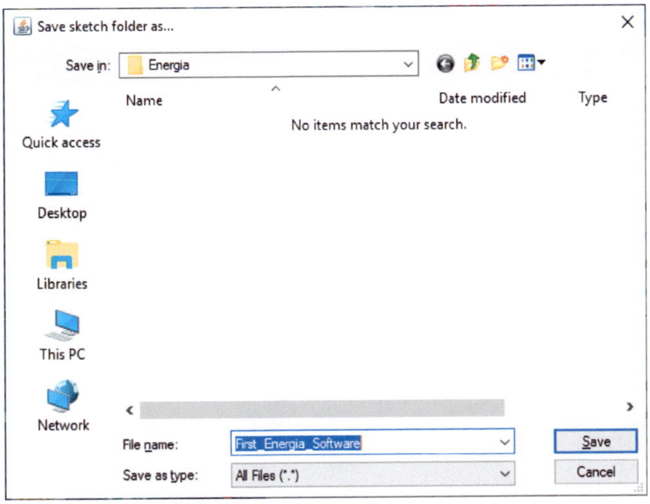

Energia will always save one single file in own directory named the same as the file itself. Looking at the file system we can find the corresponding file and directory:

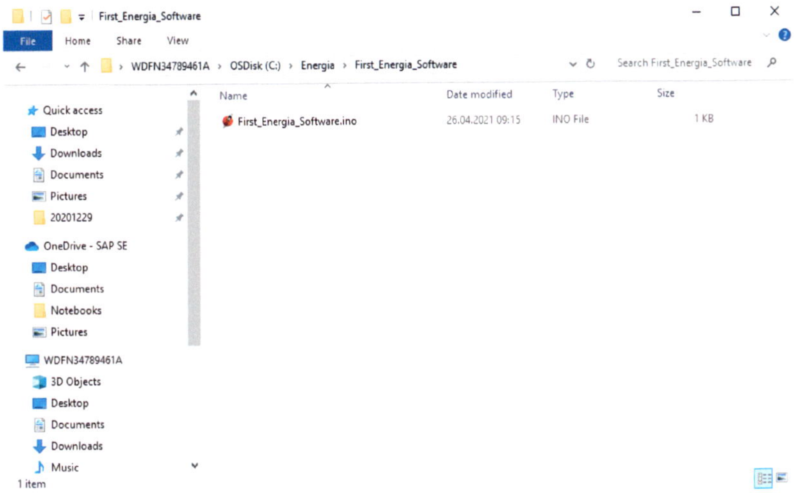

The file will have an extension ".ino", but in the end it is an ordinary text file with the coding (which can be opened e.g. in Notepad):

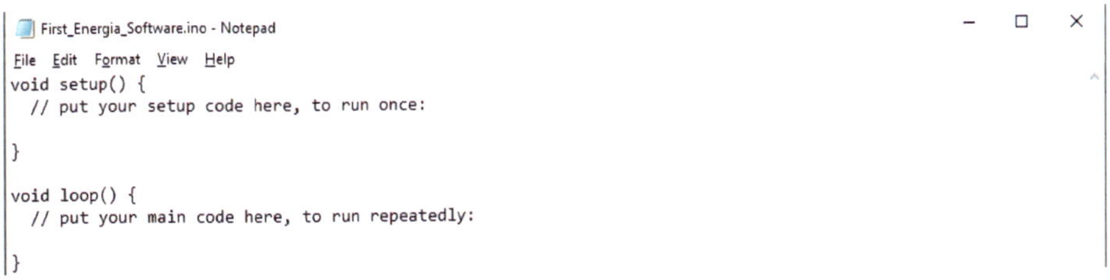

Now we can write the code itself, for example a simple firmware to let a LED blink:

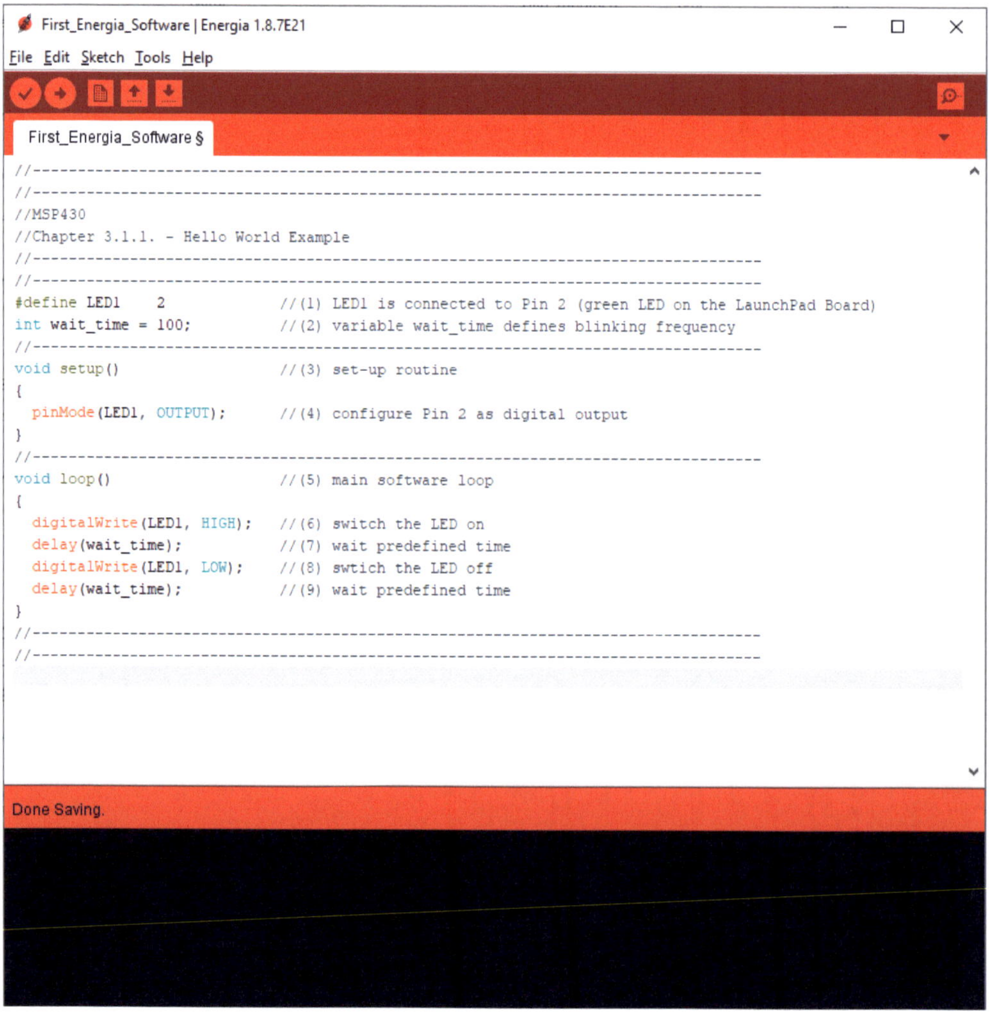

When the code is finished, we have to upload it to the microcontroller. We can do it by pressing Ctrl + U or using menu path Sketch -> Upload:

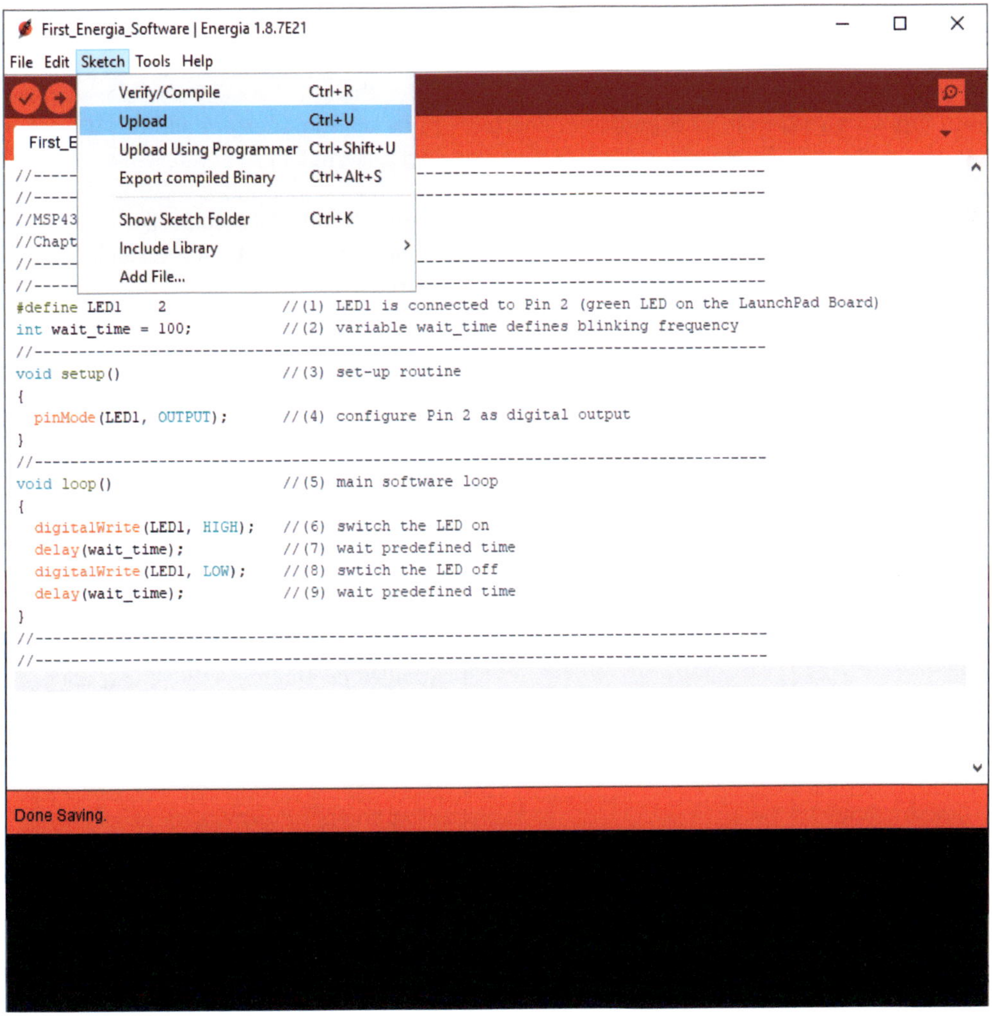

In case we do not have any syntax error in the code, Energia will compile the code und upload it to the microcontroller. Once uploading is done, the microcontroller start to execute the code.

In Energia there is no option to debug the code.

Chapter 3 • Simple Examples for MSP430G2553

I would like to give details of a couple of examples for the MSP430G2553 microcontroller with firmware written in CCS and/or in Energia - to be able to see code in both IDEs. For our examples in CCS, we will use the C-language (not assembler).

We will walk through the different available peripherals of the microcontroller. To get an overview, let's have a look at the functional block diagram of the MSP430G2553. We will take a closer look at the following peripheries of the microcontroller:

Periphery	Chapter	Short Description
GPIO	3.1	We will have a look at available ports (Port 1 & Port 2) in the context of General-Purpose Input / Output functionality. We will configure the ports as digital lines and see how to use them.
ADC10	3.2	In this chapter, we will see the possibilities of the built-in 10-bit Analog to Digital Converter
WDT+	3.3	Typical microcontroller Watchdog extended by another - MSP430-specific - functionality. This is to set up the Watchdog module to a timer mode. In timer mode, it is possible to let the WDT+ generate interrupts.
Timer0 / Timer1	3.4	16-bit timers for general purpose.
Custom	3.5	Custom Serial Communication. Here we will see the possibilities of OneWire communication utilizing a special Energia library.
COMP_A+	3.6	We will explore how we can compare two analog signals.

For some of the examples, we will use the "Serial Monitor" well known to everybody for working/playing around with the Arduino for Microchip microcontroller ATmega328P (of course - coming from Atmel). Therefore I would like to first show how to make the serial monitor work for the Energia Environment.

For the CCS-based example, we will use a 4x20 LCD to display the required values and information. Therefore we will see - already in chapter 3.1., how to easily connect and drive LCD based on an HD44780-compatible controller.

Last but not least - we will describe a very simple 3,3V power supply, which can be used do power our test applications.

We will find the following examples in this chapter:

Example	Corresponding Periphery	Chapter	Short Description
Hello World	GPIO	3.1.1.	First very simple example - blinking LED
Hello World 2	GPIO	3.1.2.	Second very simple example - two LEDs are blinking
Game Cube	GPIO	3.1.3.	Exercise with 7 LEDs and a button-playing cube construction
Connecting LCD	GPIO	3.1.4.	We will learn, how it is possible to connect an HD44780-compatible LCD to the MSP430
Reading ADC Control Registers	ADC10	3.2.1.	Getting in touch with the settings of ADC10 modules and understand the different settings by reading and explaining the ADC10 control registers
Internal Temperature Sensor	ADC10	3.2.2.	Using internal temperature sensor with ADC10 module
Own Voltage	ADC10	3.2.3.	Measurement of power supply voltage using ADC10 module and internal references.
Reading Potentiom-eter	ADC10	3.2.4.	Getting the position of an externally connected potentiometer.
WatchDog Reset	WDT+	3.3.1.	Usage of the WDT+ module as WatchDog.
WatchDog Interrupt Flag	WDT+	3.3.2.	Using the WDT+ module as a timer.
Simple 16-bit counter	Timer_A	3.4.1.	Utilization of Timer_A module as a simple 16-bit counter.
OneWire Thermometer	N/a	3.5.1.	Example of "custom" communication - implementation of OneWire communication with DS18B20 sensor.
Hit the reference	Comparator_A+	3.6.1.	Showing the usage of the Comparator_A+ module to compare two different analog signals.

Serial Monitor

Serial monitor is quite a nice and well-often used tool by Arduino fans. As the Energia supports Serial Monitor in the same way as the ATmega328P-Arduino, we look at serial monitor as well. In the examples, we will mostly use an LCD (4x20) to show the important user information.

To use serial monitor, it is important to establish a communication between the board and PC and test if serial monitor is working as expected.

Out of the box, the MSP-EXP430G2ET looks like this:

The important aspects here are the "switches" in the yellow border. As per default, the out-of-box settings do not allow the usage of serial monitor. We have to change two of them, as we can see in the picture below:

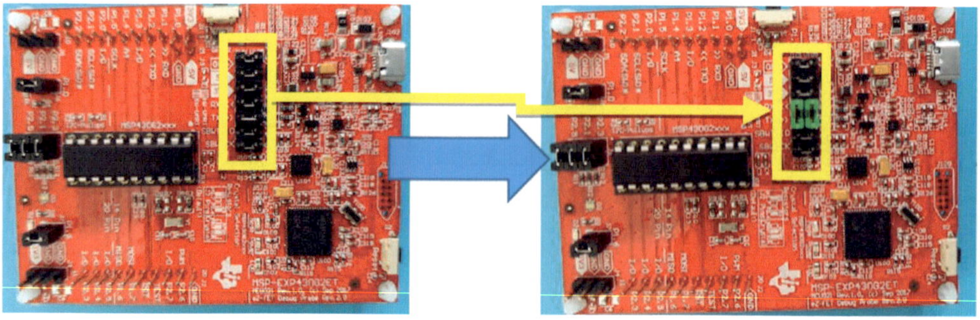

With this small change in the settings of the LaunchPad, we are still able to flash the memory of the microcontroller, do debugging (in CCS), and use the Energia Serial Monitor.

First of all we have to select the corresponding Port for communication with the board, e.g.:

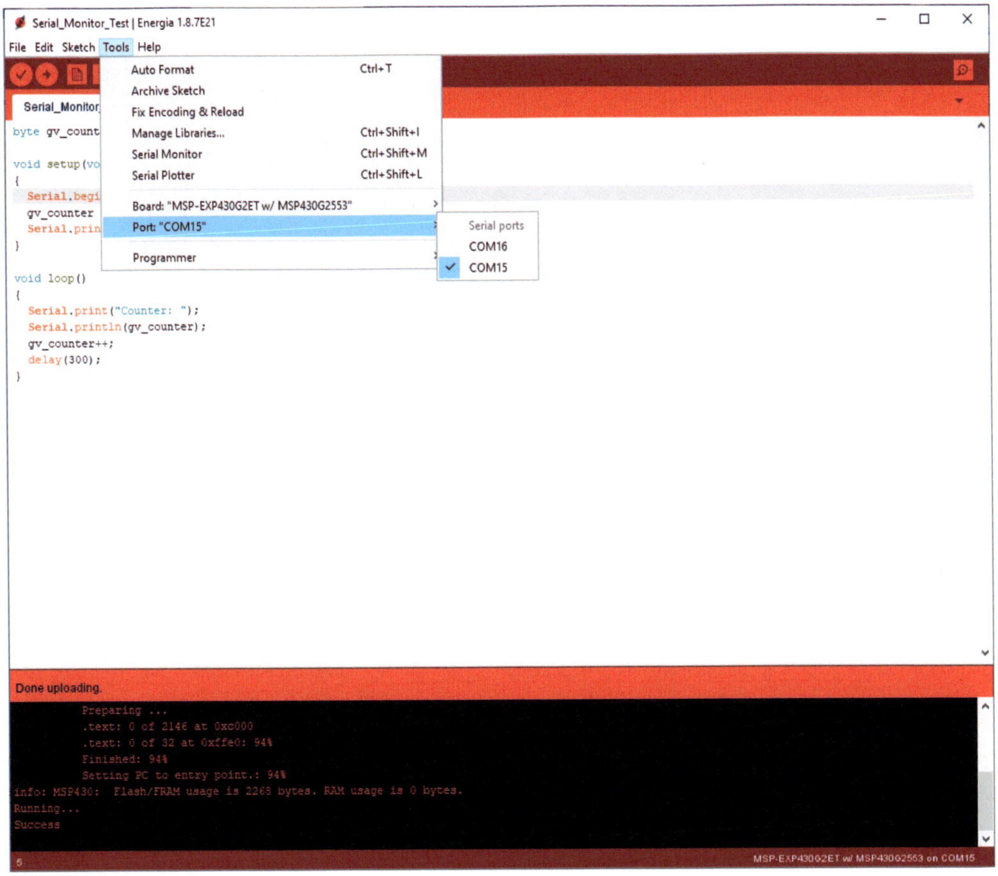

Then we can initialize the Serial Monitor Terminal from menu (Tools -> Serial Monitor), and we will get a kind of "terminal window" displayed:

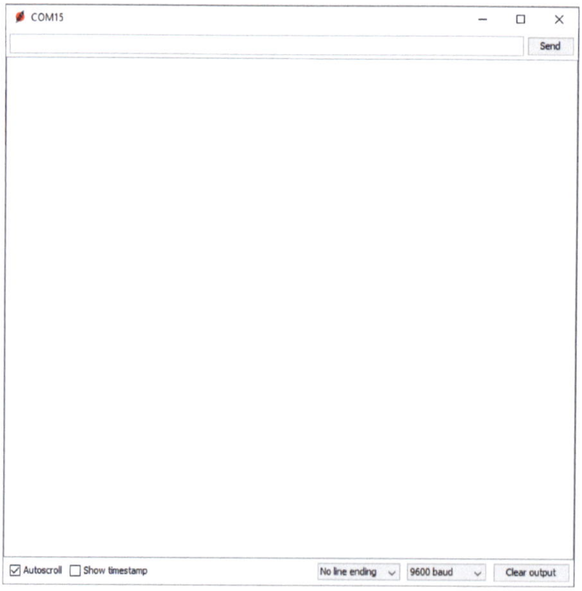

If we execute this simple program (we will not go to details now - just to see a very simple example showing the possibility to send some easy stuff to Serial Monitor), we will get the information about an internal variable of the program shown in Serial Monitor.

The program looks like this:

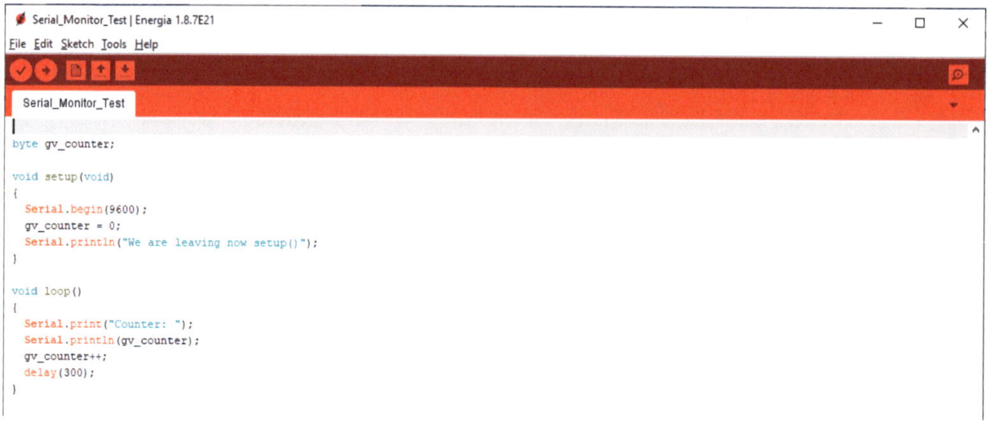

And the output (in Serial Monitor) after we upload the program and execution starts:

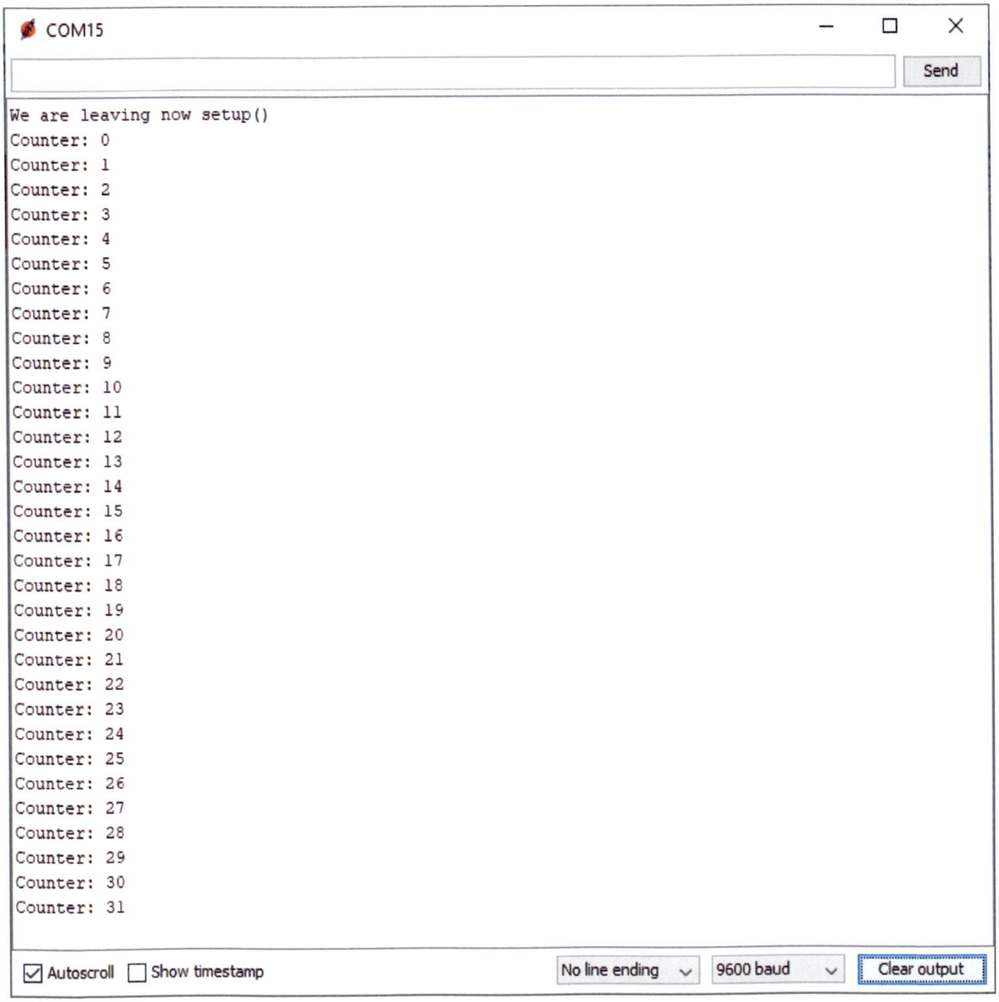

Power Supply

As we know, MSP430 microcontrollers require a power supply below 5.0V. I do not like to use batteries with these kinds of experiments but of course, using them is possible. It is not complicated to put 2x1.5V and power the tools with 3.0V. However, I like my tools to run 24/7 for a month - just to observe stability over time. It is then easier to use another kind of power supply. Over the past few years, I have used 5.0V USB power supplies from cell phones, etc., or sometimes just power banks. The only issue is, we can not supply the microcontroller with 5,0V. Therefore for the MSP430-experiments, I always use a small LDO to get 3.3V out of the 5.0V.

There are many simple LDO's on the market. I just want to show one of them: the MCP1702-3302E/TO available for example in the TO-92 and SOT-23A packages.

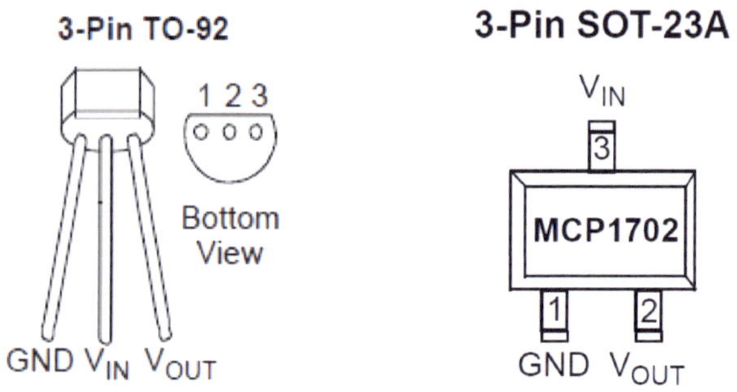

This LDO provides a 3.3V / 250mA output current. The input operating voltage can be up to 13.2V, meaning for the transformation of 5.0V - 3.3V, it is an ideal chip. 250mA is usually more than enough for the experiments.

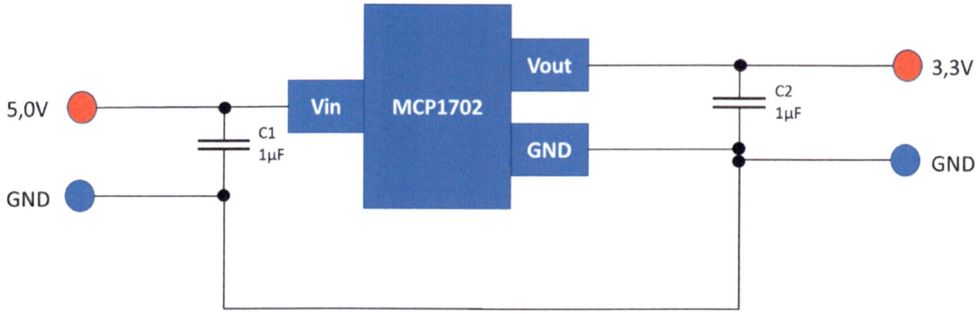

The whole module is very simple and can be built on a universal board - and for example, looks like this:

This module can then be used to provide power for experimental builds on breadboards etc. In the picture, we can see two additional LEDs. These can be used optionally to indicate power on input and output.

3.1 • GPIO

I would like to start with the digital input/output configuration. I'll say this functionality is used in almost all applications and is the easiest scenario. No special knowledge is required. We just need to know, how to configure the ports as digital input or output. And of course how to read the input or how to send the requested value (zero or one) to the output. It is beneficial to know, how to work with a single bit - e.g. how to set a value to P1.2 only, and on the other hand, how to work with the whole port, e.g. how to set all the bits of the port P1 (means - P1.0 - P1.7).

Therefore - before we start, let's have a look at the corresponding registers of the microcontrollers to learn how to set up the ports as digital inputs/outputs.

We will see that with working with Energia, we need to know next-to-nothing about the registers and corresponding hardware, as the Arduino environment, is something between Basic and C... But workings with CCS it makes sense to see a bit behind the curtain.

In the following table, the most important registers for ports as GPIO are listed. The column "register" is always the name of the register as in the datasheet referenced. We should consider that the MSP430G2553 has 2 x 8-bit ports available: P1 and P2. There are always the same control registers available for both 8-bit ports. Therefore the name shown as "PxIN" means register "P1IN" for port P1 and register "P2IN" for port P2, etc.

Register	Short Description
PxIN	To read the input value of a digital pin, we can use the P1IN / P2IN register. Each bit of the register corresponds to one pin of the microcontroller. For example bit 5 of register P1IN represents the value of the P1.5 pin (digital value), where 0 = the input is low and 1 = the input is high. There are of course - based on the nature of the register - no default after reset values for this register(s).

PxREN	This register activate or deactivate integrated pull-up / pull-down resistors. It is possible to enable / disable the pull-up/down resistors for every pin (every single bit) independently of each other. Zero in a bit of PxREN register disables the resistor for the corresponding port, value one enables the resistor. For example, if P1REN = 09h, the resistors for the port P1 are enabled / disabled as follows: P1.0 = enabled P1.1 = disabled P1.2 = disabled P1.3 = enabled P1.4 = disabled P1.5 = disabled P1.6 = disabled P1.7 = disabled why? because 09h = 0000 1001b. If the resistor will be used as pull-up or as pull-down is defined by another register: PxOUT. Summary: Bit = 0 -> Resistor is disabled (default value after reset) Bit = 1 -> Resistor is enabled
PxOUT	This register has two tasks. Either defines the output value of the port - in case the port is configured as digital output and the corresponding resistor is disabled; or it defines, if enabled resistor (by register PxREN) shall be used as pull-up or pull-down. Setting value to this register we will influence the output in case, the corresponding bit of the port is configured as digital output. For example setting value 1Eh to the register P2OUT will set the P2 output to following values: P2.0 = low P2.1 = high P2.2 = high P2.3 = high P2.4 = high P2.5 = low P2.6 = low P2.7 = low why? because 1Eh = 0001 1110b; and each bit define the value of the corresponding output pin. If port P2 is configured as digital input and all corresponding resistors are enabled, the situation will looks like: P2.0 = pull-down P2.1 = pull-up P2.2 = pull-up P2.3 = pull-up P2.4 = pull-up P2.5 = pull-down P2.6 = pull-down P2.7 = pull-down Because a 1 defines, that the resistor is used as pull-up and zero defines, that the resistor shall be pull-down. P1OUT and P2OUT registers are not affected by reset.

<table>
<tr><td>PxDIR</td><td>Definition of direction is done by this register. Setting a bit of this register to 1 will set the corresponding port to output, setting bit to 0 will defined the port as input. For example setting P1DIR register to 0Fh (= 0000 1111b) will define the port P1 as we can see here:
P1.0 = output
P1.1 = output
P1.2 = output
P1.3 = output
P1.4 = input
P1.5 = input
P1.6 = input
P1.7 = input
Summary:
Bit = 0 -> port is configured as input (default value after reset)
Bit = 1 -> port is configured as output</td></tr>
<tr><td>PxSEL & PxSEL2</td><td>For a couple of ports, there is the possibility to deactivate the primary I/O functionality and instead of that activate some specific peripheral module functions. To do that, we can modify the content of the register pair P1SEL & P1SEL2 - for Port 1, and P2SEL & P2SEL2 for Port 2.
To enable I/O function, the corresponding bits of both registers in pair shall be set to 0.
Summary:
<table>
<tr><th>PxSEL2</th><th>PxSEL</th><th>Pin Function</th></tr>
<tr><td>0</td><td>0</td><td>I/O function is selected.</td></tr>
<tr><td>0</td><td>1</td><td>Primary peripheral module function is selected.</td></tr>
<tr><td>1</td><td>0</td><td>Reserved. See device-specific data sheet.</td></tr>
<tr><td>1</td><td>1</td><td>Secondary peripheral module function is selected.</td></tr>
</table>
Default value after reset is: 00 (I/O function selected).</td></tr>
<tr><td>PxIE</td><td>Interrupt Enable Register. This register enables / disables interrupt for every single pin. Change of level on a pin can trigger an interrupt (request).
Summary:
Bit = 0 -> interrupt disabled (default value after reset)
Bit = 1 -> interrupt enabled</td></tr>
<tr><td>PxIFG</td><td>Interrupt Flag Register. A bit of this register is set, if the interrupt condition occurs. Each bit correspond to one port of the microcontroller. The interrupt request indicated in this register must be reset in the software.
Summary:
Bit = 0 -> no interrupt is pending (default value after reset)
Bit = 1 -> an interrupt is pending</td></tr>
<tr><td>PxIES</td><td>Interrupt Edge Select Register. If an interrupt is enabled by the corresponding bit of the PxIE register, this register defines, if the interrupt occurs on raising or falling edge determined on the port.
Bit = 0 -> the PxIFGx flag is set with a low-to-high transition
Bit = 1 -> the PxIFGx flag is set with a high-to-low transition</td></tr>
</table>

As we can see, even for the very basic function of digital I/O there are a couple of registers to be aware of. The beauty of Energia is that we do not need to know nearly anything about these.

Let's start now with the typical example "Hello World" - where we flash a single LED connected to the microcontroller.

3.1.1 • Hello World

What can I say? Let's make an LED flash! No handling, no buttons - just one LED to power on, and flash. A bottle of Champagne can be put on ice to be opened later.

3.1.1.1 • Hardware

"Hello World" is always a very simple example, and of course a very simple circuit. What we can see on the schematic is the connection of the stand-alone microcontroller to the other components of the experiment. As you can see, there are only a few parts required.

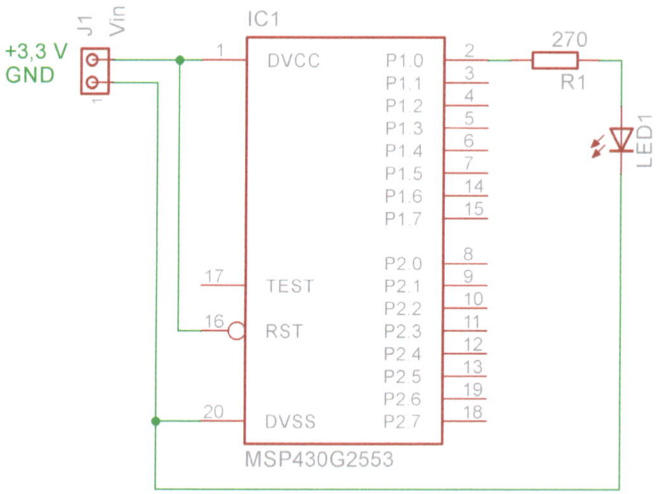

We can see, just a microcontroller, LED, and resistor. Please keep in mind that voltage must not exceed 3.6V.

The value of R1 strongly depends on LED1. In case you are using a low consumption LED, R1 can be up to 10kΩ.

On a breadboard, the circuit may look like this:

3.1.1.2 • Energia Firmware

This firmware is written and tested with Energia-1.8.7E21.

The firmware itself is of course very simple...Especially for Energia, where nearly everything is done by the IDE. A simple program letting the LED blink may look like this:

```
//----------------------------------------------------------------------------
//----------------------------------------------------------------------------
//MSP430
//Chapter 3.1.1. - Hello World Example
//----------------------------------------------------------------------------
//----------------------------------------------------------------------------
#define LED1    2               //(1) LED1 is connected to Pin 2 (green LED on the
LaunchPad Board)
int wait_time = 100;            //(2) variable wait_time defines blinking frequency
//----------------------------------------------------------------------------
void setup()                    //(3) set-up routine
{
  pinMode(LED1, OUTPUT);        //(4) configure Pin 2 as digital output
}
//----------------------------------------------------------------------------
void loop()                     //(5) main software loop
{
  digitalWrite(LED1, HIGH);     //(6) switch the LED on
  delay(wait_time);             //(7) wait predefined time
  digitalWrite(LED1, LOW);      //(8) swtich the LED off
  delay(wait_time);             //(9) wait predefined time
}
//----------------------------------------------------------------------------
//----------------------------------------------------------------------------
```

Let's walk through the code now. At the very beginning, we can see the definition of the label "LED1" (1). Here we define that LED1 is the same as number 2, meaning that our LED is connected to pin #2 of the microcontroller, port P1.0. Besides this, we define an integer variable "wait_time" and assign the value of 100 to the variable (2).

Then we start with the setup() function (3). Here we have one task - to define the P1.0 as output. We can see this is done using the command pinMode (4) - where we define that pin LED1 is used as OUTPUT; meaning - digital output.

Initialization is done with this step. And we continue with the loop() function (5), which is the main routine of the software. This is an endless loop repeating all commands inside over and over. And what do we have to repeat again and again? We have to blink with the LED, meaning we have to switch the LED on, wait a bit, switch the LED off, wait a bit... - and so on.

First, in loop (6) we switch on our LED1. We can see that to do that, we utilize the command digitalWrite. Here we specify which port we want to change (here: LED1 - means pin #2, means P1.0) and we specify the digital value, which shall be sent to the port (here: HIGH - means logical 1). We can either use "HIGH" or just "1". The following commands are always the same, just written differently:

```
digitalWrite(LED1, HIGH);
digitalWrite(LED1, 1);
digitalWrite(P1_0, HIGH);
digitalWrite(2, 1);
```

Once we switch on the LED, we will wait a pre-defined time - 100ms. To do this, we utilise the "delay" function (7).

When the wait time is over, we switch off the LED (8) using function digitalWrite. We send the value "LOW" to the output to kill the light - again as before: all commands are the same:

```
digitalWrite(LED1, LOW);
digitalWrite(LED1, 0);
digitalWrite(P1_0, LOW);
digitalWrite(2, 10);
```

The last step is again waiting (9) and the main loop is processed. As this delay is the last command in the loop, the next executed line will be again (6).

3.1.1.3 • CCS Firmware

This firmware is written and tested with CCS Version: 10.1.1.00004.

Let's have a look at the implementation in C-language using CCS. A Blinking LED can look like this:

```
//---------------------------------------------------------------------------
//---------------------------------------------------------------------------
#include <msp430.h>                   //(1) include msp430 constants & declarations

void wait001(unsigned long int i_wt); //(2) there will be "wait001" function
//---------------------------------------------------------------------------
//---------------------------------------------------------------------------
int main(void)                        //(3) main function starts here
{
    WDTCTL = WDTPW | WDTHOLD;         //(4) Stop watchdog timer
    P1DIR = 0xFF;                     //(5) Set P1.0 - P1.7 to I/O output

    for(;;)                           //(6) endless loop
    {
    P1OUT = 0b00000001;               //(7) switch on the LED on P1.0 (pin #2)
    wait001(8000);                    //(8) wait a while
    P1OUT = 0b00000000;               //(9) switch off the LED on P1.0 (pin #2)
    wait001(8000);                    //(10) wait a while
    }
}
//---------------------------------------------------------------------------
//---------------------------------------------------------------------------
void wait001(unsigned long int i_wt)  //(11) delay routine
{
        volatile unsigned long int i;             //(12) volatile to prevent optimisation
        i = i_wt;                                                     //(13) SW delay
        do i--;                       //(14) delay loop
        while(i != 0);                //(15) delay loop

        return;                       //(16) done
}
//---------------------------------------------------------------------------
```

At the very beginning, we include constants and declarations valid for the MSP430 family (1). In next line (2) we declare the "wait001" function with one input parameter called "wt" of type "unsigned long int".

Then (3) the main function start. The name of this function is always "main" and it is the function that is started after a reset. This code is put on the reset vector.

We put the initialisation to the beginning of the main function. In contrast to the Energia definition, this function is not an explicit loop. The very first instruction is to disable the WatchDog timer (4), as we do not want to use WatchDog in this example, but default settings after reset are enabling the WatchDog timer. For the next step of initialisation, we have to define the output - P1.0 to digital output. This is done in step (5) - where we set up the whole P1 (P1.0 - P1.7) to outputs. We do it by writing the value FFh (= 1111 1111b) to the register P1DIR.

At this moment we start with our coded end-less loop (6) utilising the command "for". Command "for" defines a loop in general. If we left the initialisation statement, test expression, and updated statement out, we get an endless loop.

In the loop we first switch on the LED - putting value 01h (= 0000 0001b) to the register P1OUT (7). As the least significant bit (LSb) is set to 1 - we put a logical one to as output configured port P1.0, meaning the LED is switched on. Then (8) we call our "wait001" routine to wait a while. After this (9) we switch off the LED, putting value 00h to P1 (meaning we put 0 to P1.0 as well - which switches the LED off); and wait while the LED is off (10). With this step, all commands in the endless loop are processed, and the next one will again be step (7).

The last part is to implement a delay routine (11). First, we define an integer variable "i" (12). We have to define it as a volatile data type, otherwise, the compiler will discover that nothing happens in the whole routine, and will optimise (= remove) it. Then (13) we put the input value to our defined "i"-variable and start the while-loop (14) - (15). Once the loop is over, we can return (16) to the calling routine.

That's all we have to code our first Hello World example in CCS.

3.1.2 • Hello World 2

Now we will make a small extension to the previous project by connecting another LED to our circuit. Nothing special, just slowly increasing the complexity, to develop understanding of the basics of programming.

3.1.2.1 • Hardware

In this example we have two LEDs - connected to P1.0 and P1.6. - and? correct... These are exactly the same LEDs found on the LaunchPad board.

If we want to build a stand-alone "flasher", for example on a breadboard, the circuit will look like this:

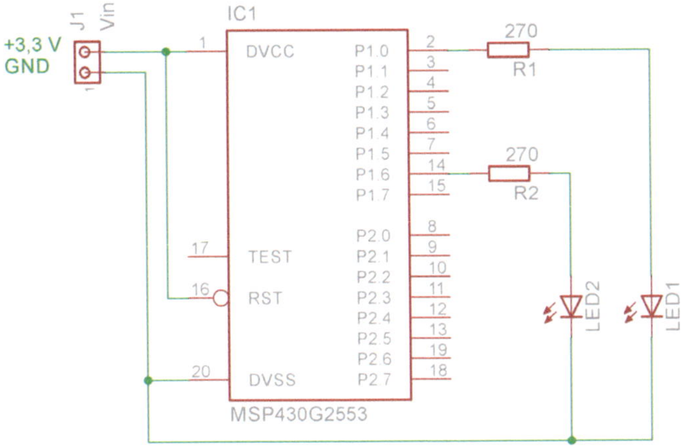

It is exactly the same circuit as before, we just added LED2 and R2.

3.1.2.2 • Energia Firmware

This firmware is written and tested with Energia-1.8.7E21.

The code of our second example is based on the first. Actually it is the same - with some extensions for LED2.

```
//-----------------------------------------------------------------------------------
//-----------------------------------------------------------------------------------
//MSP430
//Chapter 3.1.2. - Hello World 2 Example
//-----------------------------------------------------------------------------------
//-----------------------------------------------------------------------------------
#define LED1 2                //(1.1) LED1 is connected to Pin 2
#define LED2 14               //(1.2) LED1 is connected to Pin 14
int wait_time = 100;          //(2)   variable wait_time defines blinking frequency
//-----------------------------------------------------------------------------------
void setup()                  //(3)   set-up routine
{
  pinMode(LED1, OUTPUT);      //(4.1) configure Pin 2  as digital output
  pinMode(LED2, OUTPUT);      //(4.2) configure Pin 14 as digital output
}
//-----------------------------------------------------------------------------------
void loop()                   //(5)   main software loop
{
  digitalWrite(LED1, HIGH);   //(6.1) switch the LED1 on
  digitalWrite(LED2, LOW);    //(6.2) switch the LED2 off
  delay(wait_time);           //(7)   wait predefined time
  digitalWrite(LED1, LOW);    //(8.1) swtich the LED1 off
  digitalWrite(LED2, HIGH);   //(8.2) swtich the LED2 on
  delay(wait_time);           //(9)   wait predefined time}
}
//-----------------------------------------------------------------------------------
//-----------------------------------------------------------------------------------
```

We can see a new line (1.2) with a definition: LED2 is connected to pin #14. In the setup part, we will find an added line as well - step (4.2) configuring pin #14 as output. And finally in the main function - loop() we can see two new commands: (6.2) switching off the LED2 and (8.2) - switching LED2 on. With this code, LED1 and LED2 will blink "oppositely", i.e. when LED1 is on, LED2 is off and vice versa.

That's all - in all other parts, the coding is the same as in our first example.

3.1.2.3 • CCS Firmware

This firmware is written and tested with CCS Version: 10.1.1.00004.

In the CCS coding, we will do can't find any differences to the Hello World example:

```
//------------------------------------------------------------------------
//------------------------------------------------------------------------
#include <msp430.h>                     //(1) include msp430 constants & declarations

void wait001(unsigned long int i_wt);  //(2) there will be "wait001" function
//------------------------------------------------------------------------
//------------------------------------------------------------------------
int main(void)                          //(3) main function starts here
{
    WDTCTL = WDTPW | WDTHOLD;            //(4) Stop watchdog timer
    P1DIR = 0xFF;                       //(5) Set P1.0 - P1.7 to I/O output

    for(;;)                             //(6) endless loop
    {
    P1OUT = 0b00000001;                 //(7) switch on the LED on P1.0 (pin #2)
    wait001(8000);                      //(8) wait a while
    P1OUT = 0b01000000;                 //(9) switch off the LED on P1.0 (pin #2)
    wait001(8000);                      //(10) wait a while
    }
}
//------------------------------------------------------------------------
//------------------------------------------------------------------------
void wait001(unsigned long int i_wt)   //(11) delay routine
{
        volatile unsigned long int i;          //(12) volatile to prevent
optimisation
        i = i_wt;                                                   //(13) SW
delay
        do i--;                             //(14) delay loop
        while(i != 0);                      //(15) delay loop

        return;                             //(16) done
}
//------------------------------------------------------------------------
```

There has been no new single line added to the code. It is more like a game: Find 10 differences on virtually the same pictures - but here there is only one difference. Do you see it?

As in our first example, we define all ports of P1 as outputs - step (5) - there is nothing additional to be done here. The only difference is in step (9) where, instead of sending 0000 0000b, we send 0100 0000b. Do you see? We switch off LED1 because the bit 0 is equal to zero, but in addition, we switch on LED2 because bit 6 is now set to one (instead of keeping it on zero in example 1). That's the only difference in CCS C-coding.

3.1.3 • Game Cube

We can build something really useful. Useful, but still very simple to construct and code. I picked up a game cube as a good example - which is easy, but we still have to maintain 7 different LEDs and scan one button to control the cube.

The playing cube looks like this:

If we want to realise the cube-dots with LEDs, we will need 7 of them to be able to show all allowed combinations of the numbers 1 to 6:

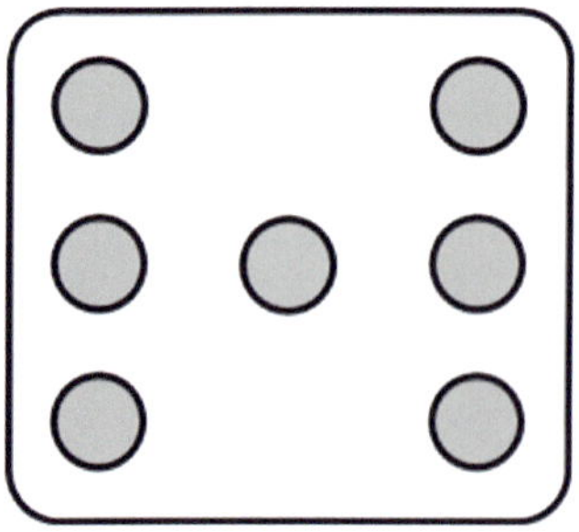

This means to connect all the LEDs and be able to drive them independently of each other (what is not 100% required for the cube application), but let's do it - we need 7 I/O ports of the microcontroller. Let's connect the LEDs to the individual ports like in this picture:

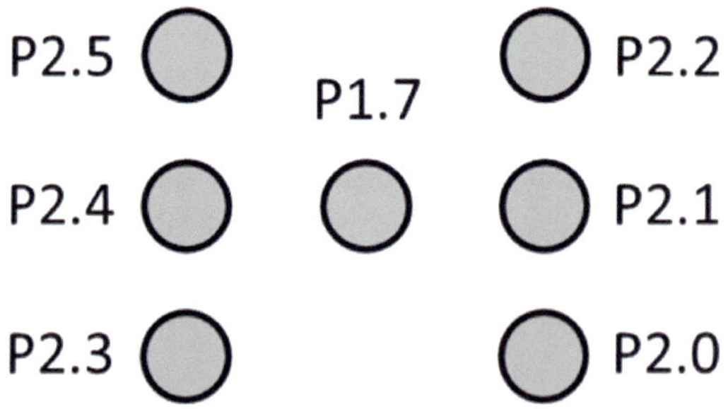

Now we need to define how we want to show the different numbers. It is quite obvious, but for writing a program it makes sense to make it very clear:

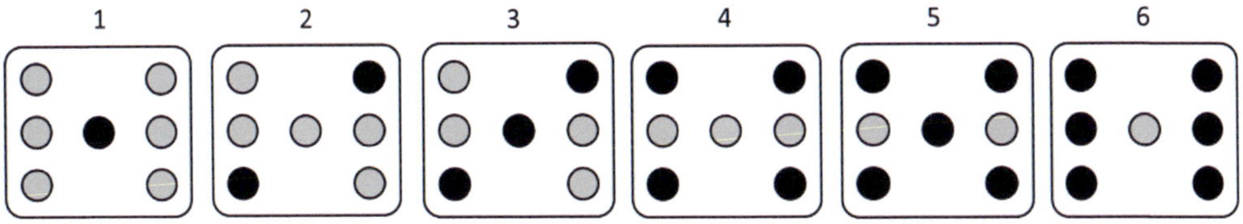

Based on the graphics, we can define the required port outputs for every allowed stage. We can summarise this in the following table - assuming we will connect our LEDs with a common cathode:

Displayed number	**P1.7**	**P2.0**	**P2.1**	**P2.2**	**P2.3**	**P2.4**	**P2.5**
1	HIGH	LOW	LOW	LOW	LOW	LOW	LOW
2	LOW	LOW	LOW	HIGH	HIGH	LOW	LOW
3	HIGH	LOW	LOW	HIGH	HIGH	LOW	LOW
4	LOW	HIGH	LOW	HIGH	HIGH	LOW	HIGH
5	HIGH	HIGH	LOW	HIGH	HIGH	LOW	HIGH
6	LOW	HIGH	HIGH	HIGH	HIGH	HIGH	HIGH

In the end, we can define any combination of LEDs to be switched on at the same time - of course even not existing on the playing cube, for example, this one:

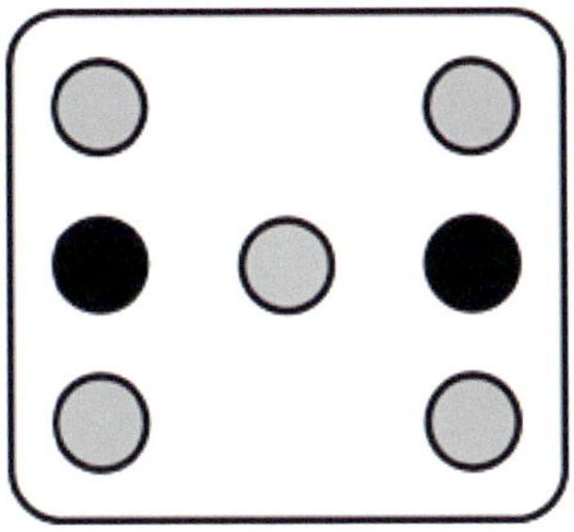

Displayed number	P1.7	P2.0	P2.1	P2.2	P2.3	P2.4	P2.5
strange 2	LOW	LOW	**HIGH**	LOW	LOW	**HIGH**	LOW

What else do we want to build? We would like to get an LED playing cube with one button. When the button is pressed, the "cube is rolling", meaning the numbers on the LEDs will be changed from 1 through 2, 3, 4, 5 to 6; and then again starting at 1 - but so fast, it will look like all the LEDs are lighting up. Once the button is released, the cube is stopped at the number which was displayed at the moment of button release.

3.1.3.1 • Hardware

The hardware for the dice is quite simple. We just have more LED compared to our Hello World examples. This is not so bad and in addition, we have one button and this is all. We even do not need to take care of the pull-up resistor, as we will utilise the internal one in the microcontroller. We already saw how the LEDs in the cube are connected to the single P2-ports. We will connect the button to P1.3 as if we build just a shield for the LaunchPad (not a stand-alone cube) we can use the button directly on the LaunchPad itself.

In the picture, we see the connection between the LEDs and MCU as well as the distribution of the LED to make the "cube" realistic.

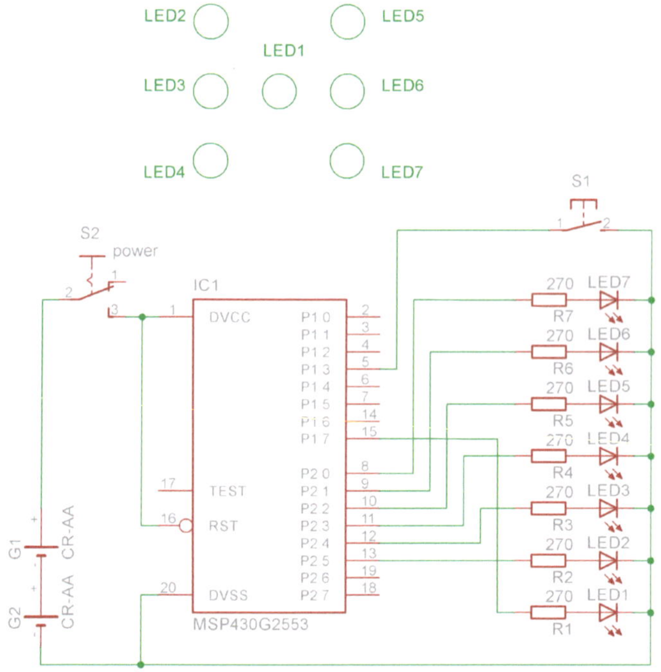

When using low-current LEDs, resistors R1 - R7 should be 1kΩ (instead of 270Ω) and the power consumption around ~4mA if 6 LEDs are lit up. This means the whole circuit can be powered using 2xAAA batteries for years, or even from a single 3V battery like a CR2032:

The cube realised as a shield for the LaunchPad may look like this:

The Cube can be built as a stand-alone device for example on a universal board powered by 2 x 1.5V AAA battery. My prototype looks like this:

Let's have a look at firmware now.

3.1.3.2 ● Energia Firmware

This firmware is written and tested with Energia-1.8.7E21.

As you can see, the firmware is a bit more complex than our first Hello World examples. On the other hand, it is a real application now, which can be used in practice. It is for example very useful for travelling with children, who want to play a game where a playing cube is required. As you know, a classic cube very often gets lost...

So - let's have a look at the firmware. It may look like this. Let's start with the setup function:

```
//--------------------------------------------------------------------------
//--------------------------------------------------------------------------
//MSP430
//Chapter 3.1.3. - Playing Cube
//--------------------------------------------------------------------------
//--------------------------------------------------------------------------
void setup()                                //(1) start of setup function
{
  pinMode(P2_0, OUTPUT);                    //(2.1) set port P2.0 to digital output
  pinMode(P2_1, OUTPUT);                    //(2.2) set port P2.1 to digital output
  pinMode(P2_2, OUTPUT);                    //(2.3) set port P2.2 to digital output
  pinMode(P2_3, OUTPUT);                    //(2.4) set port P2.3 to digital output
  pinMode(P2_4, OUTPUT);                    //(2.5) set port P2.4 to digital output
  pinMode(P2_5, OUTPUT);                    //(2.6) set port P2.5 to digital output
  pinMode(P1_7, OUTPUT);                    //(2.7) set port P1.7 to digital output

  show_test();                              //(3) execute LED test

  wm_x2();                                  //(4) display not existing combination

  pinMode(P1_3, INPUT_PULLUP);              //(5) set port P1.3 to digital input
}
//--------------------------------------------------------------------------
```

We are not using any labels/declarations here. We start directly with the setup function (1). What we have to do here, is to set the direction for ports used. Therefore we first (2.1 – 2.7) set all ports, where the LEDs are connected to digital outputs - the same way, as we did it earlier in the Hello World examples. We just use another naming. We can see, that the predefined port names correspond to the names of the pins. For example, port P2.1 is called P2_1; port P1.7 is called P1_7, etc. Once we put all output ports to digital output, we show "test" (3) - we will come to this function later. After this, we show the "strange 2" (4) - we saw earlier as a sign, that the cube has just been switched on and nobody has yet rolled the dice.

Last but not least (5) we configure port P1.3 as digital input and activate the pull-up resistor, as this port is used as input for the button.

We are now finished with the setup activities and can have a look at the main function of the firmware, an endless loop called "loop":

```
//------------------------------------------------------------------------------
void loop()                                      //(6) main - endless loop
{
  while(digitalRead(P1_3) == 0)                  //(7) another loop - the cube is rolling
                                                 //    until button is pressed (P1.3 = 0)
     {
        if(digitalRead(P1_3) == 0) wm_01();      //(8.1a) change to 1, but only if the button is still pressed
        delay(10);                               //(8.1b) wait a bit to make the LEDs flashing
        if(digitalRead(P1_3) == 0) wm_02();      //(8.2a) change to 2, but only if the button is still pressed
        delay(10);                               //(8.2b) wait a bit to make the LEDs flashing
        if(digitalRead(P1_3) == 0) wm_03();      //(8.3a) change to 3, but only if the button is still pressed
        delay(10);                               //(8.3b) wait a bit to make the LEDs flashing
        if(digitalRead(P1_3) == 0) wm_04();      //(8.4a) change 4, but only if the button is still pressed
        delay(10);                               //(8.4b) wait a bit to make the LEDs flashing
        if(digitalRead(P1_3) == 0) wm_05();      //(8.5a) change to 5, but only if the button is still pressed
        delay(10);                               //(8.5b) wait a bit to make the LEDs flashing
        if(digitalRead(P1_3) == 0) wm_06();      //(8.6a) change to 6, but only if the button is still pressed
        delay(10);                               //(8.6b) wait a bit to make the LEDs flashing
     }
}
//------------------------------------------------------------------------------
```

The main function is quite simple. We are using - well, let's say, a character generator. This means we defined functions to show all numbers used with LEDs. Function wm_01 will show number 1, function wm_02 number 2, etc. Within the main endless loop of the function "loop" (6), we used another inner loop defined by the "while" command. This loop is just showing all the allowed numbers in the ascending order: 1 -> 2 -> 3 -> 4 -> 5 -> 6 -> 1 -> 2 -> ... again and again. And very fast... It looks like all 7 LEDs are lighting up. The inner loop runs until the button connected to P1.3 is continually pressed. We can see it in the condition of the "while" command (7). What is important, the numbers change, until the button is pressed. We can see on all lines (8.1a) to (8.6a) displaying the corresponding numbers, that a number is displayed only if the button is still pressed. Why? Because the while-loop can be left only after the last command in the loop (8.6b) and this is showing the number 6. This means if we show the numbers independent of the stage of the P1.3 button, a 6 will always be the result. This is nice, but not particularly useful. Once the button is released, no new number is displayed, and the system will exit the loop "soon". Once this happens the while-loop is not entered anymore and only the main endless loop is executed without any commands. If the button is pressed again, the microcontroller starts the while-loop again and we are about to roll the dice again.

Also, after each change of the displayed number we include a short wait. This has two purposes: First - without waiting, the LEDs will light up - all of them. With this short delay, the LEDs will "blink", or "flash" - changing the displayed number so fast it is not possible to follow, but still quite clearly changing the displayed number. The second reason is, that without this delay, the highest probability will be to get the number 6. Why? Because it is the last one shown in the loop, and after 6 the loop is "restarting", and the button test is done again. There are just µs, but still, the number 6 is displayed longer than any other number. Including the delays eliminate this discrepancy, as the delays are much longer than the loop-restart, and therefore the loop-restart becomes completely irrelevant from a timing perspective.

The next function is used after power-up (or reset) to slowly switch on all the LEDs. This is useful for test purposes if we want to see the LEDs are all connected and working correctly.

```
//--------------------------------------------------------------------------
void show_test()                              //(T-1) - Test on Start-up
{
  wm_space();                                 //(T-2) - clear the display
  digitalWrite(P2_0, 1);                      //(T-3) - switch on the P2.0 LED
  delay(200);                                 //(T-4) - wait 200ms
  digitalWrite(P2_1, 1);                      //(T-5) - switch on the P2.1 LED
  delay(200);                                 //(T-6) - wait 200ms
  digitalWrite(P2_2, 1);                      //(T-7) - switch on the P2.2 LED
  delay(200);                                 //(T-8) - wait 200ms
  digitalWrite(P2_3, 1);                      //(T-9) - switch on the P2.3 LED
  delay(200);                                 //(T-10) - wait 200ms
  digitalWrite(P2_4, 1);                      //(T-11) - switch on the P2.4 LED
  delay(200);                                 //(T-12) - wait 200ms
  digitalWrite(P2_5, 1);                      //(T-13) - switch on the P2.5 LED
  delay(200);                                 //(T-14) - wait 200ms
  digitalWrite(P1_7, 1);                      //(T-15) - switch on the P1.7 LED
  delay(200);                                 //(T-16) - wait 200ms
}
//--------------------------------------------------------------------------
//--------------------------------------------------------------------------
```

The name of the function is "show_test" (T-1). If we consider the 7 LEDs as a "cube-display" - we can say, that in the first step (T-2) we clean up the display calling function wm_space(). We will see this soon. We then switch on the LED connected to P2.0 (T-3), wait 200ms (T-4), and switch on the next LED connected to P2-1 (T-5), wait again 200ms (T-6), and so on, until all LEDs are on - in step (T-15). At this moment we get "7" displayed. After the last 200ms wait time (T-16) the test is finished and the function is complete.

The next part of the code defines functions on how the different numbers will be shown on the "display" - we can more or less call it a character set.

The first character defined (WM-S) is "space" - meaning all LEDs off.

```
//--------------------------------------------------------------------------
//--------------------------------------------------------------------------
void wm_space()                                    //(WM-S) - switch off all the
LEDs
{
  digitalWrite(P2_0, 0);
  digitalWrite(P2_1, 0);
  digitalWrite(P2_2, 0);
  digitalWrite(P2_3, 0);
  digitalWrite(P2_4, 0);
  digitalWrite(P2_5, 0);
  digitalWrite(P1_7, 0);
}
//--------------------------------------------------------------------------
```

As we can see, there is nothing special about this: we just put zero (= level LOW) to all LED-driving I/Os.

The next function is to show ONE: here we put one (= level HIGH) to the I/O driving the LED in the middle, and all others are put to zero.

```
//--------------------------------------------------------------------------
void wm_01()                                       //(WM-1) - show 1
{
  digitalWrite(P2_0, 0);
  digitalWrite(P2_1, 0);
  digitalWrite(P2_2, 0);
  digitalWrite(P2_3, 0);
  digitalWrite(P2_4, 0);
  digitalWrite(P2_5, 0);
  digitalWrite(P1_7, 1);
}
//--------------------------------------------------------------------------
```

And so on. We can see here all other definitions for all other numbers from 1 to 6.

```
//--------------------------------------------------------------------------
void wm_02()                                       //(WM-2) - show 2
{
  digitalWrite(P2_0, 0);
  digitalWrite(P2_1, 0);
  digitalWrite(P2_2, 1);
  digitalWrite(P2_3, 1);
  digitalWrite(P2_4, 0);
  digitalWrite(P2_5, 0);
  digitalWrite(P1_7, 0);
```

```
}
//------------------------------------------------------------------------------
//------------------------------------------------------------------------------
void wm_03()                                    //(WM-3) - show 3
{
  digitalWrite(P2_0, 0);
  digitalWrite(P2_1, 0);
  digitalWrite(P2_2, 1);
  digitalWrite(P2_3, 1);
  digitalWrite(P2_4, 0);
  digitalWrite(P2_5, 0);
  digitalWrite(P1_7, 1);
}
//------------------------------------------------------------------------------
//------------------------------------------------------------------------------
void wm_04()                                    //(WM-4) - show 4
{
  digitalWrite(P2_0, 1);
  digitalWrite(P2_1, 0);
  digitalWrite(P2_2, 1);
  digitalWrite(P2_3, 1);
  digitalWrite(P2_4, 0);
  digitalWrite(P2_5, 1);
  digitalWrite(P1_7, 0);
}
//------------------------------------------------------------------------------
//------------------------------------------------------------------------------
void wm_05()                                    //(WM-5) - show 5
{
  digitalWrite(P2_0, 1);
  digitalWrite(P2_1, 0);
  digitalWrite(P2_2, 1);
  digitalWrite(P2_3, 1);
  digitalWrite(P2_4, 0);
  digitalWrite(P2_5, 1);
  digitalWrite(P1_7, 1);
}
//------------------------------------------------------------------------------
//------------------------------------------------------------------------------
void wm_06()                                    //(WM-6) - show 6
{
  digitalWrite(P2_0, 1);
  digitalWrite(P2_1, 1);
  digitalWrite(P2_2, 1);
  digitalWrite(P2_3, 1);
  digitalWrite(P2_4, 1);
```

```
  digitalWrite(P2_5, 1);
  digitalWrite(P1_7, 0);
}
//-----------------------------------------------------------------------------
```

The last "character" is the "strange two", shown after start-up to indicate the cube is not yet used after power-up (or reset).

```
//-----------------------------------------------------------------------------
void wm_x2()                                    //(WM-X2) - show strange 2
{
  digitalWrite(P2_0, 0);
  digitalWrite(P2_1, 1);
  digitalWrite(P2_2, 0);
  digitalWrite(P2_3, 0);
  digitalWrite(P2_4, 1);
  digitalWrite(P2_5, 0);
  digitalWrite(P1_7, 0);
}
//-----------------------------------------------------------------------------
//-----------------------------------------------------------------------------
```

3.1.3.3 • CCS Firmware

This firmware is written and tested with CCS Version: 10.1.1.00004.

The CCS-based firmware is nearly the same as the Energia-based one and may look like this example.

In the first part we see all declarations of the libraries (1), symbols (2), and implemented functions (3 - 4.9) used:

```
//--------------------------------------------------------------------------
//--------------------------------------------------------------------------
#include <msp430.h>                         //(1) include msp430 constants &
declarations

#define wait_time     500                   //(2) define wait time between number
changes

void wait001(unsigned long int i_wt);       //(3) there will be "wait001" function
void wm_01(void);                           //(4.1) character set: number 1
void wm_02(void);                           //(4.2) character set: number 2
void wm_03(void);                           //(4.3) character set: number 3
void wm_04(void);                           //(4.4) character set: number 4
void wm_05(void);                           //(4.5) character set: number 5
void wm_06(void);                           //(4.6) character set: number 6
void wm_x2(void);                           //(4.7) character set: number "strange
2"
void wm_space(void);                        //(4.8) character set: all off
void show_test(void);                       //(4.9) LED test for start-up
//--------------------------------------------------------------------------
```

I'll strongly assume for those we do not need a detailed description anymore.

The main function (5) is quite easy and is taking care of "rolling of the dice". The principle is the same, as we described in the Energia-version of the firmware:

```
//--------------------------------------------------------------------------
int main(void)                              //(5) main function starts here
{
    WDTCTL = WDTPW | WDTHOLD;               //(6) Stop watchdog timer
    P1DIR = 0b10000000;                     //(7) set-up I/O direction for P1
    P1REN = 0b00001000;                     //(8) enable resistor on P1.3
    P1OUT = 0b00001000;                     //(9) set up pull-up functionality for P1.3
    P2DIR = 0xFF;                           //(10) set P2.0 - P2.7 to I/O output

    show_test();                            //(11) execute the LED test
    wm_x2();                                //(12) show "strange 2"

    for(;;)                                 //(13) endless loop
    {
    while((P1IN & BIT3) == 0)               //(14) inner loop - when button is pressed
      {
        if ((P1IN & BIT3) == 0) wm_01();    //(15.1a) change to 1 - if the button is still pressed
        wait001(wait_time);                 //(15.1b) wait a bit to make the LEDs flashing
        if ((P1IN & BIT3) == 0) wm_02();    //(15.2a) change to 2 - if the button is still pressed
        wait001(wait_time);                 //(15.2b) wait a bit to make the LEDs flashing
        if ((P1IN & BIT3) == 0) wm_03();    //(15.3a) change to 3 - if the button is still pressed
        wait001(wait_time);                 //(15.3b) wait a bit to make the LEDs flashing
        if ((P1IN & BIT3) == 0) wm_04();    //(15.4a) change to 4 - if the button is still pressed
        wait001(wait_time);                 //(15.4b) wait a bit to make the LEDs flashing
        if ((P1IN & BIT3) == 0) wm_05();    //(15.5a) change to 5 - if the button is still pressed
        wait001(wait_time);                 //(15.5b) wait a bit to make the LEDs flashing
        if ((P1IN & BIT3) == 0) wm_06();    //(15.6a) change to 6 - if the button is still pressed
        wait001(wait_time);                 //(15.6b) wait a bit to make the LEDs flashing
      }
    }
}
//--------------------------------------------------------------------------
```

Of course, there are small differences because of the environment. What is interesting (and different) here, is the set-up of the I/O port to connect the button - port P1.3. We can see that first (7) we set the direction of all P1 ports to input except for P1.7 (where the middle LED is connected).

Then (8) we enable a pull-up/pull-down resistor on P1.3 writing the corresponding value to the P1REN register. We can see, that the "1" is written to bit 3 of the register meaning the resistor will be enabled on P1.3.

Afterward (9) we say, that the enabled resistor will be pull-up and not pull-down. This is because we write "1" to bit 3 of the P1OUT register.

The main loop of the firmware is defined utilizing the command "for" (13). It is of course an endless loop. The "dice-rolling" loop is using the "while" command (14) and, as I said already, is implemented using the same logic as the Energia-version.

The next function implemented is the LED test on start-up (T-1) - function "show_test":

```
//-----------------------------------------------------------------------
void show_test(void)                         //(T-1) LED test for start-up
{
    wm_space();                              //(T-2) clear the display
    P2OUT = 0b00000001;                      //(T-3) switch on the P2.0 LED
    wait001(20000);                          //(T-4) wait a while
    P2OUT = 0b00000011;                      //(T-5) switch on the P2.1 LED
    wait001(20000);                          //(T-6) wait a while
    P2OUT = 0b00000111;                      //(T-7) switch on the P2.2 LED
    wait001(20000);                          //(T-8) wait a while
    P2OUT = 0b00001111;                      //(T-9) switch on the P2.3 LED
    wait001(20000);                          //(T-10) wait a while
    P2OUT = 0b00011111;                      //(T-11) switch on the P2.4 LED
    wait001(20000);                          //(T-12) wait a while
    P2OUT = 0b00111111;                      //(T-13) switch on the P2.5 LED
    wait001(20000);                          //(T-14) wait a while
    P1OUT = 0x88;                            //(T-15) switch on the P1.7 LED
    wait001(20000);                          //(T-16) wait a while
}
//-----------------------------------------------------------------------
```

All other parts are just the functions for character set definition (WM-S) - (WM-6) incl. (WM-2x) and a waiting routine (wait001) for the main loop.

```
//---------------------------------------------------------------------------
void wm_space(void)                        //(WM-S) switch off all LEDs
{ P1OUT = 0x08; P2OUT = 0x00; }
//---------------------------------------------------------------------------
void wm_01(void)                           //(WM-1) show 1
{ P1OUT = 0x88; P2OUT = 0x00; }
//---------------------------------------------------------------------------
void wm_02(void)                           //(WM-2) show 2
{ P1OUT = 0x08; P2OUT = 0b00001100; }
//---------------------------------------------------------------------------
void wm_03(void)                           //(WM-3) show 3
{ P1OUT = 0x88; P2OUT = 0b00001100; }
//---------------------------------------------------------------------------
void wm_04(void)                           //(WM-4) show 4
{ P1OUT = 0x08; P2OUT = 0b00101101; }
//---------------------------------------------------------------------------
void wm_05(void)                           //(WM-5) show 5
{ P1OUT = 0x88; P2OUT = 0b00101101; }
//---------------------------------------------------------------------------
void wm_06(void)                           //(WM-6) show 6
{ P1OUT = 0x08; P2OUT = 0b00111111; }
//---------------------------------------------------------------------------
void wm_x2(void)                           //(WM-2x) show strange 2
{ P1OUT = 0x08; P2OUT = 0b00010010; }
//---------------------------------------------------------------------------
//---------------------------------------------------------------------------
void wait001(unsigned long int i_wt)       //(D-1) delay routine
{
    volatile unsigned long int i;          //(D-2) volatile to prevent optimisation
    i = i_wt;                              //(D-3) SW delay
    do i--;                                //(D-4) delay loop
    while(i != 0);                         //(D-5) delay loop
    return;                                //(D-6) done
}
//---------------------------------------------------------------------------
//---------------------------------------------------------------------------
```

I hope this part of the code is self-explanatory.

3.1.4 • Connecting an LCD

The last example of the pure digital I/O part is the connection of an LCD to the MSP430G2553 microcontroller.

If you intend to test or play around with the examples described in this book and with the CCS IDE, it makes sense to build this example as we will use it instead of Serial Monitor, especially for CCS-based examples. It makes sense to set it up as a shield for the MSP430 LaunchBoard, as it is then easy to load different firmware to the microcontroller.

In this chapter, we will see the connection of 4x20 LCD to the MSP430G2553 microcontroller using 4-bit parallel communication with the LCD. This kind of connection requires 6x I/O ports on the MCU.

3.1.4.1 ● Hardware

We will connect the LCD with an HD44780-compatible driver chip to the MSP430 LaunchPad. Typical displays are running with the same communication protocol, like 2x16 (2 rows, 16 columns), 2x20, 2x24, 4x20, etc. They all use the same connection and communication conventions. All of them can be connected in the same way, as described in this chapter.

Typical connections of this kind of LCD look like this (in the picture is 2x16 display showed):

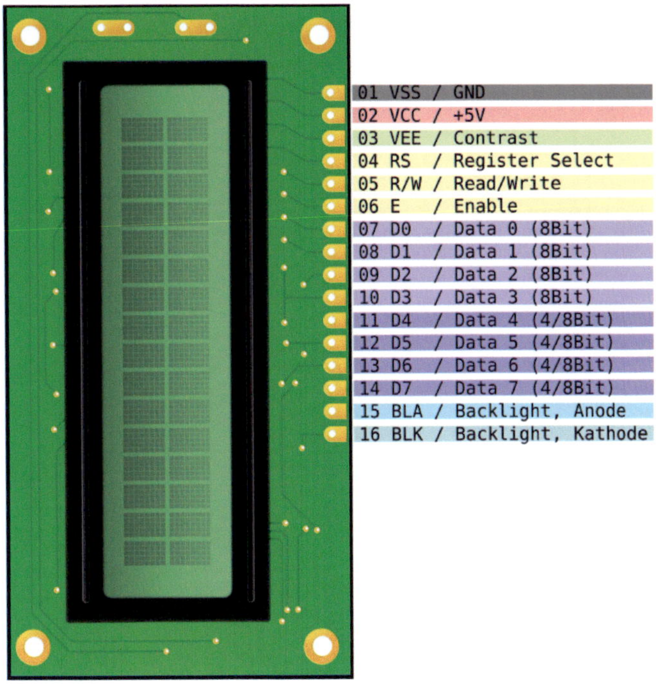

Many new LCDs can work with a power supply of 3.3V, as used for our MSP430G2553, but not all of them. To make sure that whatever display you have will work, we power the LCD with 5.0V. This is possible, as the high level of digital signals is for all displays - typically the voltage level from 2.0V upwards will be by the LCD considered as logical 1; and we do not have to be concerned about the MCU, as we do not send any data from the LCD to MCU. We will use a one-way road: MCU -> LCD.

The connection from the MCU / LaunchPad Board is defined on the following table:

LCD Pin	LCD Pin Name	Usage of the pin	Connect to
1	GND	Power: GND	GND
2	V_{cc}	Power: + 5,0V	+ 5,0 V
3	Contrast	Set-up contrast of the display	Trimmer 10k / connected between +5,0 V and GND
4	RS	0 = a command will be sent 1 = data will be sent	MSP430G2553 / P1.0 (Pin #2)
5	RW	0 = write to LCD controller 1 = read from LCD controller	GND
6	E	Communication Enable	MSP430G2553 / P1.1 (Pin #3)
7	D0	LSb for 8-bit transfer	Not connected
8	D1	Data bit 1 for 8-bit transfer	Not connected
9	D2	Data bit 2 for 8-bit transfer	Not connected
10	D3	Data bit 3 for 8-bit transfer	Not connected
11	D4	Data bit 4 for 8-bit transfer or LSb for 4-bit transfer	MSP430G2553 / P1.2 (Pin #4)
12	D5	Data bit 5 for 8-bit transfer or Data bit 1 for 4-bit transfer	MSP430G2553 / P1.3 (Pin #5)
13	D6	Data bit 6 for 8-bit transfer or Data bit 2 for 4-bit transfer	MSP430G2553 / P1.4 (Pin #6)
14	D7	MSb for 8-bit transfer or MSb for 4-bit transfer	MSP430G2553 / P1.5 (Pin #7)
15	BLA	Backlight - Anode	Trimmer 1k / connected to +5,0 V
16	BLK	Backlight - Cathode	GND

We will come back to the description later when we start to analyse the CCS-based firmware. The schematics of the connection (below the stand-alone application) are very simple and besides the microcontroller and LCD, contain only two passive elements:

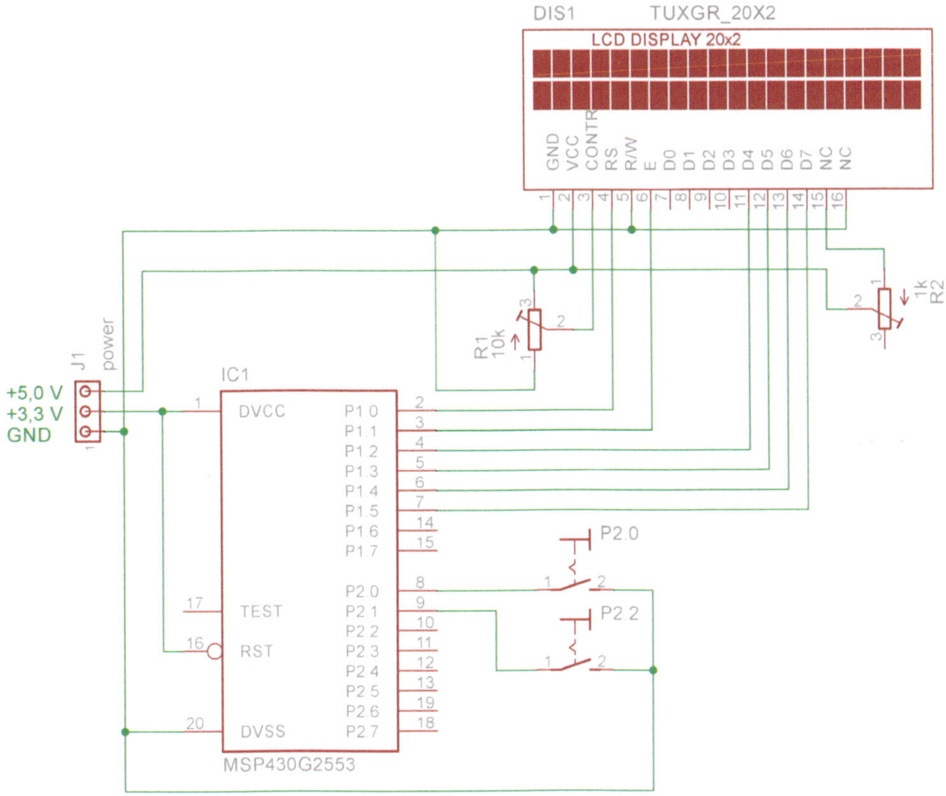

With R1 it is possible to set the contrast of the display. With R2 we can define the brightness of the backlight of the LCD.

Connection to the LaunchPad is done in the same way. On the LaunchPad connector, we will found both voltages: 5.0V and 3.3V as well.

Included are two buttons, not used in this example, but we will utilise them later.

3.1.4.2 • Energia Firmware

This firmware is written and tested with the Energia-1.8.7E21.

Energia firmware is very simple, as we will utilise the existing library for the LCD. The library is called <LiquidCrystal.h> and allows easy and conventional work with LCDs.

Our firmware will show how to write information on the LCD, and do something like definining a counter from 0 to 99.999, which will be shown on the LCD.

Let's first have a look at an important topic: "the map of the LCD"; and the command lcd. setCursor(col, row).

In the library, we can find a command to set up the position on the LCD, where the next output will be turned on aka the starting position.

As we are using an LCD 20x4 (20 columns and 4 rows), we will find coordinators for rows 0 to 3 and columns 0 to 19. The following command will set the cursor at row 0 and column 0 (the upper left corner of the LCD):

```
lcd.setCursor(0,0);
```

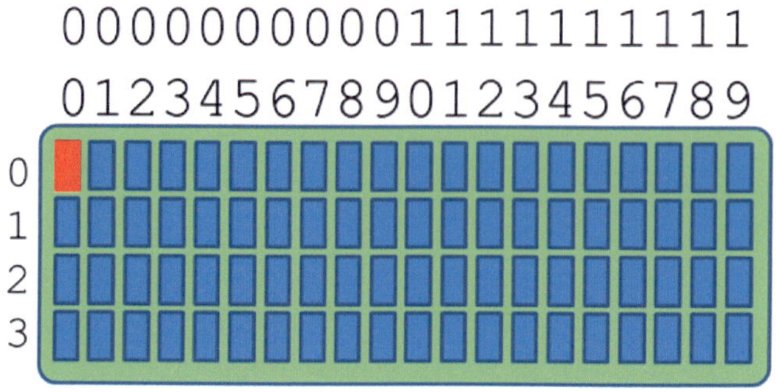

The following command:

```
lcd.setCursor(13,2);
```

will set the cursor at row number 2 and column 13:

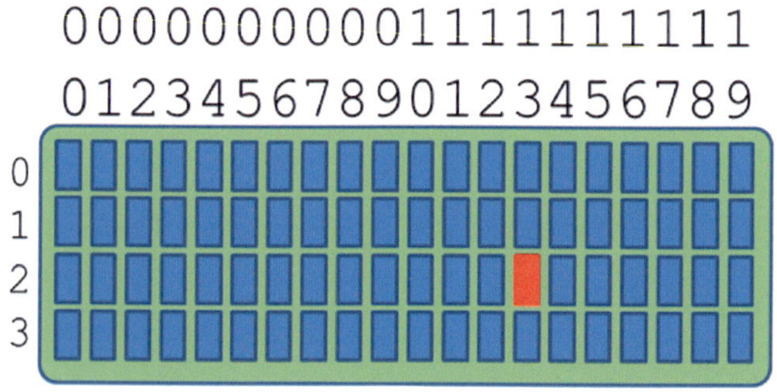

The next important command is "print", which allows the sending of data to be shown on the LCD itself. The next two commands will print the text "Release 1.24" to the 3rd row (row number 2) from the beginning of the row:

```
lcd.setCursor(0,2);
```

```
lcd.print("Release 1.24");
```

The outcome will look like this:

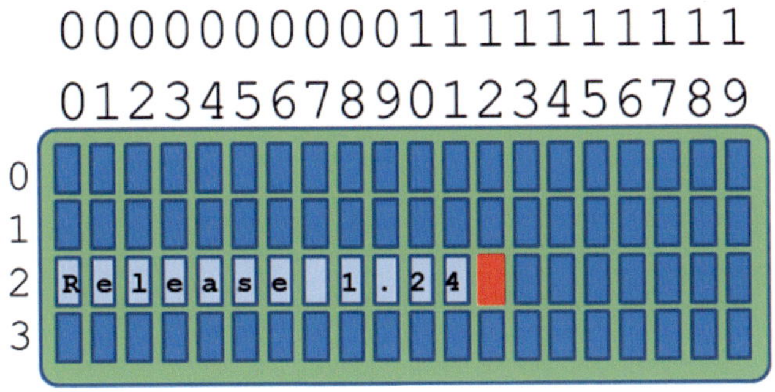

...and the cursor will stay in the next position: row 2 and column 12.

I guess it is enough for the moment. Let's have a look at one possible implementation of our simple example with a counter:

```
// -------------------------------------------------------------------------------------------
// -------------------------------------------------------------------------------------------
//MSP430
//Chapter 3.1.4. - LCD connection
// -------------------------------------------------------------------------------------------
// -------------------------------------------------------------------------------------------
#include <LiquidCrystal.h>                            //(1) include LCD communication library
LiquidCrystal lcd(P1_0, P1_1, P1_2, P1_3, P1_4, P1_5); //(2) define the connection to LCD
unsigned long int v_counter = 0;                      //(3) define counter variable
// -------------------------------------------------------------------------------------------
// -------------------------------------------------------------------------------------------
void setup()                                          //(4) Setup function
{
  lcd.begin(20, 4);                                   //(5) set-up usage of 4 rows x 20 columns

  lcd.setCursor(0,0);                                 //(6) put cursor to position col:0 / row:0
  lcd.print("MSP430 Power Book");                     //(7) write the text in quotes starting at 0,0
  lcd.setCursor(0,1);                                 //(8) put cursor to position col:0 / row:1
  lcd.print("MCU: MSP430G2553");                      //(9) write the text in quotes starting at 0,1
  lcd.setCursor(0,2);                                 //(10) put cursor to position col:0 / row:2
  lcd.print("Chapter 3.1.4");                         //(11) write the text in quotes starting at 0,2
  lcd.setCursor(0,3);                                 //(12) put cursor to position col:0 / row:3
  lcd.print("28.12.2020");                            //(13) write the text in quotes starting at 0,3

  delay(3000);                                        //(14) wait 3 sec
```

```
  lcd.clear();                                  //(15) clear the content of the LCD
}
// ---------------------------------------------------------------------------------------------------
// ---------------------------------------------------------------------------------------------------
void loop()                                     //(16) main loop starts here
{
  lcd.setCursor(0,0);                           //(17) put cursor to position col:0 / row:0
  lcd.print("LCD connection");                  //(18) write the text in quotes starting at 0,0
  lcd.setCursor(0,1);                           //(19) put cursor to position col:0 / row:1
  lcd.print("Version: Energia");                //(20) write the text in quotes starting at 0,1
  lcd.setCursor(0,2);                           //(21) put cursor to position col:0 / row:2
  lcd.print("here is a counter:");              //(22) write the text in quotes starting at 0,2
  w_print(3,3);                                 //(23) show counter information
  v_counter++;                                  //(24) increment counter
  if (v_counter > 99999) v_counter = 0;         //(25) put counter to 0 if we cross the border
}
// ---------------------------------------------------------------------------------------------------
// ---------------------------------------------------------------------------------------------------
void w_print(byte iv_col, byte iv_row)          //(26) writing counter stage
                                                //     always 5 places (with leading zeros)
{
  lcd.setCursor(iv_col,iv_row);                 //(27) put cursor to position col:3 / row:3
  lcd.print("==> ");                            //(28) write the text in quotes starting at 3,3
  if (v_counter < 10000) lcd.print("0");        //(29) for number under 10.000: write zero on this position
  if (v_counter < 1000 ) lcd.print("0");        //(30) for number under  1.000: write zero on this position
  if (v_counter < 100  ) lcd.print("0");        //(31) for number under    100: write zero on this position
  if (v_counter < 10   ) lcd.print("0");        //(32) for number under     10: write zero on this position
  lcd.print(v_counter);                         //(33) show the counter value
  lcd.print(" <==");                            //(34) write the text in quotes
}
// ---------------------------------------------------------------------------------------------------
// ---------------------------------------------------------------------------------------------------
```

As we can see, the demo-firmware "counter" is short. The reason is that all LCD-communication routines are "hidden" in the library we are going to use (1) - LiquidCrystal.h; where the parallel 4-bit communication and some flexibility regarding used LCD are implemented and available to reuse.

In the next step, we are declaring "lcd" as a class, which will be used later for communication with the LCD itself, and within this declaration provide the information on how the display is connected to the microcontroller (2). This is done with the LiquidCrystal lcd(P1_0, P1_1, P1_2, P1_3, P1_4, P1_5) definition. The syntax is LiquidCrystal **lcd**(RS, E, D4, D5, D6, D7). Based on this, we can see the assignment of the MCU I/O ports to the pins of the LCD module:

```
lcd( RS,   E,   D4,   D5,   D6,   D7)
```

```
lcd(P1_0, P1_1, P1_2, P1_3, P1_4, P1_5)
```

At the beginning we will define as well a global variable v_counter (3), which will be used to count from 00.000 to 99.999; and displayed on LCD.

We will now go through the setup routine (4) step by step to see what each command is doing.

In step (5) we define we are using LCD 4x20 (4 rows with 20 columns).

In step (6) we put the cursor on the upper left corner of the LCD - to row 0 and column zero. The LCD will be empty, just the cursor position is set. By default, we will not see the cursor on the display. We will see an empty screen, and the cursor position is as shown here:

When step (7) is finished, we will see the first line displayed and the current cursor position as shown in the following "screenshot":

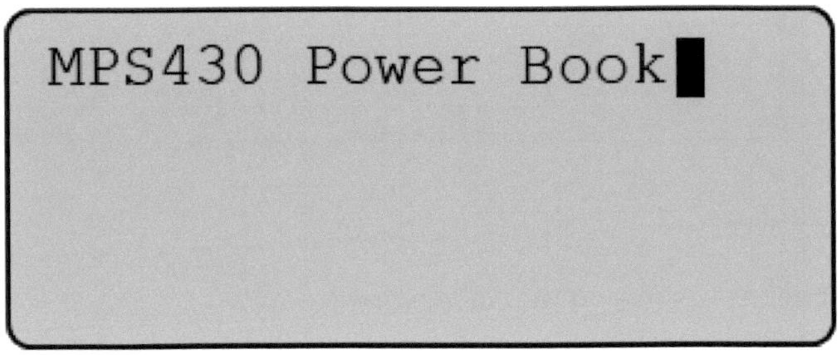

Continuing with step (8) we put the cursor in the new position:

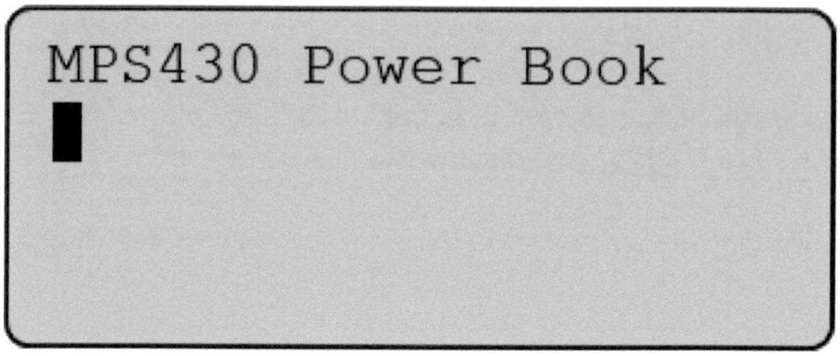

Now we can print out the next line (9):

...and put the cursor to the beginning of the next line (10):

And so on.

After step (13) the LCD is showing the full picture like this:

And the invisible cursor if of course hidden in the last line after the last "0".

As this is only the setup, we have to wait for 3 seconds (to give a chance to read the information on the LCD) - step (14). Then we clear the display (15) and finish the setup routine.

Let's summarise: We are using three different functions from the library:

`lcd.setCursor(col, row)` - to put the cursor at desired column and row position

`lcd.print(text)` - to write a text (or even content of a variable) to LCD starting from current cursor position

`lcd.clear()` - function w/o parameter to clear the display

The main loop of the firmware is a simple starting at step (16). Steps (17) to (22) will write static texts to the LCD - these are the first three lines of the LCD.

In step (23) we call another function - w_print() - to show the current value of the counter on the last line of LCD. Step (24) is incrementing the counter and (25) taking care of overflow, putting the counter value back to zero, once 100.000 has been reached.

The main loop screen looks like this:

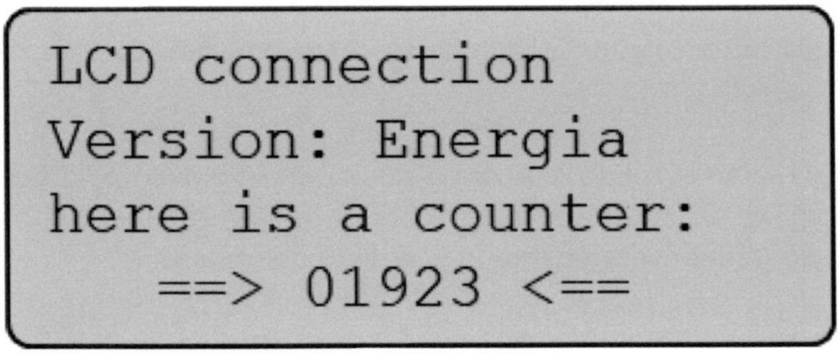

The last part of the firmware is the function to write the content of the counter (26). The reason for this function is to always write the leading zero to the current counter stage. This means, for example, if the counter value is 1923, we do not want to see "1923", but "01923". If the value is 151, we want "00151" to display... etc.

This function is then doing nothing other than putting leading zeros (based on the value) in front of the counter itself.

3.1.4.3 • CCS Firmware

This firmware is written and tested with CCS Version: 10.1.1.00004.

In the CCS-version of the firmware, we will build the communication with the LCD (without using any pre-built library). This is helpful if you later want to port the firmware to a different microcontroller, or even a different programming language. I built this software originally in assembler for Microchip PIC microcontrollers and ported it to C-language for MSP430.

To be able to understand the communication routines, let's first have look at the HD44780-based LCD communication protocol. Don't worry - we will not go through the entire theory. We just summarised what we will need to write and understand the communication routines used in this book.

We can send "command" and "data". A command is something, that will define the behaviour of the LCD, e.g. to clear the display, put the cursor to the required position, etc. Data is something that will be displayed on the LCD. We need to know, that in principle we can either write to or read from the LCD. We also need to know we can use either 8 or 4-bit communication.

Let's say we will never read any data and will use 4-bit communication. 4-bit communication makes the firmware a bit more complicated but saves 4 I/O microcontroller ports.

Communication with HD44780

We first need to learn the communication protocol to know how to send information to the LCD module.

We will ignore the timing of the R/W signal because we said, we would never read bytes in our examples from the LCD module, and put the R/W to zero. This means R/W is on zero all the time signalling that every operation is a write operation.

The host is, in general, sending two different kinds of data towards LCD: data byte - let's say something, what has to be written to the memory (simplified: an ASCII-byte, which shall be displayed on the display), and command byte - a byte controlling the behaviour of the LCD, setting the cursor position, etc.

The sending of data byte can be described with the following flow:

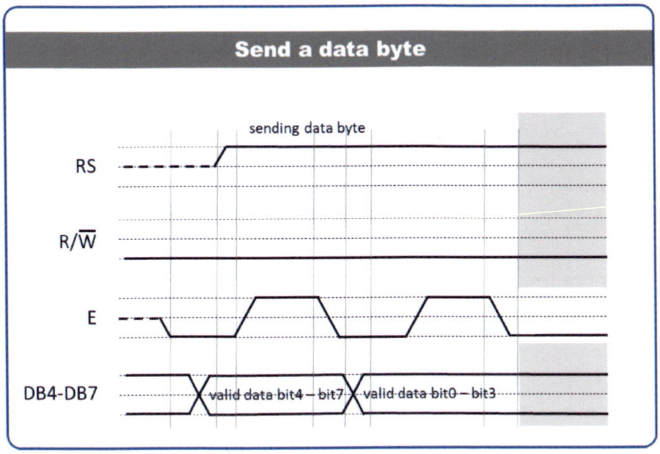

The sending of the Command byte can be described with the following flow:

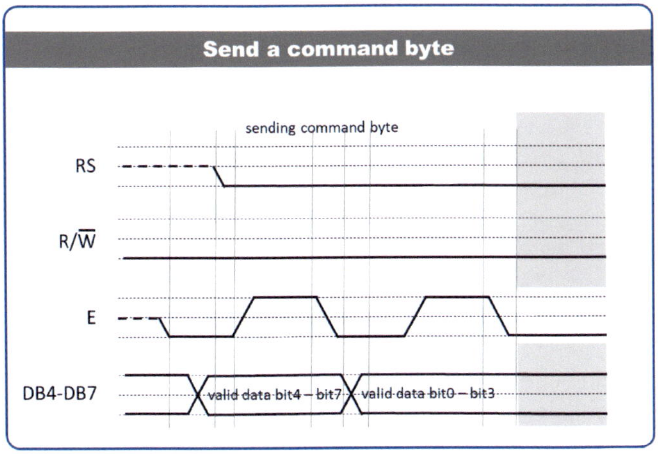

As we can see - the only difference in sending data vs command is the level of the RS-line. If we want to send a data byte, the RS-line has to be held at level one. If we are sending a command byte, the RS-line will be zero.

Based on flow, we can define a sequence of how to drive the different signals to send a byte to the LCD module. Let's call our byte to send "v_LCD_byte".

1. **put Enable line to zero** (meaning: disable communication)

   E= 0

2. **Set the used data lines** (D4-D7) to the upper part of the byte to be sent:

D4 = v_LCD_byte.bit4
D5 = v_LCD_byte.bit5
D6 = v_LCD_byte.bit6
D7 = v_LCD_byte.bit7

3. **Set the RS-line** to the appropriate value: RS will be in the step set to 1. If we intend to send a "data byte", set to 0. If we are sending a "command byte":

   RS = 1 [sending data byte]
   RS = 0 [sending command byte]

4. Now we need to indicate that all signal lines are prepared, and the LCD module will consume the data. This is done with a **pulse on Enable line**. We have to set E to 1, wait a bit, and set E back to 0 and wait again.

   E = 1
   Short wait (~1.000ns)
   E = 0
   Short wait (~1.000ns)

5. Now we can **send the second half** of the byte:

   D4 = v_LCD_byte.bit0
   D5 = v_LCD_byte.bit1
   D6 = v_LCD_byte.bit2
   D7 = v_LCD_byte.bit3

6. **Set the RS-line** in exactly the same way, as we did in step #3:

   RS = 1 [sending data byte]
   RS = 0 [sending command byte]

7. **Generate a pulse on the Enable-line** the same way as in step #4:

   E = 1
   Short wait (~1.000ns)
   E = 0
   Short wait (~1.000ns)

With step #7 the byte transfer is finished.

Now we know how to send a byte to the LCD. We also know how to send a command and data byte.

All together, we need to master three functions:

1. We need to be able to initialise the LCD (e.g. to communicate that we are using 4-bit communication)
2. We need to be able to send a command to the LCD
3. We need to be able to send data to the LCD

It is helpful for us to be aware of some abbreviations usually used in the context of LCD / HD44780:

- **DDRAM** = Display Data Ram - display memory, where displayed data is stored
- **CGRAM** = Character Generator RAM (we are not using CGRAM, as we will not define our own characters in the examples)
- **DDRAM** address corresponds to cursor position.

Initialization of the LCD

At startup, we have to initialise the LCD controller and set up 4-bit communication. To do this, we have to follow these steps:

1. After power-up, the LCD module will typically need some time for internal initialisation. We must not start immediately after power-up with initialisation of the LCD - wait a while.
2. Put all data and control signals to zero.
3. Wait 2 seconds.
4. Set DB4-DB5-DB6-DB7 to 0-0-1-1
5. Generate 0 -> 1 -> pulse on EN-line.
6. Repeat step 5 for 3x.
7. Set DB4-DB5-DB6-DB7 to 0-0-1-0
8. Generate 0 -> 1 -> pulse on EN-line.

At this point, basic initialization is complete and 4-bit communication has been established.

After this initialisation we will send a few commands to set up cursor style etc. We will later see this in the firmware listing.

Send a Command to the LCD

We already know how to send a command to the LCD. Now we get an overview of the set of commands used to drive the display. There are 8 different commands for write mode.

We will use the following instructions to drive the LCD:

Instruction	Instruction Code										Description
	RS	R/W	D7	D6	D5	D4	D3	D2	D1	D0	
Clear display	0	0	0	0	0	0	0	0	0	1	This command will clear the content of the display - putting everywhere to display memory value 20h (20h = space based on ASCII table) and set the cursor to position 0, 0
Cursor home	0	0	0	0	0	0	0	0	1	*	Set the cursor position to 0, 0
Entry-mode set	0	0	0	0	0	0	0	1	I/D	S	bits 1-0 are defining following: D1[I/D]: 0 - decrement cursor position 1 - increment cursor position D1[S]: 0 - no display shift 1 - display shift

Display On/ Off control	0	0	0	0	0	0	1	D	C	B	bits 2-0 are defining following: D2[D]: 0 - switch off display 1 - switch on display D1[C]: 0 - cursor is not visible 1 - cursor is visible D0[B] 0 - cursor blink off 1 - cursor is blinking
Cursor / Display Shift	0	0	0	0	0	1	S/C	R/L	*	*	bits 3-2 are defining following: D3[S/C] 0 - cursor move 1 - display shift D4[R/L] 0 - shift to the left 1 - shift to the right It doesn't matter, what is the value in bits D1-D0

Function Set	0	0	0	0	1	DL	N	F	*	*	bits 4-2 are defining following: D4[DL] 0 - 4-bit interface 1 - 8-bit interface D3[N] 0 - 1/8 or 1/11 duty (1 line) 1 - 1/16 duty (2 lines) D2[F] 0 - 5x7 dots 1 - 5x10 dots It doesn't matter, what is the value in bits D1-D0
Set CGRAM Address	0	0	0	1	CGRAM Address						Sets the CGRAM address.
Set DDRAM Address (set cursor position)	0	0	1	DDRAM Address							Sets the DDRAM address.

Now we've gone through the theory, we need to be able to write routines to work with the HD44780-based LCD.

A demo with a counter (as we did for Energia) in CCS may look like this:

```
// ------------------------------------------------------------------------------------
// ------------------------------------------------------------------------------------
#include <msp430.h>
#include <stdio.h>
// ------------------------------------------------------------------------------------
// P1.0 -> RS
// P1.1 -> EN
// P1.2 -> DB4
// P1.3 -> DB5
// P1.4 -> DB6
```

```
// P1.5 -> DB7
// -----------------------------------------------------------------------------------------
#define byte    unsigned short

#define LCD_RS  BIT0
#define LCD_EN  BIT1
#define LCD_DB4 BIT2
#define LCD_DB5 BIT3
#define LCD_DB6 BIT4
#define LCD_DB7 BIT5

#define LCD_W1  40
#define LCD_W2  120

void wait001(unsigned long int i_wt);
void wait_1ms(unsigned long int i_wt);
void lcd_init();
void set_LCD_D(byte v_ttt);
void set_LCD_D2(byte v_ttt);
void send_comm(byte i_byte);
void send_data(byte i_byte);
void scbc();
void scbd();
void lcd_print_c(char iv_string[20]);
void lcd_print_cc(byte iv_row, byte iv_col, char iv_string[20]);
void lcd_setcursor(byte iv_col, byte iv_row);
void lcd_clear();
void w_print(void);
void lcd_print_i(double iv_val);

double v_counter;
char v_a1p[1];
int v_a5;
double v_a6;
// -----------------------------------------------------------------------------------------
// -----------------------------------------------------------------------------------------
int main(void) {
    WDTCTL = WDTPW | WDTHOLD;   // Stop watchdog timer
    P1DIR = 0xFF;                   // Set P1.0 - P1.7 to output direction
    P1SEL = 0x00;

    lcd_init();

    lcd_print_cc(0,0, "MSP430 Power Book");
    lcd_print_cc(0,1, "MCU: MSP430G2553");
    lcd_print_cc(0,2, "Chapter 3.1.4");
```

```
    lcd_print_cc(0,3, "28.12.2020");

    wait_1ms(3000);
    lcd_clear();

    lcd_print_cc(0,0, "LCD connection");
    lcd_print_cc(0,1, "Version: CCS");
    lcd_print_cc(0,2, "here is a counter:");

    v_counter = 0;

    for(;;)
    {
        w_print();
        v_counter++;
        if(v_counter > 99999) v_counter = 0;
    }
}
// -------------------------------------------------------------------------------------
// -------------------------------------------------------------------------------------
void w_print(void)
{
    lcd_print_cc(3,3, "==> ");
    lcd_print_i(v_counter);
    lcd_print_c(" <==");
}
// -------------------------------------------------------------------------------------
// -------------------------------------------------------------------------------------
void wait_1ms(unsigned long int i_wt)
{
    long int i;

    for(i = 0; i < i_wt; i++)
    wait001(59);
}
// -------------------------------------------------------------------------------------
void wait001(unsigned long int i_wt)
{
    volatile unsigned long int i;   // volatile to prevent optimization
    i = i_wt;                      // SW Delay
    do i--;
    while(i != 0);

    return;
}
// -------------------------------------------------------------------------------------
```

```
// -----------------------------------------------------------------------------------
void lcd_init()
{
   byte i;

   wait001(10000);
   P1OUT = 0x00;
   wait001(2000);
   P1OUT &= ~LCD_RS;
   P1OUT &= ~LCD_EN;

   for(i = 1; i < 4; i++)
   {
       set_LCD_D(0b00000011);
       P1OUT |= LCD_EN;
       wait001(LCD_W1);
       P1OUT &= ~LCD_EN;
       wait001(LCD_W2);
   }
   set_LCD_D(0b00000010);
   P1OUT |= LCD_EN;
   wait001(LCD_W1);
   P1OUT &= ~LCD_EN;
   wait001(LCD_W2);

   send_comm(0b00101000);
   send_comm(0b00001000);
   send_comm(0b00001100);
   send_comm(0b00000110);
   send_comm(0b00000001);        //LCD clear
}
// -----------------------------------------------------------------------------------
// -----------------------------------------------------------------------------------
void set_LCD_D(byte v_ttt)
{
   if((v_ttt & BIT0) != 0) P1OUT |=  LCD_DB4;
   if((v_ttt & BIT0) == 0) P1OUT &= ~LCD_DB4;
   if((v_ttt & BIT1) != 0) P1OUT |=  LCD_DB5;
   if((v_ttt & BIT1) == 0) P1OUT &= ~LCD_DB5;
   if((v_ttt & BIT2) != 0) P1OUT |=  LCD_DB6;
   if((v_ttt & BIT2) == 0) P1OUT &= ~LCD_DB6;
   if((v_ttt & BIT3) != 0) P1OUT |=  LCD_DB7;
   if((v_ttt & BIT3) == 0) P1OUT &= ~LCD_DB7;

}
```

```
void set_LCD_D2(byte v_ttt)
{
    if((v_ttt & BIT4) != 0) P1OUT |=  LCD_DB4;
    if((v_ttt & BIT4) == 0) P1OUT &= ~LCD_DB4;
    if((v_ttt & BIT5) != 0) P1OUT |=  LCD_DB5;
    if((v_ttt & BIT5) == 0) P1OUT &= ~LCD_DB5;
    if((v_ttt & BIT6) != 0) P1OUT |=  LCD_DB6;
    if((v_ttt & BIT6) == 0) P1OUT &= ~LCD_DB6;
    if((v_ttt & BIT7) != 0) P1OUT |=  LCD_DB7;
    if((v_ttt & BIT7) == 0) P1OUT &= ~LCD_DB7;
}

void send_data(byte i_byte)
{
    P1OUT &= ~LCD_EN;
    set_LCD_D2(i_byte);
    scbd();
    set_LCD_D(i_byte);
    scbd();
}

void send_comm(byte i_byte)
{
    P1OUT &= ~LCD_EN;
    set_LCD_D2(i_byte);
    scbc();
    set_LCD_D(i_byte);
    scbc();
}

void scbc()
{
    P1OUT &= ~LCD_RS;
    P1OUT |= LCD_EN;
    wait001(100);
    P1OUT &= ~LCD_EN;
    wait001(200);
}

void scbd()
{
    P1OUT |= LCD_RS;
    P1OUT |= LCD_EN;
    //NOP
    P1OUT &= ~LCD_EN;
    //NOP
```

```
}
// ------------------------------------------------------------------------------------
// ------------------------------------------------------------------------------------
// ------------------------------------------------------------------------------------
void lcd_print_cc(byte iv_row, byte iv_col, char iv_string[20])
{
    lcd_setcursor(iv_row, iv_col);
    lcd_print_c(iv_string);
}
// ------------------------------------------------------------------------------------
// ------------------------------------------------------------------------------------
void lcd_print_c(char iv_string[20])
{
    int i;

    i = 0;
    while(iv_string[i] != 0)
    {
        send_data(iv_string[i]);
        i++;
    }
}
// ------------------------------------------------------------------------------------
// ------------------------------------------------------------------------------------
void lcd_print_i(double iv_val)
{
    v_a5 = iv_val / 10000;
    v_a6 = v_a5;
    sprintf(v_a1p, "%d", v_a5);
    lcd_print_cc(7, 3, v_a1p);
    iv_val = iv_val - 10000 * v_a6;         //here we need to use "long enough" data type for multiplication

    v_a5 = iv_val / 1000;
    sprintf(v_a1p, "%d", v_a5);
    lcd_print_cc(8, 3, v_a1p);
    iv_val = iv_val - 1000 * v_a5;

    v_a5 = iv_val / 100;
    sprintf(v_a1p, "%d", v_a5);
    lcd_print_cc(9, 3, v_a1p);
    iv_val = iv_val - 100 * v_a5;

    v_a5 = iv_val / 10;
    sprintf(v_a1p, "%d", v_a5);
    lcd_print_cc(10, 3, v_a1p);
    iv_val = iv_val - 10 * v_a5;
```

```
    v_a5 = iv_val / 1;
    sprintf(v_a1p, "%d", v_a5);
    lcd_print_cc(11, 3, v_a1p);
    iv_val = iv_val - 1 * v_a5;
}
// ---------------------------------------------------------------------------------------
// ---------------------------------------------------------------------------------------
void lcd_setcursor(byte iv_col, byte iv_row)
{
    int lv_a;

    lv_a = 0b10000000;
    switch(iv_row)
    {
        case 0x00:
           lv_a = 0b10000000;
           break;
        case 0x01:
           lv_a = 0b11000000;
           break;
        case 0x02:
           lv_a = 0b10010100;
           break;
        case 0x03:
           lv_a = 0b11010100;
           break;
    }

    lv_a = lv_a + iv_col;
    send_comm(lv_a);
}
// ---------------------------------------------------------------------------------------
// ---------------------------------------------------------------------------------------
void lcd_clear()
{
    send_comm(0b00000001);       //LCD clear
}
// ---------------------------------------------------------------------------------------
// ---------------------------------------------------------------------------------------
```

3.1.4.4 • CCS Firmware - The Library

This firmware is written and tested using CCS Version: 10.1.1.00004.

To be able to use the LCD communication routines easily in other examples, extract them to a library file - let's call it: <LCD4x20.h>.

We will extract all LCD-related functionalities to the library file. It doesn't make sense to show the listing again now - just have a look how the main program will look like after extraction:

```
// ---------------------------------------------------------------------------------
// ---------------------------------------------------------------------------------
#include <msp430.h>
#include <LCD4x20.h>

void w_print(void);

double v_counter;
// ---------------------------------------------------------------------------------
// ---------------------------------------------------------------------------------
int main(void) {
    WDTCTL = WDTPW | WDTHOLD;        // Stop watchdog timer
    P1DIR = 0xFF;                    // Set P1.0 - P1.7 to output direction
    P1SEL = 0x00;

    lcd_init();

    lcd_print_cc(0,0, "MSP430 Power Book");
    lcd_print_cc(0,1, "MCU: MSP430G2553");
    lcd_print_cc(0,2, "Chapter 3.1.4");
    lcd_print_cc(0,3, "07.01.2021");

    wait_1ms(3000);
    lcd_clear();

    lcd_print_cc(0,0, "LCD connection");
    lcd_print_cc(0,1, "Version: CCS & lib");
    lcd_print_cc(0,2, "here is a counter:");

    v_counter = 0;

    for(;;)
    {
        w_print();
        v_counter++;
        if(v_counter > 99999) v_counter = 0;
    }
}
// ---------------------------------------------------------------------------------
// ---------------------------------------------------------------------------------
void w_print(void)
{
```

```
    lcd_print_cc(3,3, "==> ");
    lcd_print_ic(7,3,v_counter);
    lcd_print_c(" <==");
}
// ---------------------------------------------------------------------------------
// ---------------------------------------------------------------------------------
```

In the library are following functions implemented:

Function	Parameters	Functionality
lcd_init	n/a	initialization of the LCD for 4-bit data transfer
send_data	i_byte	one byte is sent to the LCD (typically a character to be shown on the display)
send_comm	i_byte	one command is sent to the LCD; for example to set a cursor to the desired position on the display
lcd_clear	n/a	content of the LCD is cleared
lcd_print_c	iv_string	String of characters is shown on the current position of LCD, the string can be max. 20 characters
lcd_print_ic	iv_col iv_row iv_string	exactly as lcd_print_c; just in addition the cursor is set to position iv_col / iv_row before writing
lcd_print_f	iv_val	float variable is written on LCD / current position. One decimal place will be shown
lcd_setcursor	iv_col iv_row	cursor is set to position iv_col / iv_row on LCD
w_bin16	v_word	16-bit numbers are written in binary form to the LCD
w_bin8	v_word	8-bit numbers are written in binary form to the LCD

3.2 • ADC10

Now we know roughly how to maintain digital outputs. But what about analog input? There are lots of different examples, where it is important to measure many different analog values i.e. voltage, light, temperature, ... whatever.

It is quite easy to read analog values with the integrated ADC10 module of the MSP430G2553. Let's have a short look at the possibilities. The following examples will explain how the ADC10 module can be customised. Also, an example to measure the voltage of the power supply of the microcontroller itself is shown in addition to utilizing the built-in temperature sensor with the ADC10 module.

As the name of the module suggests, the resolution of the measurement is always 10 bits. The examples will include the Energia command: "analogReadResolution(8)". Once seen, it can awaken the denotation that it is possible to set the resolution of the measurement. But it is not. This will just add some code to the background of the execution to re-calculate the results of 10 bits to another one - of 8 bits.

Let's now start with the possibilities regarding the ADC10.

There are two important control registers to configure the functionality of ADC10: ADC10CTL0 and ADC10CTL1.

Both of them are 16-bit registers. Let's have a look at them now.

ADC10CTL0 register:

bit 15	*bit 14*	*bit 13*	*bit 12*	*bit 11*	*bit 10*	*bit 9*	*bit 8*
SREFx			**ADSC10SHTx**		**ARC10SR**	**REFOUT**	**REFBURST**
rw-0	*rw-0*	*rw-0*	*rw-0*	*rw-0*	*rw-0*	*rw-0*	*rw-0*

bit 7	*bit 6*	*bit 5*	*bit 4*	*bit 3*	*bit 2*	*bit 1*	*bit 0*
MSC	**REF2_5V**	**REFON**	**ADC10ON**	**ADC10IE**	**ADC10IFG**	**ENC**	**ADC10SC**
rw-0	*rw-0*	*rw-0*	*rw-0*	*rw-0*	*rw-0*	*rw-0*	*rw-0*

bit name	bit(s)	usage
SREFx	15 - 13	Reference selection: 000: $V_{R+} = V_{CC}$ $V_{R-} = V_{SS}$ 001: $V_{R+} = V_{REF+}$ $V_{R-} = V_{SS}$ 010: $V_{R+} = V_{eREF+}$ $V_{R-} = V_{SS}$ 011: V_{R+} = buffered V_{eREF+} $V_{R-} = V_{SS}$ 100: $V_{R+} = V_{CC}$ $V_{R-} = V_{REF-} / V_{eREF-}$ 101: $V_{R+} = V_{REF+}$ $V_{R-} = V_{REF-} / V_{eREF-}$ 110: $V_{R+} = Ve_{REF+}$ $V_{R-} = V_{REF-} / V_{eREF-}$ 111: V_{R+} = buffered V_{eREF+} $V_{R-} = V_{REF-} / V_{eREF-}$
ADSC10SHTx	*12 - 11*	ADC10 sample and hold time: 00: 4 × ADC10CLKs (default value) 01: 8 × ADC10CLKs 10: 16 × ADC10CLKs 11: 64 × ADC10CLKs
ARC10SR	*10*	ADC10 sampling rate: 0: up to ~ 200ksps (default value) 1: up to ~ 50ksps
REFOUT	*9*	Reference out: 0: reference output is off (default value) 1: reference output is on
REFBURST	*8*	Reference burst: 0: Reference buffer on continuously (default value) 1: Reference buffer on only during sample-and-conversion
MSC	*7*	Multiple sample and conversion - for sequence and repeated modes only.
REF2_5V	*6*	If reference generator is active (on) - we can with this bit choose one of the possible reference voltages: 0: reference voltage is: 1,5V (default) 1: reference voltage is: 2,5V
REFON	*5*	Reference generator enable bit: 0: reference generator is off 1: reference generator is on
ADC10ON	*4*	ADC10 main switch - activate or deactivate ADC10 module: 0: ADC10 module is off (default value) 1: ADC10 is on

ADC10IE	*3*	ADC10 interrupt enable bit: 0: interrupt from ADC10 module is disabled (default value) 1: interrupt from ADC10 module is enabled
ADC10IFG	*2*	ADC10 interrupt flag; this bit is activated once the ADC10 result register (ADC10MEM) is filled with the result of conversion. This bit is filled independent of the fact, if interrupt is enabled or disabled. 0: no ADC10 interrupt is pending 1: ADC10 interrupt is pending
ENC	*1*	Enable conversion bit: 0: ADC10 conversion is disabled 1: ADC10 conversion is enabled
ADC10SC	*0*	Start of a conversion - this bit is cleared automatic. Writing 1 to this bit will trigger the conversion (of course, only if the ADC10 module is on and enabled): 0: no sample-and-conversion 1: trigger conversion

In our examples we will use just a couple of bits from the ADC10CTL0 register - we will later see which ones.

The ADC10CTL1 register is as described here:

ADC10CTL1 register

bit 15	bit 14	bit 13	bit 12	bit 11	bit 10	bit 9	bit 8
INCHx				**SHSx**		**ADC10DF**	**ISSH**
rw-0	rw-0	rw-0	rw-0	rw-0	rw-0	rw-0	rw-0

bit 7	bit 6	bit 5	bit 4	bit 3	bit 2	bit 1	bit 0
ADC10DIVx				**ADC10SSELx**		**CONSEQx**	**ADC10BUSY**
rw-0	rw-0	rw-0	rw-0	rw-0	rw-0	rw-0	r-0

bit name	bit(s)	usage
INCHx	15 - 12	Input channel select: 0000: A0 0001: A1 0010: A2 0011: A3 0100: A4 0101: A5 0110: A6 0111: A7 1000: V_{eREF+} 1001: V_{REF-} / V_{eREF-} 1010: Internal Temperature Sensor 1011: $(V_{CC} - V_{SS}) / 2$ 1100: $(V_{CC} - V_{SS}) / 2$ or A12 on devices with A12 input 1101: $(V_{CC} - V_{SS}) / 2$ or A13 on devices with A13 input 1110: $(V_{CC} - V_{SS}) / 2$ or A14 on devices with A14 input 1111: $(V_{CC} - V_{SS}) / 2$ or A15 on devices with A15 input Note: MSP430G2553 does not provide A12-A15 inputs
SHSx	11 - 10	Sample-and-hold source select: 00: ADC10SC bit 01: TIMER_A.OUT1 10: TIMER_A.OUT0 11: TIMER_A.OUT2
ADC10DF	9	ADC10 data format: 0: Straight binary 1: 2s complement
ISSH	8	Invert signal sample-and-hold: 0: The sample-input signal is not inverted. 1: The sample-input signal is inverted.

ADC10DIVx	7 - 5	ADC10 clock divider: 000: divided by 1 001: divided by 2 010: divided by 3 011: divided by 4 100: divided by 5 101: divided by 6 110: divided by 7 111: divided by 8
ADC10SSELx	4 - 3	ADC10 clock source select: 00: ADC10OSC 01: ACLK 10: MCLK 11: SMCLK
CONSEQx	2 - 1	Conversion sequence mode select: 00: Single-channel-single-conversion 01: Sequence-of-channels 10: Repeat-single-channel 11: Repeat-sequence-of-channels
ADC10BUSY	0	ADC10 busy. This bit indicates an active sample or conversion operation: 0: No operation is active. 1: A sequence, sample, or conversion is active.

Once a measurement is complete, with just a simple read of the **ADC10MEM** register we get the result. In other words, the ADC10MEM register is keeping the result of the ADC10 execution.

3.2.1 • First simple exercise: reading the ADC10 control registers

An example will demonstrate the current settings of the ADC10 module. It is a good exercise to become acquainted with the real stuff.

There will be the possibility of seeing the content of the ADC10CTL0, ADC10CTL1, ADC10AE0, and ADC10MEM registers.

We can see as well, how the Energia command "analogRead" influences the content of the corresponding registers.

In our example, we executed the command "sensorValue = analogRead(TEMPSENSOR);".

Besides this, later on, the Vcc-measurement will be shown - it is quite simple. The Following commands can do this:

```
ADC10CTL1 = 0b1011000000000000;
ADC10CTL0 = 0b0011100001111011;
delay(50);
adc10_read = ADC10MEM;
Vadc10 = adc10_read / 1023.0 * 2.5;
Vcc = Vadc10 * 2;
```

This exercise will be shown only with the Energia IDE as there are a lot of texts and descriptions. Providing the firmware in CCS will not add any value.

3.2.1.1 ● Hardware

There are no extensions or special hardware needed for the exercise. The only thing that is used is the LaunchPad itself.

3.2.1.2 ● Energia Firmware

This firmware is written and tested with Energia-1.8.7E21.

I will keep this example more or less without comments. We can see how the content of the settings of the ADC10 module can be explained easily. Therefore I prefer to keep the whole listing as (because of the nature of the example) is it self-explanatory.

```
//-----------------------------------------------------------------------------
//-----------------------------------------------------------------------------
//MSP430
//Chapter 3.2.1. - ADC10 - read and explain registers
//-----------------------------------------------------------------------------
//-----------------------------------------------------------------------------
byte v_done;
int adc10_read;
float Vcc;
float Vadc10;
//-----------------------------------------------------------------------------
//-----------------------------------------------------------------------------
void setup() {
  pinMode(14, OUTPUT);

  Serial.begin(9600);
  v_done = 0;

  Serial.println("Read & show content of the ADC10 registers.");
```

```
  Serial.println("Firmware version: 1.0.0 / 10.02.2021");
  Serial.println("-------------------------------------------");
}
//--------------------------------------------------------------------------------
//--------------------------------------------------------------------------------
void loop() {
  digitalWrite(14, 1);
  delay(100);
  digitalWrite(14, 0);
  delay(100);           //(9) wait predefined time

  ADC10CTL1 = 0b1011000000000000;
  ADC10CTL0 = 0b0011100001111011;
  delay(50);
  adc10_read = ADC10MEM;
  Vadc10 = adc10_read / 1023.0 * 2.5;
  Vcc = Vadc10 * 2;

  write_once();
}
//--------------------------------------------------------------------------------
//--------------------------------------------------------------------------------
void write_once()
{
  if (v_done == 0)
    {
      Serial.println("");
      Serial.
println("---------------------------------------------------------------------------------------");
      explain_CTL0(ADC10CTL0);
      Serial.
println("---------------------------------------------------------------------------------------");
      explain_CTL1(ADC10CTL1);
      Serial.
println("---------------------------------------------------------------------------------------");
      explain_AE0(ADC10AE0);
      Serial.
println("---------------------------------------------------------------------------------------");
      explain_MEM(ADC10MEM);
      Serial.
println("---------------------------------------------------------------------------------------");

      Serial.print("Vadc10 = ");
      Serial.print(Vadc10);
      Serial.println(" V");
```

```
      Serial.print("Vcc = ");
      Serial.print(Vcc);
      Serial.println(" V");

      v_done = 1;
    }
}
//--------------------------------------------------------------------------------
//--------------------------------------------------------------------------------
void write_bin(int i_word)
{
  if ((i_word & 0b1000000000000000) == 32768) Serial.print("1"); else Serial.print("0");
  if ((i_word & 0b0100000000000000) == 16384) Serial.print("1"); else Serial.print("0");
  if ((i_word & 0b0010000000000000) == 8192 ) Serial.print("1"); else Serial.print("0");
  if ((i_word & 0b0001000000000000) == 4096 ) Serial.print("1"); else Serial.print("0");
  Serial.print("-");
  if ((i_word & 0b0000100000000000) == 2048 ) Serial.print("1"); else Serial.print("0");
  if ((i_word & 0b0000010000000000) == 1024 ) Serial.print("1"); else Serial.print("0");
  if ((i_word & 0b0000001000000000) == 512  ) Serial.print("1"); else Serial.print("0");
  if ((i_word & 0b0000000100000000) == 256  ) Serial.print("1"); else Serial.print("0");
  Serial.print("--");
  if ((i_word & 0b0000000010000000) == 128  ) Serial.print("1"); else Serial.print("0");
  if ((i_word & 0b0000000001000000) == 64   ) Serial.print("1"); else Serial.print("0");
  if ((i_word & 0b0000000000100000) == 32   ) Serial.print("1"); else Serial.print("0");
  if ((i_word & 0b0000000000010000) == 16   ) Serial.print("1"); else Serial.print("0");
  Serial.print("-");
  if ((i_word & 0b0000000000001000) == 8    ) Serial.print("1"); else Serial.print("0");
  if ((i_word & 0b0000000000000100) == 4    ) Serial.print("1"); else Serial.print("0");
  if ((i_word & 0b0000000000000010) == 2    ) Serial.print("1"); else Serial.print("0");
  if ((i_word & 0b0000000000000001) == 1    ) Serial.print("1"); else Serial.print("0");
}
//--------------------------------------------------------------------------------
//--------------------------------------------------------------------------------
void write_bin8(int i_word)
{
  if ((i_word & 0b0000000010000000) == 128  ) Serial.print("1"); else Serial.print("0");
  if ((i_word & 0b0000000001000000) == 64   ) Serial.print("1"); else Serial.print("0");
  if ((i_word & 0b0000000000100000) == 32   ) Serial.print("1"); else Serial.print("0");
  if ((i_word & 0b0000000000010000) == 16   ) Serial.print("1"); else Serial.print("0");
  Serial.print("-");
  if ((i_word & 0b0000000000001000) == 8    ) Serial.print("1"); else Serial.print("0");
  if ((i_word & 0b0000000000000100) == 4    ) Serial.print("1"); else Serial.print("0");
  if ((i_word & 0b0000000000000010) == 2    ) Serial.print("1"); else Serial.print("0");
  if ((i_word & 0b0000000000000001) == 1    ) Serial.print("1"); else Serial.print("0");
}
//--------------------------------------------------------------------------------
```

```
//--------------------------------------------------------------------------------
void write_bin4(byte i_byte)
{
  if ((i_byte & 0b1000) == 8    ) Serial.print("1"); else Serial.print("0");
  if ((i_byte & 0b0100) == 4    ) Serial.print("1"); else Serial.print("0");
  if ((i_byte & 0b0010) == 2    ) Serial.print("1"); else Serial.print("0");
  if ((i_byte & 0b0001) == 1    ) Serial.print("1"); else Serial.print("0");
}
//--------------------------------------------------------------------------------
//--------------------------------------------------------------------------------
void write_bin3(byte i_byte)
{
  if ((i_byte & 0b0100) == 4    ) Serial.print("1"); else Serial.print("0");
  if ((i_byte & 0b0010) == 2    ) Serial.print("1"); else Serial.print("0");
  if ((i_byte & 0b0001) == 1    ) Serial.print("1"); else Serial.print("0");
}
//--------------------------------------------------------------------------------
//--------------------------------------------------------------------------------
void write_bin2(byte i_byte)
{
  if ((i_byte & 0b0010) == 2    ) Serial.print("1"); else Serial.print("0");
  if ((i_byte & 0b0001) == 1    ) Serial.print("1"); else Serial.print("0");
}
//--------------------------------------------------------------------------------
//--------------------------------------------------------------------------------
void write_bin1(byte i_byte)
{
  if ((i_byte & 0b0001) == 1    ) Serial.print("1"); else Serial.print("0");
}
//--------------------------------------------------------------------------------
//--------------------------------------------------------------------------------
void explain_CTL1(int v_word)
{
  Serial.print("ADC10 Control Register 1: ");
  Serial.print("ADC10CTL1: "); write_bin(v_word); Serial.println("b");
  Serial.
println("-----------------------------------------------------------------------------------------------");
  int v_INCHx      = (v_word >> 12) & 15;
  int v_SHSx       = v_word >> 10; v_SHSx = v_SHSx & 3;
  int v_ADC10DF    = (v_word & 512) >> 9;
  int v_ISSH       = (v_word & 256) >> 8;
  int v_ADC10DIVx  = (v_word & 0b11100000) >> 5;
  int v_ADC10SSELx = (v_word & 0b00011000) >> 3;
  int v_CONSEQx    = (v_word & 0b00000110) >> 1;
  int v_ADC10BUSY  = v_word & 1;
```

```
Serial.print("  INCHx:     (bits 15-12) Input channel select      : ");
write_bin4(v_INCHx); Serial.print("b => ");
switch (v_INCHx)
{
  case 0b0000: Serial.println("A0"); break;
  case 0b0001: Serial.println("A1"); break;
  case 0b0010: Serial.println("A2"); break;
  case 0b0011: Serial.println("A3"); break;
  case 0b0100: Serial.println("A4"); break;
  case 0b0101: Serial.println("A5"); break;
  case 0b0110: Serial.println("A6"); break;
  case 0b0111: Serial.println("A7"); break;
  case 0b1000: Serial.println("Veref+"); break;
  case 0b1001: Serial.println("Vref- / Veref-"); break;
  case 0b1010: Serial.println("Temperature Sensor"); break;
  case 0b1011: Serial.println("(Vcc - Vss) / 2"); break;
}

Serial.print("  SHSx:      (bits 11-10) Sample-and-hold source sel:   ");
write_bin2(v_SHSx); Serial.print("b => ");
switch (v_SHSx)
{
  case 0b00: Serial.println("ADC10SC bit"); break;
  case 0b01: Serial.println("Timer_A.OUT1"); break;
  case 0b10: Serial.println("Timer_A.OUT0"); break;
  case 0b11: Serial.println("Timer_A.OUT2"); break;
}

Serial.print("  ADC10DF:   (bit 9)      ADC10 data format         :    ");
write_bin1(v_ADC10DF); Serial.print("b => ");
switch (v_ADC10DF)
{
  case 0: Serial.println("Straight binary"); break;
  case 1: Serial.println("2s complement"); break;
}

Serial.print("  ISSH:      (bit 8)      Invert signal sample-and-h:    ");
write_bin1(v_ISSH); Serial.print("b => ");
switch (v_ISSH)
{
  case 0: Serial.println("The sample-input signal is not inverted"); break;
  case 1: Serial.println("The sample-input signal is inverted"); break;
}

Serial.print("  ADC10DIVx: (bits 7-5)   ADC clock divider         :  ");
write_bin3(v_ADC10DIVx); Serial.print("b => ");
```

```
  Serial.print(":"); Serial.println(v_ADC10DIVx + 1);

  Serial.print("  ADC10SSELx:(bits 4-3)   ADC10 clock source select :   ");
  write_bin2(v_ADC10SSELx); Serial.print("b => ");
  switch (v_ADC10SSELx)
  {
    case 0b00: Serial.println("ADC10OSC"); break;
    case 0b01: Serial.println("ACLK"); break;
    case 0b10: Serial.println("MCLK"); break;
    case 0b11: Serial.println("SMCLK"); break;
  }

  Serial.print("  CONSEQx:   (bits 2-1)   Conversion sequence sel   :   ");
  write_bin2(v_CONSEQx); Serial.print("b => ");
  switch (v_CONSEQx)
  {
    case 0b00: Serial.println("Single-channel-single-conversion"); break;
    case 0b01: Serial.println("Sequence-of-channels"); break;
    case 0b10: Serial.println("Repeat-single-channel"); break;
    case 0b11: Serial.println("Repeat-sequence-of-channels"); break;
  }

  Serial.print("  ADC10BUSY: (bit 0)      ADC10 busy                :    ");
  write_bin1(v_ADC10BUSY); Serial.print("b => ");
  switch (v_ADC10BUSY)
  {
    case 0: Serial.println("No operation is active"); break;
    case 1: Serial.println("Conversion is ongoing"); break;
  }
}
//-----------------------------------------------------------------------------------
//-----------------------------------------------------------------------------------
void explain_CTL0(int v_word)
{
  Serial.print("ADC10 Control Register 0: ");
  Serial.print("ADC10CTL0: "); write_bin(v_word); Serial.println("b");
  Serial.
println("-----------------------------------------------------------------------------------------------");
  int v_SREFx      = v_word >> 13;
  int v_ADC10SHTx = v_word >> 11; v_ADC10SHTx = v_ADC10SHTx & 0x03;
  int v_ADC10SR    = (v_word & 1024) >> 10;
  int v_REFOUT     = (v_word & 512) >> 9;
  int v_REFBURST   = (v_word & 256) >> 8;
  int v_MSC        = (v_word & 128) >> 7;
  int v_REF2_5V    = (v_word & 64) >> 6;
  int v_REFON      = (v_word & 32) >> 5;
```

```
int v_ADC10ON   = (v_word & 16) >> 4;
int v_ADC10IE   = (v_word & 8) >> 3;
int v_ADC10IFG  = (v_word & 4) >> 2;
int v_ENC       = (v_word & 2) >> 1;
int v_ADC10SC   = v_word & 1;

Serial.print("  SREFx:     (bits 15-13) Select Reference          :  ");
write_bin3(v_SREFx); Serial.print("b => ");
switch (v_SREFx)
{
  case 0b000: Serial.println("Vr+ = Vcc and Vr- = Vss"); break;
  case 0b001: Serial.println("Vr+ = Vref+ and Vr- = Vss"); break;
  case 0b010: Serial.println("Vr+ = Veref+ and Vr- = Vss"); break;
  case 0b011: Serial.println("Vr+ = buffered Veref+ and Vr- = Vss"); break;
}

Serial.print("  ADC10SHTx: (bits 12-11) ADC10 sample-and-hold time:   ");
write_bin2(v_ADC10SHTx); Serial.print("b => ");
switch (v_ADC10SHTx)
{
  case 0b00: Serial.println("4 x ADC10CLKs"); break;
  case 0b01: Serial.println("8 x ADC10CLKs"); break;
  case 0b10: Serial.println("16 x ADC10CLKs"); break;
  case 0b11: Serial.println("64 x ADC10CLKs"); break;
}

Serial.print("  ADC10SR:   (bit 10)     ADC10 sampling rate       :    ");
write_bin1(v_ADC10SR); Serial.print("b => ");
switch (v_ADC10SR)
{
  case 0: Serial.println("up to ~200 ksps"); break;
  case 1: Serial.println("up to ~50 ksps"); break;
}

Serial.print("  REFOUT:    (bit  9)     Reference output          :    ");
write_bin1(v_REFOUT); Serial.print("b => ");
switch (v_REFOUT)
{
  case 0: Serial.println("Reference output OFF"); break;
  case 1: Serial.println("Reference output ON"); break;
}

Serial.print("  REFBURST:  (bit  8)     Reference burst           :    ");
write_bin1(v_REFBURST); Serial.print("b => ");
switch (v_REFBURST)
{
```

```
  case 0: Serial.println("Reference buffer on continuously"); break;
  case 1: Serial.println("Reference buffer on only during sample-and-conversion"); break;
}

Serial.print("  MSC:       (bit  7)    Multiple sample and conv. :    ");
write_bin1(v_MSC); Serial.print("b => ");
switch (v_MSC)
{
  case 0: Serial.println("OFF"); break;
  case 1: Serial.println("ON"); break;
}

Serial.print("  REF2_5V:   (bit  6)    Reference-gen. Voltage    :    ");
write_bin1(v_REF2_5V); Serial.print("b => ");
switch (v_REF2_5V)
{
  case 0: Serial.println("1,5V"); break;
  case 1: Serial.println("2,5V"); break;
}

Serial.print("  REFON:     (bit  5)    Reference generator ON    :    ");
write_bin1(v_REFON); Serial.print("b => ");
switch (v_REFON)
{
  case 0: Serial.println("Reference OFF"); break;
  case 1: Serial.println("Reference ON"); break;
}

Serial.print("  ADC10ON:   (bit  4)    ADC10 ON                  :    ");
write_bin1(v_ADC10ON); Serial.print("b => ");
switch (v_ADC10ON)
{
  case 0: Serial.println("ADC10 OFF"); break;
  case 1: Serial.println("ADC10 ON"); break;
}

Serial.print("  ADC10IE:   (bit  3)    ADC10 Interrupt Enable    :    ");
write_bin1(v_ADC10IE); Serial.print("b => ");
switch (v_ADC10IE)
{
  case 0: Serial.println("Interrupt Disabled"); break;
  case 1: Serial.println("Interrupt Enabled"); break;
}

Serial.print("  ADC10IFG:  (bit  2)    ADC10 Interrupt Flag      :    ");
write_bin1(v_ADC10IFG); Serial.print("b => ");
```

```
  switch (v_ADC10IFG)
  {
    case 0: Serial.println("No interrupt pending"); break;
    case 1: Serial.println("Interrupt pending"); break;
  }

  Serial.print("  ENC:      (bit  1)     Enable Conversion         :    ");
  write_bin1(v_ENC); Serial.print("b => ");
  switch (v_ENC)
  {
    case 0: Serial.println("ADC10 disabled"); break;
    case 1: Serial.println("ADC10 enabled"); break;
  }

  Serial.print("  ADC10SC:   (bit  0)     Start conversion          :    ");
  write_bin1(v_ADC10SC); Serial.print("b => ");
  switch (v_ADC10SC)
  {
    case 0: Serial.println("No sample-and-conversion start"); break;
    case 1: Serial.println("Start sample-and-conversion"); break;
  }
}
//-------------------------------------------------------------------------------------
//-------------------------------------------------------------------------------------
void explain_AE0(byte v_word)
{
  Serial.print("ADC10 Analog Input Enable Control Register 0: ");
  Serial.print("ADC10AE0: "); write_bin8(v_word); Serial.println("b");
  Serial.print("   A7: "); w_en_dis(v_word, 7);
  Serial.print("   A6: "); w_en_dis(v_word, 6);
  Serial.print("   A5: "); w_en_dis(v_word, 5);
  Serial.print("   A4: "); w_en_dis(v_word, 4);
  Serial.print("   A3: "); w_en_dis(v_word, 3);
  Serial.print("   A2: "); w_en_dis(v_word, 2);
  Serial.print("   A1: "); w_en_dis(v_word, 1);
  Serial.print("   A0: "); w_en_dis(v_word, 0);
}
//-------------------------------------------------------------------------------------
//-------------------------------------------------------------------------------------
void w_en_dis(byte v_word, byte v_bit)
{
  v_word = (v_word >> v_bit) & 1;
  if (v_word == 1) Serial.print("Analog input enabled  ("); else Serial.print("Analog input disabled (");
  Serial.print(v_word);
  Serial.println(")");
}
```

```
//-----------------------------------------------------------------------------
//-----------------------------------------------------------------------------
void explain_MEM(int v_word)
{
  Serial.print("ADC10 Conversion-Memory Register: ");
  Serial.print("ADC10MEM: "); write_bin(v_word); Serial.println("b");
  Serial.print("Value: "); Serial.print(v_word); Serial.println();
}
//-----------------------------------------------------------------------------
//-----------------------------------------------------------------------------
```

Once the firmware is executed, in the serial monitor following information can be found:

```
Read & show content of the ADC10 registers.
Firmware version: 1.0.0 / 10.02.2021
-------------------------------------------


----------------------------------------------------------------------------------------------
ADC10 Control Register 0: ADC10CTL0: 0011-1000--0111-1010b
----------------------------------------------------------------------------------------------
  SREFx:     (bits 15-13) Select Reference          :  001b => Vr+ = Vref+ and Vr- = Vss
  ADC10SHTx: (bits 12-11) ADC10 sample-and-hold time:   11b => 64 x ADC10CLKs
  ADC10SR:   (bit 10)     ADC10 sampling rate       :    0b => up to ~200 ksps
  REFOUT:    (bit  9)     Reference output          :    0b => Reference output OFF
  REFBURST:  (bit  8)     Reference burst           :    0b => Reference buffer on continuously
  MSC:       (bit  7)     Multiple sample and conv. :    0b => OFF
  REF2_5V:   (bit  6)     Reference-gen. Voltage    :    1b => 2,5V
  REFON:     (bit  5)     Reference generator ON    :    1b => Reference ON
  ADC10ON:   (bit  4)     ADC10 ON                  :    1b => ADC10 ON
  ADC10IE:   (bit  3)     ADC10 Interrupt Enable    :    1b => Interrupt Enabled
  ADC10IFG:  (bit  2)     ADC10 Interrupt Flag      :    0b => No interrupt pending
  ENC:       (bit  1)     Enable Conversion         :    1b => ADC10 enabled
  ADC10SC:   (bit  0)     Start conversion          :    0b => No sample-and-conversion start
----------------------------------------------------------------------------------------------
ADC10 Control Register 1: ADC10CTL1: 1011-0000--0000-0000b
----------------------------------------------------------------------------------------------
  INCHx:     (bits 15-12) Input channel select      : 1011b => (Vcc - Vss) / 2
  SHSx:      (bits 11-10) Sample-and-hold source sel:   00b => ADC10SC bit
  ADC10DF:   (bit 9)      ADC10 data format         :    0b => Straight binary
  ISSH:      (bit 8)      Invert signal sample-and-h:    0b => The sample-input signal is not inverted
  ADC10DIVx: (bits 7-5)   ADC clock divider         :  000b => :1
  ADC10SSELx:(bits 4-3)   ADC10 clock source select :   00b => ADC10OSC
  CONSEQx:   (bits 2-1)   Conversion sequence sel   :   00b => Single-channel-single-conversion
  ADC10BUSY: (bit 0)      ADC10 busy                :    0b => No operation is active
----------------------------------------------------------------------------------------------
ADC10 Analog Input Enable Control Register 0: ADC10AE0: 0000-0000b
```

```
  A7: Analog input disabled (0)
  A6: Analog input disabled (0)
  A5: Analog input disabled (0)
  A4: Analog input disabled (0)
  A3: Analog input disabled (0)
  A2: Analog input disabled (0)
  A1: Analog input disabled (0)
  A0: Analog input disabled (0)
-------------------------------------------------------------------------------------------
ADC10 Conversion-Memory Register: ADC10MEM: 0000-0010--1001-1001b
Value: 665
-------------------------------------------------------------------------------------------
Vadc10 = 1.63 V
Vcc = 3.25 V
```

In the following section, the settings highlighted are the most important ones. With these settings, we define the following parameters for the ADC10 module in the example shown.

```
ADC10 Control Register 0: ADC10CTL0: 0011-1000--0111-1010b
-------------------------------------------------------------------------------------------
  SREFx:      (bits 15-13) Select Reference          :  001b => Vr+ = Vref+ and Vr- = Vss
  ADC10SHTx:  (bits 12-11) ADC10 sample-and-hold time:   11b => 64 x ADC10CLKs
  ADC10SR:    (bit 10)     ADC10 sampling rate       :    0b => up to ~200 ksps
  REFOUT:     (bit  9)     Reference output          :    0b => Reference output OFF
  REFBURST:   (bit  8)     Reference burst           :    0b => Reference buffer on continuously
  MSC:        (bit  7)     Multiple sample and conv. :    0b => OFF
  REF2_5V:    (bit  6)     Reference-gen. Voltage    :    1b => 2,5V
  REFON:      (bit  5)     Reference generator ON    :    1b => Reference ON
  ADC10ON:    (bit  4)     ADC10 ON                  :    1b => ADC10 ON
  ADC10IE:    (bit  3)     ADC10 Interrupt Enable    :    1b => Interrupt Enabled
  ADC10IFG:   (bit  2)     ADC10 Interrupt Flag      :    0b => No interrupt pending
  ENC:        (bit  1)     Enable Conversion         :    1b => ADC10 enabled
  ADC10SC:    (bit  0)     Start conversion          :    0b => No sample-and-conversion start
-------------------------------------------------------------------------------------------
ADC10 Control Register 1: ADC10CTL1: 1011-0000--0000-0000b
-------------------------------------------------------------------------------------------
  INCHx:      (bits 15-12) Input channel select      : 1011b => (Vcc - Vss) / 2
  SHSx:       (bits 11-10) Sample-and-hold source sel:   00b => ADC10SC bit
  ADC10DF:    (bit 9)      ADC10 data format         :    0b => Straight binary
  ISSH:       (bit 8)      Invert signal sample-and-h:    0b => The sample-input signal is not inverted
  ADC10DIVx:  (bits 7-5)   ADC clock divider         :  000b => :1
  ADC10SSELx:(bits 4-3)    ADC10 clock source select :   00b => ADC10OSC
  CONSEQx:    (bits 2-1)   Conversion sequence sel   :   00b => Single-channel-single-conversion
  ADC10BUSY:  (bit 0)      ADC10 busy                :    0b => No operation is active
-------------------------------------------------------------------------------------------
```

3.2.2 • Internal Temperature Sensor

The MSP430G2553 has an integrated temperature sensor. It is not the intention for it to be used to measure environmental temperature, as the sensor is not very precise, but to get an idea about the temperature inside a microcontroller, we can use it. The temperature sensor is, as we know, one possible input for the ADC10+ module.

This example will be built and coded in CCS.

3.2.2.1 • Hardware

We do not need any special hardware for this exercise, we will just reuse our LCD shield to show the results of the temperature measurement.

3.2.2.2 • CCS Firmware

This firmware is written and tested with CCS Version: 10.1.1.00004.

Let's have a look at the CCS firmware which utilises the internal temperature sensor of the MSP430G2553. As already mentioned, we have to consider that this sensor is not a stand-alone chip to measure external temperature. It is a built-in sensor measuring the temperature within the MCU. This temperature will be always higher than the outside temperature.

What is the firmware doing and showing?

Besides the "welcome screen" are the results of the measurement shown on the LCD in this way:

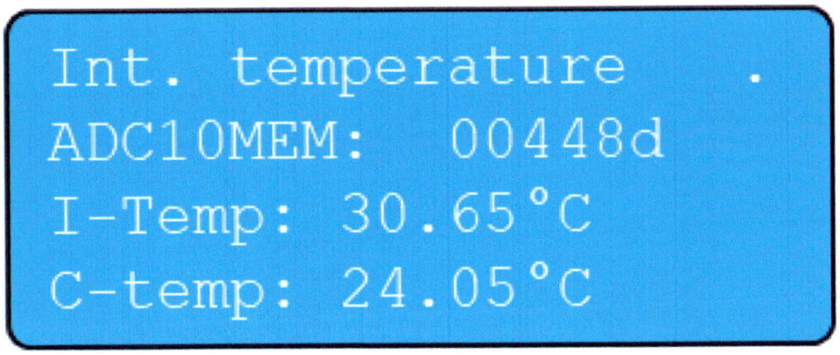

We can see in the first line "Int. temperature" (generated in line (19.1) of the coding); then in the second line, we see the decimal value of the ADC10MEM-register; which is the result of the conversion of the ADC10 module. In the next line, we see the internal temperature within the chip (on the sensor) calculated based on the ADC10MEM value and reference voltage used. In the last line we see what I call "calibrated temperature". This is just the internal temperature decreased by 6.6°C - which in my example was more or less the real outside temperature. I just compared the result of MSP430G2553 with a "real thermometer" placed at the same location, and the constant 6.6°C was appropriate for temperatures between 3°C and 30°C...

The "dot" we can see in the first line - at the end of the line is kind of "alive-indicator". This kind of device (like a thermometer) can show the same value for a long time because the temperature is quite stable. In the end you never know if the temperature is stable, or the firmware has crashed and isn't working anymore; just the LCD is showing the last communicated data for a longer timer already. Therefore I usually build in something to say: "hey, I'm still here". It can be a flashing LED, or like in the example, a falling dot. The dot is displayed after every measurement always in the next line. This means that even the result of the measurement is the same for a longer period, there is still something changing on the LCD:

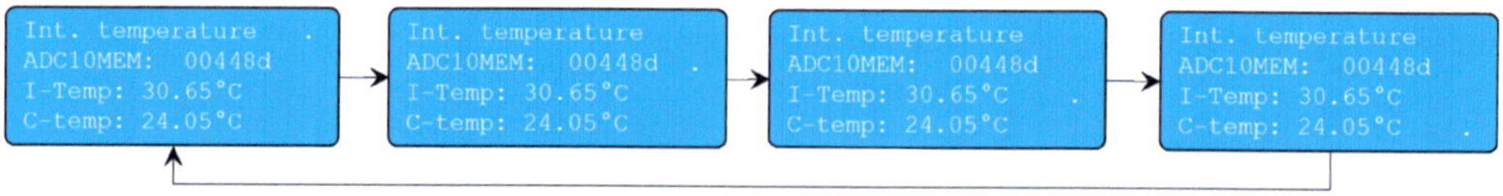

The CCS-based firmware in "C" can look like this:

```
// -------------------------------------------------------------------------------
// -------------------------------------------------------------------------------
#include <msp430.h>                     //(1) include msp430 constants & declarations
#include <LCD4x20.h>                    //(2) include own LCD library

void wait_ms(unsigned int iv_ms);       //(3) declaration of wait function

float temp_i=0;                         //(4) calculated internal MCU temperature
float temp_c=0;                         //(5) calibrated temperature
short v_dot;
// -------------------------------------------------------------------------------
// -------------------------------------------------------------------------------
void main(void)                         //(6) start of main function
{
    WDTCTL=WDTPW+WDTHOLD;               //(7) stop WDT

    P1DIR = 0xFF;                       //(8) Set P1.0 - P1.7 to output
    lcd_init();                         //(9) LCD initialization
    lcd_print_cc(0,0, "MSP430 Power Book");  //(10.1) welcome screen
    lcd_print_cc(0,1, "MCU: MSP430G2553");   //(10.2) welcome screen
    lcd_print_cc(0,2, "Chapter 3.2.2");      //(10.3) welcome screen
    lcd_print_cc(0,3, "09.01.2021");         //(10.4) welcome screen
    wait_1ms(3000);                     //(11) wait 3 seconds
    lcd_clear();                        //(12) clear LCD
    ADC10CTL1 = 0b1010000000000000;     //(13) set-up ADC10CTL1
    v_dot = 0;
```

```
    for(;;)                                     //(14) Main software-loop
    {
        ADC10CTL0 = 0b0011100001110011;         //(15) set-up ADC10CTL0 and start conversion
        while(ADC10CTL1&ADC10BUSY);             //(16) wait until conversion is finished

        temp_i = (((2.5*(float)ADC10MEM)/1023)-0.986)/0.00355;
                                                //(17) calculate internal MCU temperature
        temp_c = temp_i - 6.6;                  //(18) "calibration" for external temperature

        lcd_print_cc(0,0,"Int. temperature");   //(19.1) write result to LCD
        lcd_print_cc(0,1,"ADC10MEM: ");         //(19.2) write result to LCD
        lcd_print_ic(11,1,ADC10MEM);            //(19.3) write result to LCD
        lcd_print_c("d");                       //(19.4) write result to LCD

        lcd_print_cc(0,2,"I-Temp: ");           //(19.5) write result to LCD
        lcd_print_f(temp_i);                    //(19.6) write result to LCD
        send_data(223);                         //(19.7) write result to LCD
        lcd_print_c("C");                       //(19.8) write result to LCD

        lcd_print_cc(0,3,"C-Temp: ");           //(19.9) write result to LCD
        lcd_print_f(temp_c);                    //(19.10) write result to LCD
        send_data(223);                         //(19.11) write result to LCD
        lcd_print_c("C");                       //(19.12) write result to LCD

        wait_ms(500);                           //(20) wait 0,5 sec

        lcd_print_cc(19,v_dot++," ");           //(21.1) still alive indicator
        if(v_dot == 4) v_dot = 0;               //(21.2) still alive indicator
        lcd_print_cc(19,v_dot,".");             //(21.3) still alive indicator
    }
}
// ------------------------------------------------------------------------------
// ------------------------------------------------------------------------------
void wait_ms(unsigned int iv_ms)                //(22) wait-function
{
    while(iv_ms--) __delay_cycles(1000);
}
// ------------------------------------------------------------------------------
// ------------------------------------------------------------------------------
```

Let's keep the comment for this firmware effective, meaning short. Besides the declarations and commands writing texts and measurement results on the LCD, only steps (15) - (18) are important.

In step (15) is the ADC10+ module configured in a way that temperature measurement is possible. How? We can have a look at the settings used, which are written to the ADC10CTL0 register (the value is: 0b0011100001110011):

bit name	bit(s)	usage
SREFx	15 - 13	Reference selection: 001: $V_{R+} = V_{REF+}$ $V_{R-} = V_{SS}$
ADSC10SHTx	12 - 11	ADC10 sample and hold time: 11: 64 × ADC10CLKs
ARC10SR	10	ADC10 sampling rate: 0: up to ~ 200ksps (default value)
REFOUT	9	Reference out: 0: reference output is off (default value)
REFBURST	8	Reference burst: 0: Reference buffer on continuously (default value)
MSC	7	Multiple sample and conversion - for sequence and repeated modes only. 0: not used
REF2_5V	6	If the reference generator is active (on) - we can with this bit choose one of the possible reference voltages: 1: reference voltage is: 2,5V
REFON	5	Reference generator enable bit: 1: reference generator is on
ADC10ON	4	ADC10 main switch - activate or deactivate ADC10 module: 1: ADC10 is on
ADC10IE	3	ADC10 interrupt enable bit: 0 interrupt from ADC10 module is disabled

ADC10IFG	2	ADC10 interrupt flag; this bit is activated once the ADC10 result register (ADC10MEM) is filled with the result of conversion. This bit is filled independent of the fact if the interrupt is enabled or disabled. 0 no ADC10 interrupt is pending 1 ADC10 interrupt is pending
ENC	1	Enable conversion bit: 1 ADC10 conversion is enabled
ADC10SC	0	Start of a conversion - this bit is cleared automatically. Writing 1 to this bit will trigger the conversion (of course, only if the ADC10 module is on and enabled): 1 trigger conversion

Important here is to consider that the voltage reference module has been activated. The voltage reference is set to 2.5V; the reference has been selected to GDN and the voltage reference (2,5V) and storing the settings to the ADC10CTL0 register will be the module itself activated and in the same shot the conversion started.

Another important setting is made earlier in the firmware in step (13), by writing the value needed to the ADC10CTL1 register. The Internal Temperature Sensor will be input for ADC10 conversions (see the 4 most significant bits of the value): 0b**1010**000000000000. In step (16) the firmware waits until the measurement is finished and in steps (17) and (18) it is possible to see the calculation (and correction) of the temperature based on the measurement results. The measurement result is stored in the ADC10MEM register.

3.2.3 • Own Voltage

As we already learned with the ADC10 module and appropriate configuration we can measure the supply voltage of the microcontroller.

To do this, we will utilise the possibility of usage of a fixed internal voltage reference, and another possibility: to connect the input to ADC10 to the voltage divider providing half of V_{cc} (input select will be: 1011).

We will perform a configuration of the ADC10 based on the following settings of the ADC10CTL0 and ADC10CTL1 registers:

ADC10CTL0 register:

bit name	bit(s)	usage
SREFx	15 - 13	Reference selection: 000: $V_{R+} = V_{CC}$ $V_{R-} = V_{SS}$ 001: $V_{R+} = V_{REF+}$ $V_{R-} = V_{SS}$ 010: $V_{R+} = V_{eREF+}$ $V_{R-} = V_{SS}$ 011: V_{R+} = buffered V_{eREF+} $V_{R-} = V^{SS}$ 100: $V_{R+} = V_{CC}$ $V_{R-} = V_{REF-}$ / V_{eREF-} 101: $V_{R+} = V_{REF+}$ $V_{R-} = V_{REF-}$ / V_{eREF-} 110: $V_{R+} = V_{eREF+}$ $V_{R-} = V_{REF-}$ / V_{eREF-} 111: V_{R+} = buffered V_{eREF+} $V_{R-} = V_{REF-}$ / V_{eREF-}
ADSC10SHTx	12 - 11	ADC10 sample and hold time: 00: 4 × ADC10CLKs (default value) 01: 8 × ADC10CLKs 10: 16 × ADC10CLKs 11: 64 × ADC10CLKs
ARC10SR	10	Default value used: 0
REFOUT	9	Default value used: 0
REFBURST	8	Default value used: 0
MSC	7	Default value used: 0
REF2_5V	6	If reference generator is active (on) - we can with this bit choose one of the possible reference voltages: 0: reference voltage is: 1,5V (default) 1: reference voltage is: 2,5V
REFON	5	Reference generator enable bit: 0: reference generator is off 1: reference generator is on
ADC10ON	4	ADC10 main switch - activate or deactivate ADC10 module: 0: ADC10 module is off (default value) 1: ADC10 is on
ADC10IE	3	ADC10 interrupt enable bit: 0: interrupt from ADC10 module is disabled (default value) 1: interrupt from ADC10 module is enabled
ADC10IFG	2	ADC10 interrupt flag; not relevant for configuration - set to 0
ENC	1	Enable conversion bit: 0: ADC10 conversion is disabled 1: ADC10 conversion is enabled
ADC10SC	0	Start of a conversion - this bit is cleared automatically. Writing 1 to this bit will trigger the conversion (of course, only if the ADC10 module is on and enabled): 0: no sample-and-conversion 1: trigger conversion

ADC10CTL1 register:

bit name	bit(s)	usage
INCHx	15 - 12	Input channel select: 0000: A0 0001: A1 0010: A2 0011: A3 0100: A4 0101: A5 0110: A6 0111: A7 1000: V_{eREF+} 1001: V_{REF-} / V_{eREF-} 1010: Internal Temperature Sensor 1011: $(V_{CC} - V_{SS}) / 2$ 1100: $(V_{CC} - V_{SS}) / 2$ or A12 on devices with A12 input 1101: $(V_{CC} - V_{SS}) / 2$ or A13 on devices with A13 input 1110: $(V_{CC} - V_{SS}) / 2$ or A14 on devices with A14 input 1111: $(V_{CC} - V_{SS}) / 2$ or A15 on devices with A15 input
SHSx	11 - 10	Default value used: 00
ADC10DF	9	Default value used: 0
ISSH	8	Default value used: 0
ADC10DIVx	7 - 5	Default value used: 000
ADC10SSELx	4 - 3	Default value used: 00
CONSEQx	2 - 1	Default value used: 00
ADC10BUSY	0	Not relevant for the settings (set as 0)

Regarding settings it may be important to say, that we have to select the reference voltage of 2.5V (instead of 1.5V). Why? Because we will measure one half of the power supply. The allowed range of Vcc for the MSP430G2553 is 1.8V to 3.6V max. This means the half of the V_{cc} is in the range: 0.9V to 1.8V; meaning that 1.8V already exceeds the default reference voltage of 1.5V by 0.3V. With a reference voltage of 1.5V, we also can measure a maximum

V_{cc} of 3.0V, which will reduce the possibilities and stop the measurement of the V_{cc} on the LaunchPad, where 3.3V is used.

Sometimes, especially during initial experiments something doesn't really work as expected. To make sure the microcontroller is alive, an LED blinks. Therefore, if for example, we do not see anything on the serial monitor or later on LCD (but the LED is blinking), we know the program is running, but something about the showing the results is wrong. To avoid the need for an external LED we will use the LED connected to P1.6 as this is already integrated on the LaunchPad.

3.2.3.1 • Hardware

For this example, we do not need any hardware for the Energia-version of the firmware as we will send the results to the serial monitor. For the CCS version, we will reuse the LCD shield described in chapter 3.1.4.

3.2.3.2 • Energia Firmware / Serial Monitor

This firmware is written and tested with Energia-1.8.7E21.

The software written with Energia IDE to measure the supply voltage is quite simple. We just need to set up the two control registers as described above, and then periodically read the result of the conversion from the ADC10MEM register.

```
//-----------------------------------------------------------------------------
//-----------------------------------------------------------------------------
//MSP430 - Own Voltage measurement
//Output to serial monitor
//-----------------------------------------------------------------------------
//-----------------------------------------------------------------------------
#define LED1    14                  //(1) LED1 is connected to Pin 14
int adc10_read;                     //(2) variable to store value from analog input
float Vcc;                          //(3) calculated supply voltage
float Vadc10;                       //(4) calculated voltage on ADC10
//-----------------------------------------------------------------------------
void setup()                        //(5) set-up routine
{
  pinMode(LED1, OUTPUT);            //(6) configure Pin 14 as digital output
  Serial.begin(9600);               //(7) serial communication initialization
}
//-----------------------------------------------------------------------------
void loop()                         //(8) main software loop
{
  digitalWrite(LED1, 1);            //(9) switch on the LED
  delay(100);                       //(10) wait 100ms
  digitalWrite(LED1, 0);            //(11) switch off the LED
  delay(100);                       //(12) wait 100ms

  ADC10CTL1 = 0b1011000000000000;   //(13) select input: (Vcc - Vss) / 2
  ADC10CTL0 = 0b0011100001111011;   //(14) set up references etc. and start the conversion
  delay(50);                        //(15) wait until conversion is done
  adc10_read = ADC10MEM;            //(16) get the result from ADC10MEM register
  Vadc10 = adc10_read / 1023.0 * 2.5;  //(17) calculate ADC10 voltage based on used resolution and ref.voltage
  Vcc = Vadc10 * 2;                 //(18) calculate Vcc

  Serial.print("Vadc10 = ");        //(19) send result to the serial monitor
  Serial.print(Vadc10);             //(20) send result to the serial monitor
  Serial.println(" V");             //(21) send result to the serial monitor

  Serial.print("Vcc    = ");        //(22) send result to the serial monitor
  Serial.print(Vcc);                //(23) send result to the serial monitor
  Serial.println(" V");             //(24) send result to the serial monitor
  Serial.println("-----------------------------------");
}
//-----------------------------------------------------------------------------
//-----------------------------------------------------------------------------
```

It doesn't make sense to describe the software line by line. I will just talk about a few commands that concern ADC and the calculation of voltage.

There are a couple of preparation steps done at the beginning: (1) - (8); inclusive of the LED blink in steps (9) - (12). We then put the required setup-value in register ADC10CTL1 (13), and finally to ADC10CTL0 (14). Why are we doing it in "wrong order"? Because writing the value to ADC10CTL0 will perform 4 steps in 1:

1. Finalise the setup if the ADC0
2. Switch the ADC10 module on (ADC10ON <- 1)
3. Enable the conversion on ADC10 (ENC <- 1)
4. Trigger the conversion itself (ADC10SC <- 1)

All of these steps can be done in one write to the ADC10CTL0 register. We do not need to do it step by step. But at the end, triggering the conversion, we want to have everything prepared first - including the correct settings in the ADC10CTL1 register. Therefore we write the desired values to this register in the first place.

In our example, we are not in hurry and therefore wait 50ms (15) to let the ADC10 finish the conversion and then read the result from the ARC10MEM register (16).

In the next step (17) we calculate the voltage measured by the ADC10 module using the range of the ADC (10 bit leads to a maximum digital value of 0b0000 0011 1111 1111 = 0x03FF = 1.023) and the applied reference voltage (2.5 V). In the final step of measurement and calculation, we have to multiply this value by 2 (18), as the input to the ADC10 was half of V_{cc}. We then just send the results to the serial monitor - in steps (19) - (24).

And the endless loop starts again.

The result on serial monitor look like shown here:

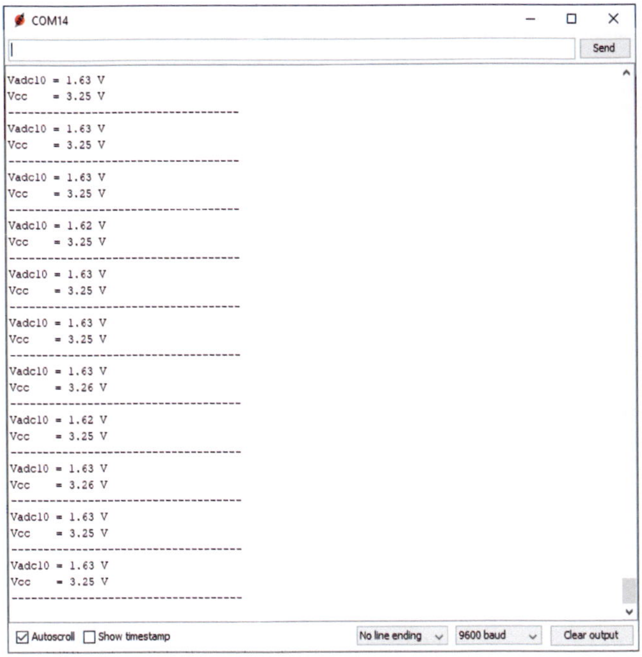

3.2.3.3 • Energia Firmware / LCD

This firmware is written and tested with Energia-1.8.7E21.

If we want to use our 4x20 LCD instead of the serial monitor, we can replace the serial monitor communication by communication with the LCD. The adjusted firmware for writing the results to LCD instead of the serial monitor may look like this:

```
//--------------------------------------------------------------------------------
//--------------------------------------------------------------------------------
//MSP430 - Own Voltage measurement
//Output to serial monitor & to LCD
//--------------------------------------------------------------------------------
//--------------------------------------------------------------------------------
#include <LiquidCrystal.h>
LiquidCrystal lcd(P1_0,P1_1,P1_2,P1_3,P1_4,P1_5);

#define LED1    14                  //(1) LED1 is connected to Pin 14
int adc10_read;                     //(2) variable to store value from analog input
float Vcc;                          //(3) calculated supply voltage
float Vadc10;                       //(4) calculated voltage on ADC10
//--------------------------------------------------------------------------------
void setup()                        //(5) set-up routine
{
  pinMode(LED1, OUTPUT);            //(6) configure Pin 14 as digital output
  lcd.begin(20,4);
```

```
}
//-------------------------------------------------------------------------------
void loop()                              //(8) main software loop
{
  digitalWrite(LED1, 1);                 //(9) switch on the LED
  delay(100);                            //(10) wait 100ms
  digitalWrite(LED1, 0);                 //(11) switch off the LED
  delay(100);                            //(12) wait 100ms

  ADC10CTL1 = 0b1011000000000000;        //(13) select input: (Vcc - Vss) / 2
  ADC10CTL0 = 0b0011100001111011;        //(14) set up references etc. and start the conversion
  delay(50);                             //(15) wait until conversion is done
  adc10_read = ADC10MEM;                 //(16) get the result from ADC10MEM register
  Vadc10 = adc10_read / 1023.0 * 2.5;    //(17) calculate ADC10 voltage based on used resolution and ref.voltage
  Vcc = Vadc10 * 2;                      //(18) calculate Vcc

  lcd.setCursor(0,0);                    //(19) write results to LCD
  lcd.print("Vadc10 = ");                //(20) write results to LCD
  lcd.print(Vadc10);                     //(21) write results to LCD
  lcd.print(" V");                       //(22) write results to LCD

  lcd.setCursor(0,1);                    //(23) write results to LCD
  lcd.print("Vcc    = ");                //(24) write results to LCD
  lcd.print(Vcc);                        //(25) write results to LCD
  lcd.print(" V");                       //(26) write results to LCD
}
//-------------------------------------------------------------------------------
//-------------------------------------------------------------------------------
```

We can see that everything is the same, we are just using the LCD routines, not the serial monitor routines.

If everything is ok, on the LCD we will see an image like this:

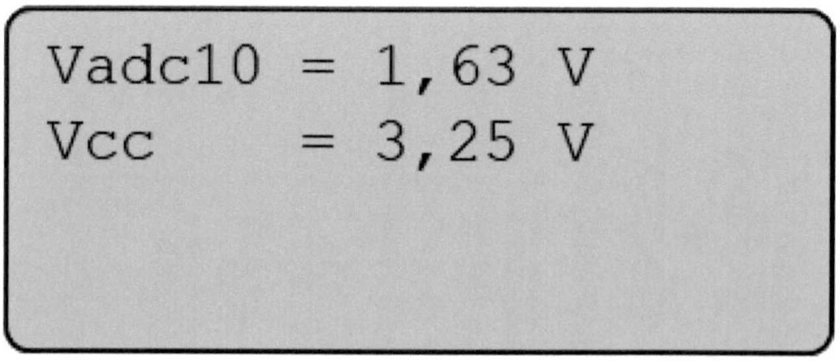

3.2.3.4 • CCS Firmware

This firmware is written and tested with CCS Version: 10.1.1.00004.

We will of course use our LCD library in this example; and will see the software is almost the same as Energia. I have to admit, I first wrote the Energia-version, and then took over the majority of the code with copy & paste... with a few minor adjustments.

This is the result:

```
// -------------------------------------------------------------------------------------
// -------------------------------------------------------------------------------------
#include <msp430.h>
#include <LCD4x20.h>
void delay_ms(unsigned int iv_delay_ms);

int adc10_read;                         //(2) variable to store value from analog input
float Vcc;                              //(3) calculated supply voltage
float Vadc10;                           //(4) calculated voltage on ADC10
// -------------------------------------------------------------------------------------
// -------------------------------------------------------------------------------------
int main(void) {
    WDTCTL = WDTPW | WDTHOLD;   // Stop watchdog timer
    P1DIR = 0xFF;                   // Set P1.0 - P1.7 to output direction
    P1SEL = 0x00;

    lcd_init();

    lcd_print_cc(0,0, “MSP430 Power Book”);
    lcd_print_cc(0,1, “MCU: MSP430G2553”);
    lcd_print_cc(0,2, “Chapter 3.2.3”);
    lcd_print_cc(0,3, “07.01.2021”);

    wait_1ms(3000);
    lcd_clear();

    lcd_print_cc(0,0, “Own Voltage”);
    lcd_print_cc(0,1, “Version: CCS”);

    ADC10CTL1 = 0b1011000000000000;        //(13) set-up ADC10CTL1

    P1DIR |= BIT6;
    //  ---------------------------------------------------------------------------------
    for(;;)
    {
        P1OUT |= BIT6;
        delay_ms(100);
```

```
        P1OUT &= ~BIT6;
        delay_ms(50);
        ADC10CTL0 = 0b0011100001111011;       //(14) set up ADC10CTL0 and start conversion
        delay_ms(50);
        adc10_read = ADC10MEM;                //(16) get the result from ADC10MEM register
        Vadc10 = adc10_read / 1023.0 * 2.5;   //(17) calculate ADC10 voltage based on used resolution and ref.voltage
        Vcc = Vadc10 * 2;                     //(18) calculate Vcc

        lcd_print_cc(0,2,"Vadc10 = ");
        lcd_print_f(Vadc10);
        lcd_print_c(" V");

        lcd_print_cc(0,3,"Vcc    = ");
        lcd_print_f(Vcc);
        lcd_print_c(" V");
    }
}
// ------------------------------------------------------------------------------------------
// ------------------------------------------------------------------------------------------
void delay_ms(unsigned int iv_delay_ms)     //(19) delay routine
{ while(iv_delay_ms--) __delay_cycles(1000); }
// ------------------------------------------------------------------------------------------
// ------------------------------------------------------------------------------------------
```

3.2.4 ● Potentiometer

In this example, we will see how to read an input voltage on one of the analog inputs. We will connect a potentiometer to A0-input (pin #2 / P1.0).

We can build a simple shield as shown in the photos below, or of course, use the breadboard and connect the potentiometer with flexible connections.

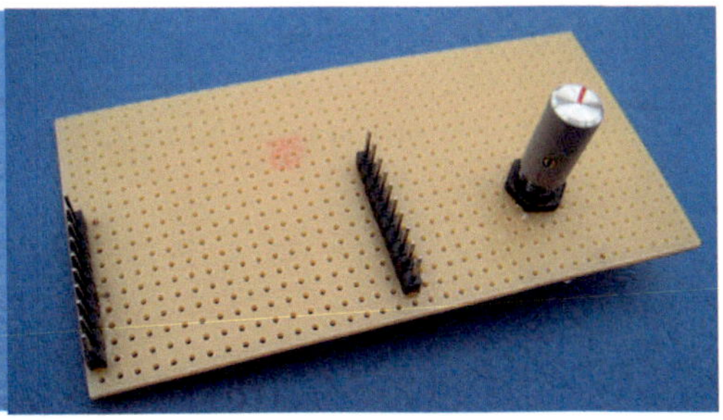

It is nice to attach a simple analog or digital voltmeter to the potentiometer as we will see the "outside microcontroller" voltage measured, and then the MCU measured voltage.

In this example we will use serial monitor to display the results of the measurement. Will will therefore stick to the Energia-Version of the firmware.

3.2.4.1 ● Hardware

The circuit is very simple and voltmeter P1 is optional.

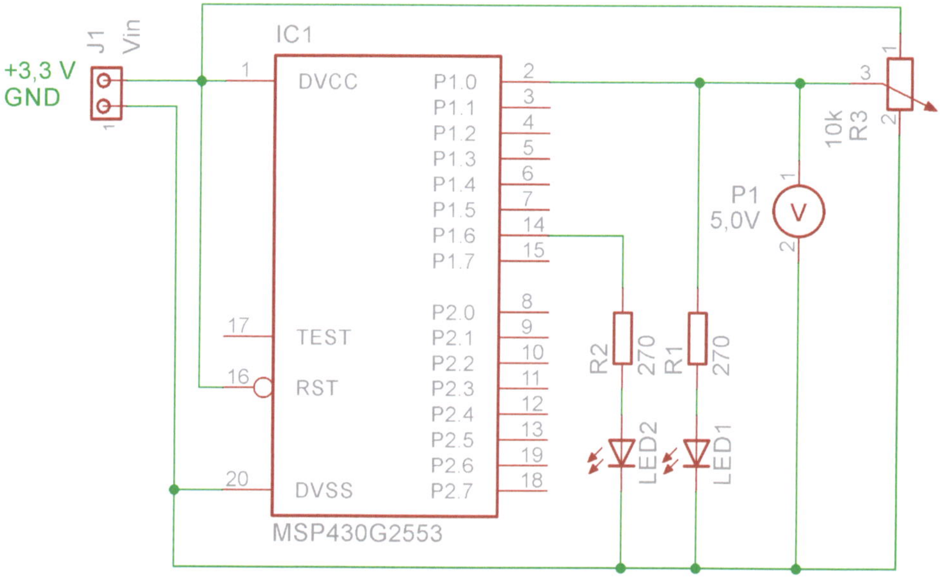

If we build the shield (and not a stand-alone board), we have LED1, LED2, R1, and R2 on the LaunchPad and should NOT connect it again.

The only obligatory part is potentiometer R3.

3.2.4.2 ● Energia Firmware - Version 1

This firmware is written and tested with Energia-1.8.7E21.

Our first software example will measure the voltage on A0 input (based on the position of the pot) and send the measured value and calculated voltage through the serial monitor to the PC. Additionally, we will flash an LED. The speed of the flashes will correspond to the position of the pot.

After first, ok - second - looking at the software it is clear that the majority of the code is taking care of sending data to the PC using serial monitor. The measurement itself is very uncomplicated.

```
//-----------------------------------------------------------------------------
//-----------------------------------------------------------------------------
//MSP430 - Read Potentiometer on A0
//Output to serial monitor and LED
//-----------------------------------------------------------------------------
//-----------------------------------------------------------------------------
#define LED1    14                     //(1) LED1 is connected to Pin 14
byte PotiValue;                        //(2) variable to store value from analog input
int wait_time;                         //(3) variable wait_time defines blinking frequency
float v_help1;                         //(4) help variable: conversion of byte to float
float Vin;                             //(5) calculated voltage
//-----------------------------------------------------------------------------
void setup()                           //(6) set-up routine
{
  pinMode(LED1, OUTPUT);               //(7) configure Pin 14 as digital output
  analogReadResolution(8);             //(8) define 8-bit resolution for the A/D

  Serial.begin(9600);                  //(9) serial communication initialization
  Serial.println("Now we can start..."); //(10) send the string to the setial port
}
//-----------------------------------------------------------------------------
void loop()                            //(11) main software loop
{
  PotiValue = analogRead(A0);          //(12) get poti position
  wait_time = PotiValue + 50;          //(13) lowest delay is 50 ms
  v_help1 = PotiValue;                 //(14) convert ADC10 byte value to float
  Vin = v_help1 / 255 * 3.3;           //(15) calculate the meassured voltage
  Serial.print("Value from A0: ");     //(16) send the string to the setial port
  Serial.print(PotiValue);             //(17) send the value from ADC
  Serial.print(" / Voltage: ");        //(18) send the string to the setial port
  Serial.print(Vin);                   //(19) show calculated voltage
  Serial.print("V");                   //(20) send the string to the setial port
  Serial.print(" >> waiting time: ");  //(21) send the string to the setial port
  Serial.print(wait_time);             //(22) write calculated waiting time
  Serial.println(" ms");               //(23) send the string to the setial port
  digitalWrite(LED1, 1);               //(24) switch on the LED
  delay(wait_time);                    //(25) wait predefined time
  digitalWrite(LED1, 0);               //(26) switch off the LED
  delay(wait_time);                    //(27) wait predefined time
}
//-----------------------------------------------------------------------------
//-----------------------------------------------------------------------------
```

At the beginning, we declare a couple of global variables and define the symbol "LED1" - see steps (1) to (5).

During the set-up phase (6) we configure the LED-port as output (7) and the resolution of conversion is put down to 8-bits (8). The setting-up of the ADC10 conversion resolution is a pure Energia "trick", as the MSP430G2553 does not support the change of resolution on a hardware level.

We then (9) initialise serial monitor and send out a first "test message" (10). With the test message, the setup is finished and the execution continues with the main loop (11).

The main part is just about step (12). With help from "analogRead(A0)", we will get a value of 0 (pot at GND-position) to 255 (pot at V_{cc} position). The maximal value is 255, as we put the resolution at 8-bit. The rest of the code concerns the calculating of the delay for LED-blinking and sending the information to the serial port. We can see in step (15) the calculation of voltage (based on the assumption, that the power supply is equal to 3.30V).

3.2.4.3 • Energia Firmware - Version 2

This firmware is written and tested with Energia-1.8.7E21.

Now we do a simplification and remove all parts concerning serial monitor communication. We just include measurement and LED flashing. Let's see how much simpler the firmware is:

```
//------------------------------------------------------------------------------
//------------------------------------------------------------------------------
//Praktická Elektronika - MSP430 seriál, časť III.
//Štvrtý príklad: Čítanie pozície potenciometra
//komentáre sú stále anglicky - ale stále len zopár slov
//------------------------------------------------------------------------------
//------------------------------------------------------------------------------
#define LED1    14            //(1) LED1 is connected to Pin 14
byte PotiValue;               //(2) variable to store value from analog input
int wait_time;                //(3) variable wait_time defines blinking frequency
//------------------------------------------------------------------------------
void setup()                  //(4) set-up routine
{
  pinMode(LED1, OUTPUT);      //(5) configure Pin 14 as digital output
  analogReadResolution(8);    //(6) define 8-bit resolution for the A/D
}
//------------------------------------------------------------------------------
void loop()                   //(7) main software loop
{
  PotiValue = analogRead(A0); //(8)  get poti position
  wait_time = PotiValue + 50; //(9)  lowest delay is 50 ms
  digitalWrite(LED1, 1);      //(10) switch on the LED
```

```
  delay(wait_time);           //(11) wait predefined time
  digitalWrite(LED1, 0);      //(12) switch off the LED
  delay(wait_time);           //(13) wait predefined time
}
//-------------------------------------------------------------------------------------
//-------------------------------------------------------------------------------------
```

We can see that instead of 27 steps, we now only have 13. What is important are steps (6) - setting up the resolution of the measurement; and step (8), the measurement itself. Other parts of the code concern flashing the LED and few declarations.

3.3 • WDT+

The MSP430G2553 Microcontroller has an integrated WatchDog Timer module - WDT+. Usually, the WatchDog is used to make sure, that if for whatever reason the firmware crashes, the MCU will restart and the electronic equipment will not just "freeze", but can recover and continue work. The WDT+ is based on a counter, which has to be cleared periodically by the firmware itself. If the timer is not cleared, the WDT will typically make sure, that the MCU will receive a reset signal.

The Watchdog Timer+ within the MSP430G2553 module can be used for one additional purpose, and therefore in two different main modes - either as a "real" WatchDog or as a timer generating interrupts. The real WatchDog is intended to remedy the "firmware crash" issue. Interrupt mode can be used by the firmware to observe pre-defined and firmware time-outs.

The WatchDog uses one control register, called WDTCTL; then the watchdog counter itself, WDTCNT. This is not accessible from software, and one bit of the interrupt enable register (bit WDTIE - bit 0 of the register IE1), and one bit of the IFG1 register (bit WDTIFG - bit 0 of the register IFG1).

Register	Short-form	Address	Width	Initial State (after reset)
WatchDog timer+ control register	WDTCTL	0120h	16 bit	6900h
SFR interrupt enable register 1	IE1	0000h	8 bit	00h
SFR interrupt flag register 1	IFG1	0002h	8 bit	00h

With the different bits of the IE1 register (Interrupt Enable 1 Register) it is possible to enable or disable interrupts raised from different sources. For WDT+ is important bit 0 (called WDTIE = Watchdog Timer Interrupt Enable) - as already mentioned, which enables or disables the WDT interrupt:

WDTIE = 0:	WDT interrupt is disabled (default value)
WDTEI = 1:	WDT interrupt is enabled

Register IFG1 (Interrupt Flag Register 1) collects interrupt flags. Even if the corresponding interrupt is disabled, the flag will be set. For WDT+ we can use the WDTIFG bit of this register (bit 0):

WDTIFG = 0:	No WDT interrupt pending
WDTIFG = 0:	WDT interrupt

Let's have a look at a summary of the WDTCTL register - firstly at the lowest 8 bits (LSB) of the register:

bit 7	bit 6	bit 5	bit 4	bit 3	bit 2	bit 1	bit 0
WDTHOLD	**WDTNMIES**	**WDTNMI**	**WDTTMSEL**	**WDTCNTCL**	**WDTSSEL**	**WDTISx**	
rw-0	rw-0	rw-0	rw-0	r0(w)	rw-0	rw-0	

As already mentioned, the WDTCTL is a 16-bit wide register. The highest 8 bits (MSB) are using as a "WatchDog Password".

When writing to the WDTCTL register, the WatchDog password must always be equal to 5Ah - otherwise, the device will generate PUC (and reset). During the read operation, the WDT-password is always 69h.

bit name	bit(s)	usage
WDTPW	Bits 15 - 8	WatchDog timer+ password (as just mentioned) - always read as 69h, must be written as 5Ah, otherwise, a PUC (power-up clear) is generated
WDTHOLD	Bit 7	WDT+ hold bit. This bit enables or disables WDT+ operation: 0 WDT+ is enabled (default) 1 WDT+ is disabled

WDTNMIES	Bit 6	Watchdog timer+ NMI edge select. This bit selects the interrupt edge for the NMI interrupt when WDTNMI = 1. Modifying this bit can trigger an NMI. Modify this bit when WDTIE = 0 to avoid triggering an accidental NMI. 0 NMI on rising edge 1 NMI on falling edge
WDTNMI	Bit 5	WDT+ NMI select. This bit selects the function for the RST/NMI pin: 0 Reset function (default) 1 NMI function
WDTTMSEL	Bit 4	WDT+ mode select: 0 WatchDog mode 1 Interval Timer mode
WDTCNTCL	Bit 3	WDT+ timer reset. Setting this bit to 1 will clear the WDTCNT register - means will clear the WDT timer. This bit is always read as 0.
WDTSSEL	Bit 2	WDT+ clock source select: 0 SMCLK 1 ACLK
WDTISx	Bits 1 - 0	WDT+ interval select. Selection of divider for the WatchDog counter: 00 WDT+ clock source divided by 32.768 01 WDT+ clock source divided by 8.192 10 WDT+ clock source divided by 512 11 WDT+ clock source divided by 64

3.3.1 • WatchDog Reset

We can start with this first kind of usage of the WDT+. This is the MCU reset after time-out. This is as well the default setting after the power-up of the MCU. Therefore we find in all out CCS-based examples the first instruction, deactivating the WDT+.

The Energia IDE does this for us; the WDT+ is not deactivated but switched to Interval-Timer mode, where no reset takes place.

The "Reset-Example" is demonstrated with IDE Energia, as here the serial monitor has been utilised.

3.3.1.1 • Specification

It makes sense to first specify what the demo will do.

The exercise intends to demonstrate the reset feature of the WDT+ module. Therefore the firmware initialises the Watchdog and executes MCU reset once the Watchdog timer overflows.

The firmware blinks with an LED connected to P1.6 (red LED on the MSP430 LaunchPad). Besides this, the firmware will allow Clearing of the Watchdog-timer by pressing a button connected to P1.3 (push button on the MSP430 LaunchPad board).

In addition, the firmware will use Serial Monitor to provide additional information about the WDT+ settings and the content of the IE1 and IFG1 registers. And, last but not least, the firmware will write the user configuration of the WDT+ module explaining the settings of the WDTCTL register.

The output seen on the serial monitor will look like the following screenshot:

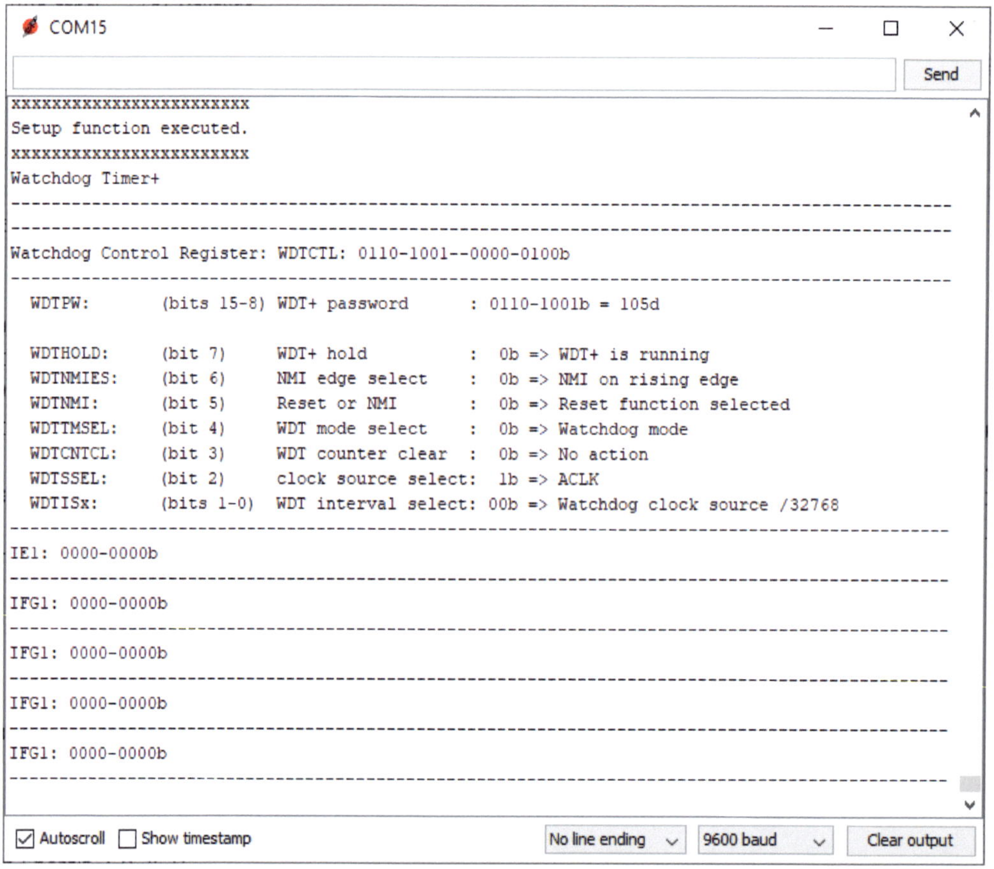

The text at the beginning ("Setup function executed") informs the user of the execution of the initialization routine. The text at the end, provides information about the RESET executed earlier.

The section "Watchdog Control Register: ..." provides the current value of the WDTCRL register as a 16-bit binary number; followed by the explanation of every single bit.

After an explanation, the content of the IE1 register is displayed as an 8-bit binary number. Then the current content of the IFG1 register is displayed periodically until RESET is triggered by the WDT+ module.

If the P1.3-button is pressed, information about the initialisation of the watchdog counter is shown:

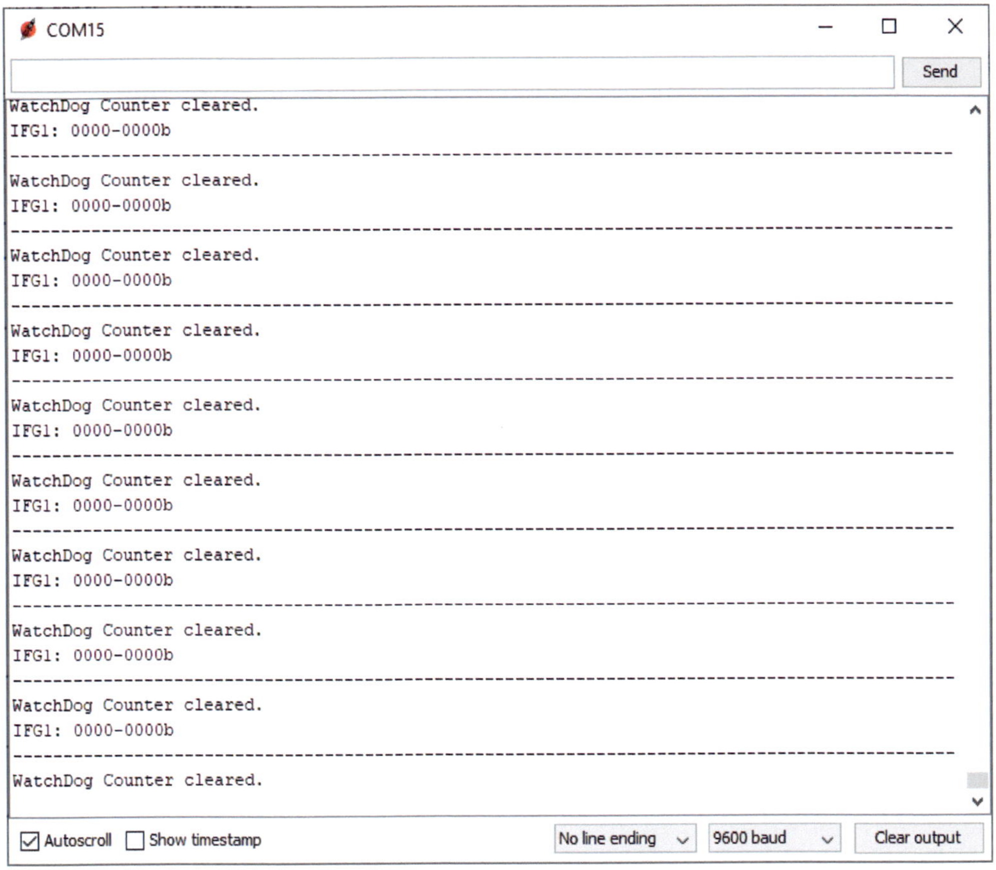

Now everything is specified - let's do it.

3.3.1.2 • Hardware

There is no need for any special hardware. For the Energia-based firmware, it is enough to have the MSP430 LaunchBoard and a working serial monitor.

3.3.1.3 • Energia Firmware

This firmware is written and tested with Energia-1.8.7E21.

Let's have a look at the firmware for the WDT-Reset demonstration. Let's take it step-by-step, or in other words, function by function.

```
//-----------------------------------------------------------------------------
//-----------------------------------------------------------------------------
// MSP430G2553 - Peripherie
// Chapter 3.3.1. Watchdog WDT+ -> Reset
//
// Register WDTCNT is not accessible by the software (read always as 0000h)
// delay() function can not be used here...
// button P1.3 can be used to clear WDTCNT and to clear the interrupt flag
//-----------------------------------------------------------------------------
//-----------------------------------------------------------------------------
byte v_done;                                  //(1) Help Variable 1
word v_WDTCTL;                                //(2) Help Variable 2
//-----------------------------------------------------------------------------
//-----------------------------------------------------------------------------
void setup()
{
  pinMode(14, OUTPUT);                        //(3) configure P1.6 as output (LED)
  Serial.begin(9600);                         //(4) initialize serial monitore
  v_done = 0;                                 //(5) nothing has been printed yet
  //(6) print textual information
  Serial.println("xxxxxxxxxxxxxxxxxxxxxxxxx");
  Serial.println("Setup function executed.");
  Serial.println("xxxxxxxxxxxxxxxxxxxxxxxxx");
  IE1  = 0x00;                                //(7) disable interrupts
  IFG1 = 0x00;                                //(8) clear interrupt flags
//          PPPPPPPP76543210
  WDTCTL = 0b0101101000001100;                //(9) WDTCTL settings: reset will be forced
  }
//-----------------------------------------------------------------------------
//-----------------------------------------------------------------------------
```

The initialisation part of the software is very easy and short. First (1) - (2) we define global help variables used later. In setup(), P1.6 is configured as an output (3) to be able to drive the LED for flashing. The v_done variable is then set to zero (4) and a "welcome text" is sent to the serial monitor (6). Right after, the interrupts are disabled (7) and all pending interrupt flags are cleared (8).

The most important step is (9). Here the desired WDT+ module settings are made by putting the appropriate value to the WDTCTL register. The appropriate value for this exercise is:

```
WDTCTL = 0b0101101000001100; //bits 15 - 8
```
WDT password = 5Ah (01011010b) - always the same value

```
WDTCTL = 0b0101101000001100; //bit 7
```
WDT+ module is enabled

```
WDTCTL = 0b0101101000001100; // bit 6
```
NMI on rising edge selected - not relevant for this example

```
WDTCTL = 0b0101101000001100; //bit 5
```
Reset function of WDT+ module selected

```
WDTCTL = 0b0101101000001100; //bit 4
```
Watchdog mode selected (not interval timer mode)

```
WDTCTL = 0b0101101000001100; //bit 3
```
Watchdog timer reset will be executed

```
WDTCTL = 0b0101101000001100; //bit 2
```
ACLK is selected as WDT+ clock

```
WDTCTL = 0b0101101000001100; //bits 1 - 0
```
WDT+ clock source will be divided by 32.768

Now the initialisation is performed.

Let's have a short look at the loop() function:

```
//-------------------------------------------------------------------------------
//-------------------------------------------------------------------------------
void loop()
{
  digitalWrite(14, 1);                  //(10) switch on  LED connected to P1.6
  wait_a2(2);                           //(11) wait a while
  digitalWrite(14, 0);                  //(12) switch off LED connected to P1.6
  wait_a2(2);                           //(13) wait a while
  write_once();                         //(14) write info to serial monitor
  Serial.print("IFG1: ");               //(15) show content of IFG1 register
  write_bin8(IFG1);                     //(16) show content of IFG1 register
  Serial.println("b");                  //(17) show content of IFG1 register
  Serial.
println("---------------------------------------------------------------------------------------------");
  if (digitalRead(P1_3) == 0)           //(19) test the button, if pressed clear the counter and flags
    {
      WDTCTL = 0b0101101000001100;      //(20) clear WDT+ counter
      IFG1 = 0x00;                      //(21) clear interrupt flags
```

```
      Serial.println("WatchDog Counter cleared.");
    }
}
//---------------------------------------------------------------------------------
//---------------------------------------------------------------------------------
```

The main firmware loop is very simple. (10) - (13) take care of blinking the LED connected to port P1.6. In step (14) is the "one-time information" shown using the corresponding function. One-time info will inform the user about WDT+ settings, explaining the content of the WDTCTL register. Steps (15) - (16) periodically provide the content of the IFG1 register. In this example, the content will always be 00h - shown in binary form (00000000b) as the WDT+ is configured to trigger reset and not interrupt. The button is then tested (19) and in case, it is pressed, the WDT+ counter will be cleared (20) by initialising the WDTCTL register again with the same value as we saw earlier. Important is, that bit 3 is set to 1, which will clear the counter. Consequently, the IFG1 register is cleared (20) and that's the end of the main loop as well.

The rest part of the firmware takes care of waiting and providing information to be sent to the serial monitor - especially an explanation of the WDTCTL register.

```
//---------------------------------------------------------------------------------
//---------------------------------------------------------------------------------
void wait_a2(int time1)
{
  int a1;
  float a2;
//------------------------------
  a1 = time1;
  while(a1 > 0)
  {
    a2 = 1000;
    while(a2 > 0) a2--;
    a1--;
  }
}
//---------------------------------------------------------------------------------
//---------------------------------------------------------------------------------
void write_once()
{
  if (v_done == 0)
    {
      v_WDTCTL = WDTCTL;
      Serial.println("Watchdog Timer+");
      Serial.
println("--------------------------------------------------------------------------------");
      Serial.
```

```
println("----------------------------------------------------------------------------------------");
      explain_WDTCTL();
      Serial.
println("----------------------------------------------------------------------------------------");
      Serial.print("IE1: ");
      write_bin8(IE1);
      Serial.println("b");
      Serial.
println("----------------------------------------------------------------------------------------");
      v_done = 1;
    }
}
//---------------------------------------------------------------------------------
//---------------------------------------------------------------------------------
void write_bin(int i_word)
{
  if ((i_word & 0b1000000000000000) == 32768) Serial.print("1"); else Serial.print("0");
  if ((i_word & 0b0100000000000000) == 16384) Serial.print("1"); else Serial.print("0");
  if ((i_word & 0b0010000000000000) == 8192 ) Serial.print("1"); else Serial.print("0");
  if ((i_word & 0b0001000000000000) == 4096 ) Serial.print("1"); else Serial.print("0");
  Serial.print("-");
  if ((i_word & 0b0000100000000000) == 2048 ) Serial.print("1"); else Serial.print("0");
  if ((i_word & 0b0000010000000000) == 1024 ) Serial.print("1"); else Serial.print("0");
  if ((i_word & 0b0000001000000000) == 512  ) Serial.print("1"); else Serial.print("0");
  if ((i_word & 0b0000000100000000) == 256  ) Serial.print("1"); else Serial.print("0");
  Serial.print("--");
  if ((i_word & 0b0000000010000000) == 128  ) Serial.print("1"); else Serial.print("0");
  if ((i_word & 0b0000000001000000) == 64   ) Serial.print("1"); else Serial.print("0");
  if ((i_word & 0b0000000000100000) == 32   ) Serial.print("1"); else Serial.print("0");
  if ((i_word & 0b0000000000010000) == 16   ) Serial.print("1"); else Serial.print("0");
  Serial.print("-");
  if ((i_word & 0b0000000000001000) == 8    ) Serial.print("1"); else Serial.print("0");
  if ((i_word & 0b0000000000000100) == 4    ) Serial.print("1"); else Serial.print("0");
  if ((i_word & 0b0000000000000010) == 2    ) Serial.print("1"); else Serial.print("0");
  if ((i_word & 0b0000000000000001) == 1    ) Serial.print("1"); else Serial.print("0");
}
//---------------------------------------------------------------------------------
//---------------------------------------------------------------------------------
void write_bin8(int i_word)
{
  if ((i_word & 0b0000000010000000) == 128  ) Serial.print("1"); else Serial.print("0");
  if ((i_word & 0b0000000001000000) == 64   ) Serial.print("1"); else Serial.print("0");
  if ((i_word & 0b0000000000100000) == 32   ) Serial.print("1"); else Serial.print("0");
  if ((i_word & 0b0000000000010000) == 16   ) Serial.print("1"); else Serial.print("0");
  Serial.print("-");
  if ((i_word & 0b0000000000001000) == 8    ) Serial.print("1"); else Serial.print("0");
```

```
  if ((i_word & 0b0000000000000100) == 4    ) Serial.print("1"); else Serial.print("0");
  if ((i_word & 0b0000000000000010) == 2    ) Serial.print("1"); else Serial.print("0");
  if ((i_word & 0b0000000000000001) == 1    ) Serial.print("1"); else Serial.print("0");
}
//--------------------------------------------------------------------------------
//--------------------------------------------------------------------------------
void write_bin4(byte i_byte)
{
  if ((i_byte & 0b1000) == 8    ) Serial.print("1"); else Serial.print("0");
  if ((i_byte & 0b0100) == 4    ) Serial.print("1"); else Serial.print("0");
  if ((i_byte & 0b0010) == 2    ) Serial.print("1"); else Serial.print("0");
  if ((i_byte & 0b0001) == 1    ) Serial.print("1"); else Serial.print("0");
}
//--------------------------------------------------------------------------------
//--------------------------------------------------------------------------------
void write_bin3(byte i_byte)
{
  if ((i_byte & 0b0100) == 4    ) Serial.print("1"); else Serial.print("0");
  if ((i_byte & 0b0010) == 2    ) Serial.print("1"); else Serial.print("0");
  if ((i_byte & 0b0001) == 1    ) Serial.print("1"); else Serial.print("0");
}
//--------------------------------------------------------------------------------
//--------------------------------------------------------------------------------
void write_bin2(byte i_byte)
{
  if ((i_byte & 0b0010) == 2    ) Serial.print("1"); else Serial.print("0");
  if ((i_byte & 0b0001) == 1    ) Serial.print("1"); else Serial.print("0");
}
//--------------------------------------------------------------------------------
//--------------------------------------------------------------------------------
void write_bin1(byte i_byte)
{
  if ((i_byte & 0b0001) == 1    ) Serial.print("1"); else Serial.print("0");
}
//--------------------------------------------------------------------------------
//--------------------------------------------------------------------------------
void explain_WDTCTL(void)
{
  Serial.print("Watchdog Control Register: ");
  Serial.print("WDTCTL: "); write_bin(v_WDTCTL); Serial.println("b");
  Serial.
println("--------------------------------------------------------------------------------------------");
  int v_WDTPW      = (v_WDTCTL >> 8) & 255;
  int v_WDTHOLD    = (v_WDTCTL & 128) >> 7;
  int v_WDTNMIES   = (v_WDTCTL & 64) >> 6;
  int v_WDTNMI     = (v_WDTCTL & 32) >> 5;
```

```
  int v_WDTTMSEL    = (v_WDTCTL & 16) >> 4;
  int v_WDTCNTCL    = (v_WDTCTL & 8) >> 3;
  int v_WDTSSEL     = (v_WDTCTL & 4) >> 2;
  int v_WDTISx      = (v_WDTCTL & 3);
//----------------------------------------------------------------------------------
  Serial.print("  WDTPW:        (bits 15-8) WDT+ password      : ");
  write_bin8(v_WDTPW); Serial.print("b = ");
  Serial.print(v_WDTPW);
  Serial.println("d");
  Serial.println();

  Serial.print("  WDTHOLD:      (bit 7)     WDT+ hold          :  ");
  write_bin1(v_WDTHOLD); Serial.print("b => ");
  switch (v_WDTHOLD)
  {
    case 0: Serial.println("WDT+ is running"); break;
    case 1: Serial.println("WDT+ is stopped"); break;
  }

  Serial.print("  WDTNMIES:     (bit 6)     NMI edge select    :  ");
  write_bin1(v_WDTNMIES); Serial.print("b => ");
  switch (v_WDTNMIES)
  {
    case 0: Serial.println("NMI on rising edge"); break;
    case 1: Serial.println("NMI on falling edge"); break;
  }

  Serial.print("  WDTNMI:       (bit 5)     Reset or NMI       :  ");
  write_bin1(v_WDTNMI); Serial.print("b => ");
  switch (v_WDTNMI)
  {
    case 0: Serial.println("Reset function selected"); break;
    case 1: Serial.println("NMI function selected"); break;
  }

  Serial.print("  WDTTMSEL:     (bit 4)     WDT mode select    :  ");
  write_bin1(v_WDTTMSEL); Serial.print("b => ");
  switch (v_WDTTMSEL)
  {
    case 0: Serial.println("Watchdog mode"); break;
    case 1: Serial.println("Interval timer mode"); break;
  }

  Serial.print("  WDTCNTCL:     (bit 3)     WDT counter clear  :  ");
  write_bin1(v_WDTCNTCL); Serial.print("b => ");
  switch (v_WDTCNTCL)
```

```
  {
    case 0: Serial.println("No action"); break;
    case 1: Serial.println("WDTCNT = 0000h"); break;
  }

  Serial.print("  WDTSSEL:     (bit 2)     clock source select:  ");
  write_bin1(v_WDTSSEL); Serial.print("b => ");
  switch (v_WDTSSEL)
  {
    case 0: Serial.println("SMCLK"); break;
    case 1: Serial.println("ACLK"); break;
  }

  Serial.print("  WDTISx:      (bits 1-0)  WDT interval select: ");
  write_bin2(v_WDTISx); Serial.print("b => ");
  switch (v_WDTISx)
  {
    case 0b00: Serial.println("Watchdog clock source /32768"); break;
    case 0b01: Serial.println("Watchdog clock source /8192"); break;
    case 0b10: Serial.println("Watchdog clock source /512"); break;
    case 0b11: Serial.println("Watchdog clock source /64"); break;
  }
}
//-----------------------------------------------------------------------------------
//-----------------------------------------------------------------------------------
```

3.3.2 • WatchDog Interrupt Flag

In this exercise, interval timer mode is demonstrated to show the clear difference with watchdog mode. Firmware utilising Energia and CCS can be found in this chapter.
There is no need to specify the behaviour of the construction now. The expectation is the same - just with other WDT+ settings.

3.3.2.1 • Hardware

In this example, we do not need any special hardware. For the Energia-based firmware, it is enough to have the MSP430 LaunchBoard and a working serial monitor. Nevertheless, for the CCS-based firmware, we will reuse the hardware described in Chapter 3.1.4. - Connecting an LCD.

3.3.2.2 • Energia Firmware

This firmware is written and tested using Energia-1.8.7E21.

The firmware is the same as in the previous example, just the WDT-Settings are different. Therefore we will just have a look at the first part of the software as it doesn't make sense to list the same code again.

There is no need for a firmware listing. Let's have a look just at step (9) - defining the value written to the WDTCTL register. Step (9) in this version looks like this:

```
//            PPPPPPPP76543210
  WDTCTL = 0b0101101000011100;          //(9) WDTCTL settings: interrupt flag will be set
```

Compared to the settings of the former exercise:

```
  WDTCTL = 0b0101101000001100;          //(9) WDTCTL settings: reset will be forced
  WDTCTL = 0b0101101000011100;          //(9) WDTCTL settings: interrupt flag will be set
```

It becomes quite obvious that only visible change is in the settings of bit #4. Here the interval timer mode is defined as active. The result is that instead of getting the MCU-reset after a while, the information in serial monitor will be altered:

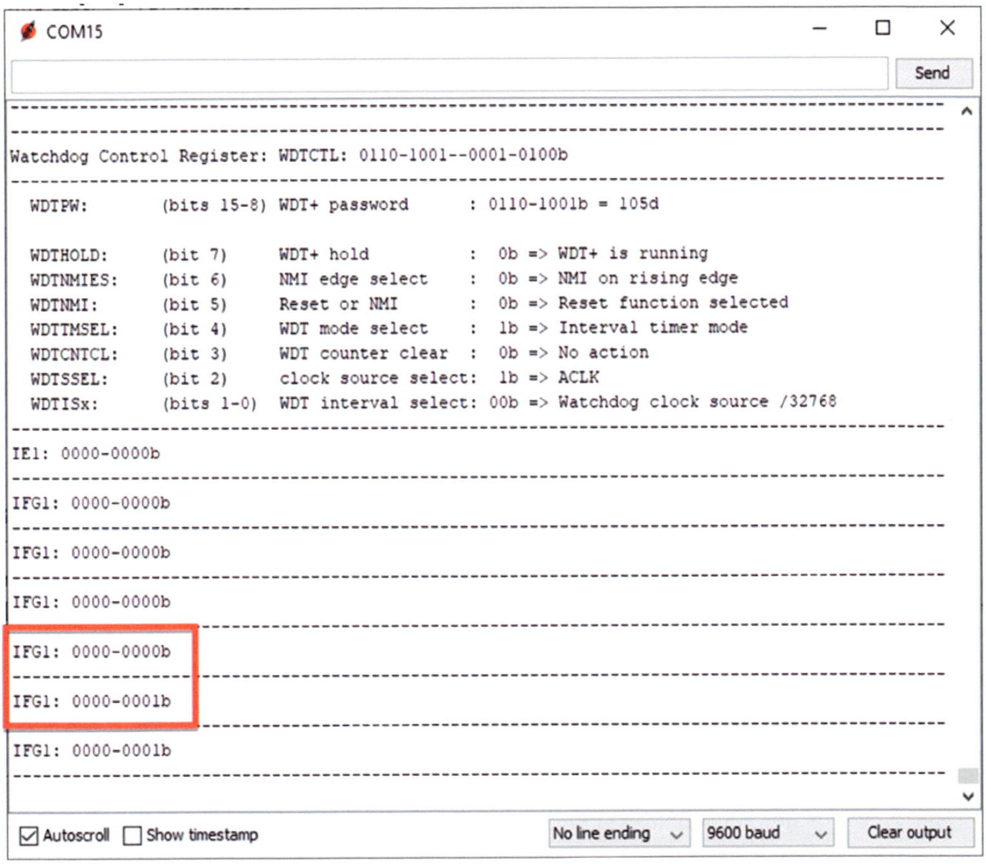

The change can be seen within the red border. Bit 0 of the IFG1 register changed from 0 to 1. This is the so-called WDTIFG - Watchdog timer interrupt flag. As the interrupt is disabled by WDT counter overflow, the WDTIFG bit is set and nothing more happens. In software, the bit can be tested and some activities can be undertaken. In the exercise firmware, this flag is cleared once the P1.3 button is pressed:

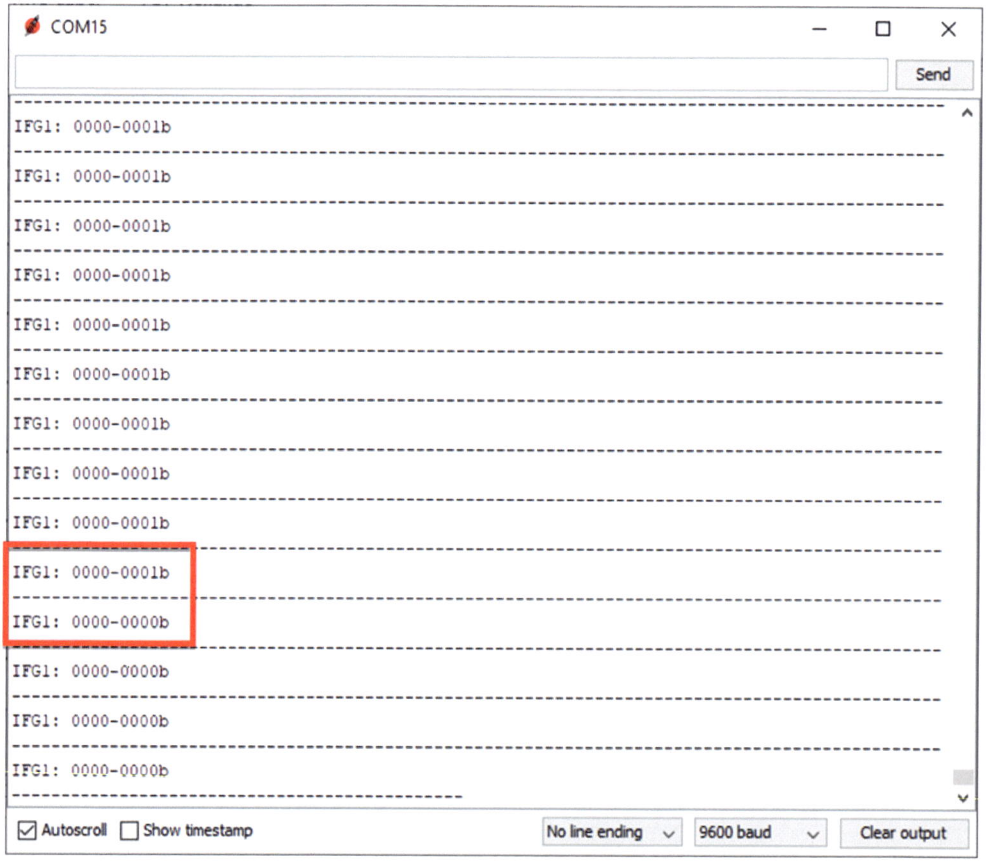

After a while, the bit will again be set to 1 as the watch dog is still running.

3.3.2.3 • CCS Firmware

This firmware is written and tested with CCS Version: 10.1.1.00004.

To see how the WDT+ can be used in the CCS environment, here is a short example demonstrating a preference. The only real difference to the Energia IDE Version is the "explaining-component". As there is only a 4x20 LCD available (and not the whole computer screen), the explanation is quite lean but is still sufficient.

On the other hand, the whole firmware is very simple.

```
// ------------------------------------------------------------------------------
// ------------------------------------------------------------------------------
#include <msp430.h>                              //(1) basic include
#include <LCD4x20.h>                             //(2) own LCD driver

void explain_WDTCTL(unsigned int iv_word);       //(3) declaration of explain-function

double v_counter;                                //(4) help variable
unsigned int v_WDTCTL;                           //(5) help variable
// ------------------------------------------------------------------------------
// ------------------------------------------------------------------------------
int main(void) {
    WDTCTL = WDTPW | WDTHOLD;                    //(6) Stop watchdog timer
    P1DIR = 0xFF;                                //(7) Set P1.0 - P1.7 to output direction
    P1SEL = 0x00;                                //(8) Set P1.0 - P1.7 to output direction
    P2DIR = 0x00;                                //(9) Set P2.0 - P2.7 to input direction
    P2REN = 0b000000001;                         //(10) activate pull-up for P2.0
    P2OUT = 0b000000001;                         //(11) activate pull-up for P2.0

    lcd_init();                                  //(12) LCD initialization

    lcd_print_cc(0,0, “MSP430 Power Book”);      //(13) Welcome Screen
    lcd_print_cc(0,1, “WDT+ Interrupt Flag”);    //(14) Welcome Screen
    lcd_print_cc(0,2, “Chapter 3.3.2”);          //(15) Welcome Screen
    lcd_print_cc(0,3, “29.12.2020”);             //(16) Welcome Screen

    wait_1ms(3000);                              //(17) wait 3 seconds
    lcd_clear();                                 //(18) clear LCD

    WDTCTL = 0b0101101000011101;                 //(19) set-up WDT+
    v_counter = 0;                               //(20) initialize help variable
// ------------------------------------------------------------------------------
// ------------------------------------------------------------------------------
```

After reset (power-on) the welcome screen is shown:

After 3 seconds (17) the welcome screen will disappear (18) and the main settings can be made (19). The settings of the WDTCTL register are the same as in the Energia IDE exercise shown previously.

The help variable v_counter is initialised (20). It is used to give a "still alive sign"; and the endless loop may start:

```
// ------------------------------------------------------------------------------------
// ------------------------------------------------------------------------------------
    for(;;)                                     //(21) main endless loop
    {
        lcd_print_cc(0,0, "CTL:");              //(22) write main screen content
        v_WDTCTL = WDTCTL;                      //(23) show WDTCTL register - binary
        w_bin16(v_WDTCTL);                      //(24) show WDTCTL register - binary
        explain_WDTCTL(v_WDTCTL);               //(25) explain WDTCTL register

        lcd_setcursor(0,3);                     //(26) show the status of interrupt flag
        if((IFG1 & BIT0) == 0)                  //(27) show the status of interrupt flag
            lcd_print_c("No interrupt   ");     //(28) show the status of interrupt flag
            else lcd_print_c("WDT IR pending"); //(29) show the status of interrupt flag

        if((P2IN & BIT0) == 0)                  //(30) if button pressed - clear WDT & flag
        {
            WDTCTL = 0b0101101000011101;
            IFG1 &= ~BIT0;
            lcd_print_cc(17,3,"CLR");
        }
        else
        {
            if (v_counter < 10) lcd_print_cc(17,3,"  X");
            else lcd_print_cc(17,3,"  *");
        }
        v_counter++;
        if(v_counter>20) v_counter = 0;
    }
}
// ------------------------------------------------------------------------------------
// ------------------------------------------------------------------------------------
```

The main endless loop started at (21) is writing the main screen and taking care of the button. If the button is pressed, the code coming after (27) is executed - and the WDT counter and interrupt flag are cleared.

The main screen displays like this:

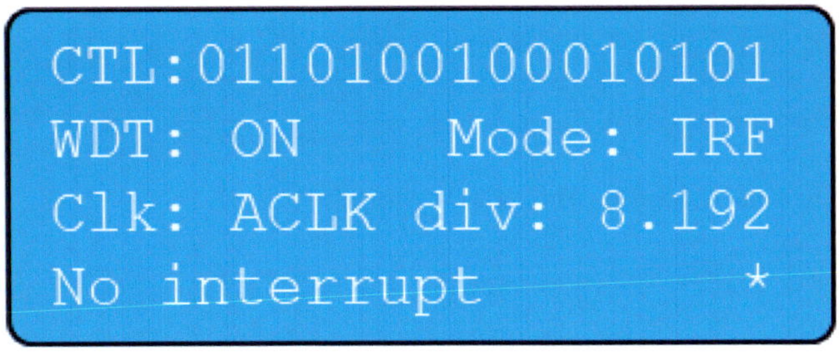

On the first line, the content of the 16-bit WDTCTL register is shown. Regarding this, are steps (22) - (24). The next two lines are explanations of settings, triggered by step (25).

The last line is handled in steps (26) - (29), where based on LSb (bit 0) of the IFG1 register, it is decided what should be shown. If this bit is equal to zero, no interrupt request is pending (there was no WDT counter overflow) and the "No interrupt" is shown. If this bit is equal to one, the comment "WDT IR pending" will be displayed:

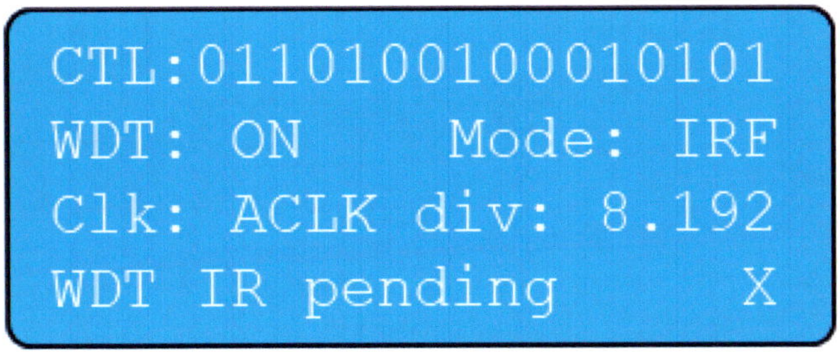

The last column in the last line is the "still alive sign". This is changed from "X" to "*" and back, to make sure the MCU is still running. Otherwise, the information shown on the LCD is quite stable.

The explanation implementation is the last part of firmware - function explain_WDTCTL():

```
// ---------------------------------------------------------------------------------
// ---------------------------------------------------------------------------------
void explain_WDTCTL(unsigned int iv_word)
{
    lcd_setcursor(0,1);
    if((iv_word & BIT7) == 0) lcd_print_c(“WDT: ON     “); else lcd_print_c(“WDT: OFF    “);
    if((iv_word & BIT4) == 0) lcd_print_c(“Mode: WDT”); else lcd_print_c(“Mode: IRF”);
    lcd_setcursor(0,2);
    if((iv_word & BIT2) == 0) lcd_print_c(“Clk:SMCLK “); else lcd_print_c(“Clk: ACLK “);
    if((iv_word & 3) == 0x00) lcd_print_c(“div:32.768”);
    if((iv_word & 3) == 0x01) lcd_print_c(“div: 8.192”);
    if((iv_word & 3) == 0x02) lcd_print_c(“div:   512”);
    if((iv_word & 3) == 0x03) lcd_print_c(“div:    64”);
```

```
}
// ------------------------------------------------------------------------------
// ------------------------------------------------------------------------------
```

This is all from my side regarding the WDT+ module.

3.4 • Timer_A module

There are two 16-bits counters provided by the MSP430G2553 microcontroller. These can be used for a couple of purposes - we will focus on simple counter functionality.

Timer_A for the MSP430-family microcontrollers is built as shown in the following block diagram:

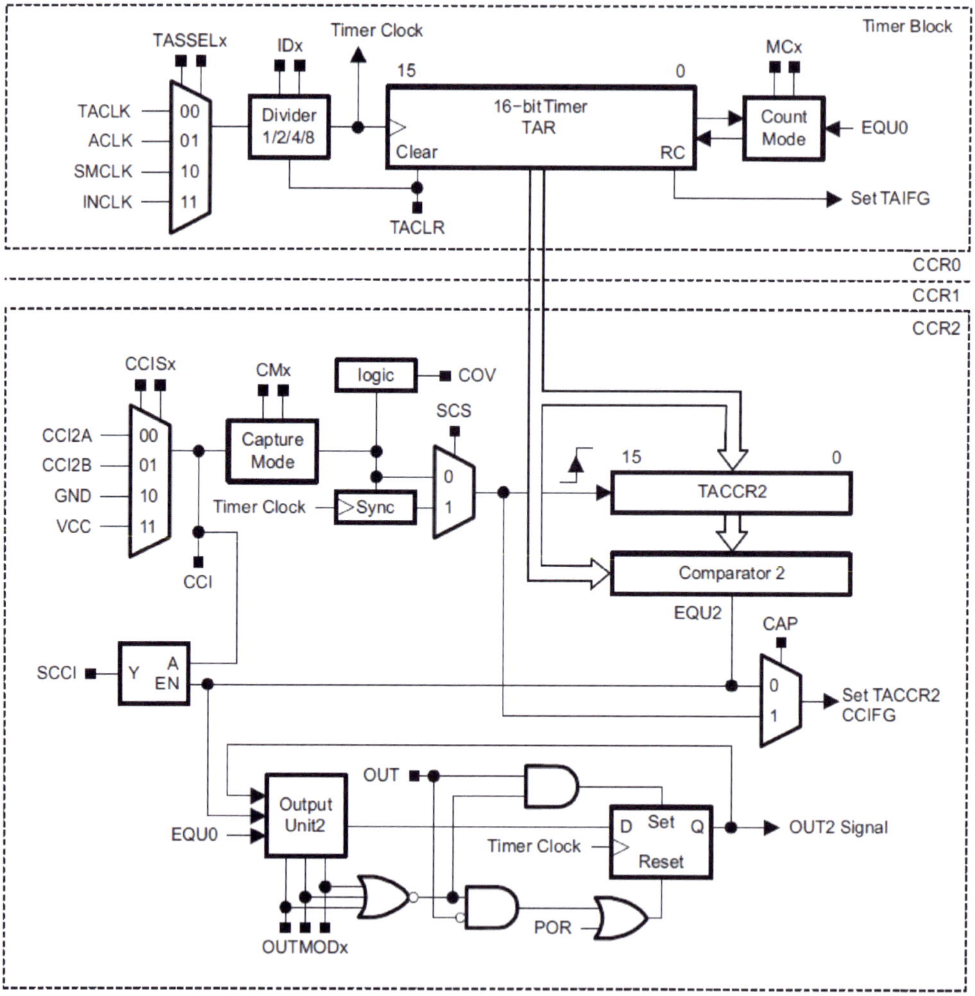

The whole functionality can be configured in the software using a small number of configuration registers.

The module can be used either as a timer or capture module to count different kinds of events. And of course, the module can be connected to the interrupt system of the microcontroller.

There are a couple of registers associated with the Timer_A+ module:

Register	Short Form	Register Type	Address	Initial State
Timer_A control	TACTL	Read/write	0160h	Reset with POR
Timer_A counter	TAR	Read/write	0170h	Reset with POR
Timer_A capture/compare control 0	TACCTL0	Read/write	0162h	Reset with POR
Timer_A capture/compare 0	TACCR0	Read/write	0172h	Reset with POR
Timer_A capture/compare control 1	TACCTL1	Read/write	0164h	Reset with POR
Timer_A capture/compare 1	TACCR1	Read/write	0174h	Reset with POR
Timer_A capture/compare control 2	TACCTL2[(1)]	Read/write	0166h	Reset with POR
Timer_A capture/compare 2	TACCR2[(1)]	Read/write	0176h	Reset with POR
Timer_A interrupt vector	TAIV	Read only	012Eh	Reset with POR

(1) Not present on MSP430 devices with Timer_A2 like MSP430F20xx and other devices.

The most important register regarding settings is TACTL. As we have two 16-bit timers available, all registers are doubled. Therefore there is a 16-bit register accessible as **TA0CTL** and **TA1CTL**:

bit 15	bit 14	bit 13	bit 12	bit 11	bit 10	bit 9	bit 8
Unused						**TASSELx**	
rw-0	rw-0	rw-0	rw-0	rw-0	rw-0	rw-0	

bit 7	bit 6	bit 5	bit 4	bit 3	bit 2	bit 1	bit 0
IDx		**MCx**		**Unused**	**TACLR**	**TAIE**	**TAIFG**
rw-0	rw-0	rw-0	rw-0	rw-0	rw-0	rw-0	rw-0

bit name	bit(s)	usage
Unused	15 - 10	No used bits
TASSELx	9 - 8	Timer_A clock source select: 00 - TACLK 01 - ACLK 10 - SMCLK 11 - INCLK
IDx	7 - 6	Input divider. The input clock can be divided by following values - before hitting the counter itself: 00 - input clock:1 (no divider) 01 - input clock:2 10 - input clock:4 11 - input clock:8
MCx	5 - 4	Definition of timer mode: 00 - timer is not running 01 - up mode - the timer counts up to the value stored in register TACCRx 10 - continuous mode: the timer counts up to FFFFh 11 - Up/down mode: the timer counts up to TACCR0 and then down to 0000h
Unused	3	Not used bit
TACLR	2	Timer clear bit
TAIE	1	Timer_A interrupt enable: 0 - interrupt is disabled 1 - interrupt is enabled
TAIFG	0	Timer_A interrupt flag: 0 - no Timer_A interrupt pending 1 - interrupt pending

The counter value can be obtained at any time by reading the corresponding 16-bit counter register: **TAxR** (**TA0R** / **TA1R**).

The **TACCRx** (**TACCR0** / **TACCR1**) register holds a compare value for the timer itself. In "up" and "up/down" modes there is a stored "final" value, after which an overflow takes place.

No other registers (compare/capture) will be used in the exercise.

3.4.1 • Simple 16-bit counter

In this exercise, Timer0 is utilised, and therefore registers related to Timer0 are used. Very simple software for CCS will be shown doing basic settings of Timer0 to count up or up/down and showing the content of the counter on the LCD. There will be no Energia-Firmware, as the code will be almost the same, just for another IDE.

After startup, the firmware will show a kind of "welcome screen" like this:

After 3 seconds, the LCD will clear, and the main screen will be displayed:

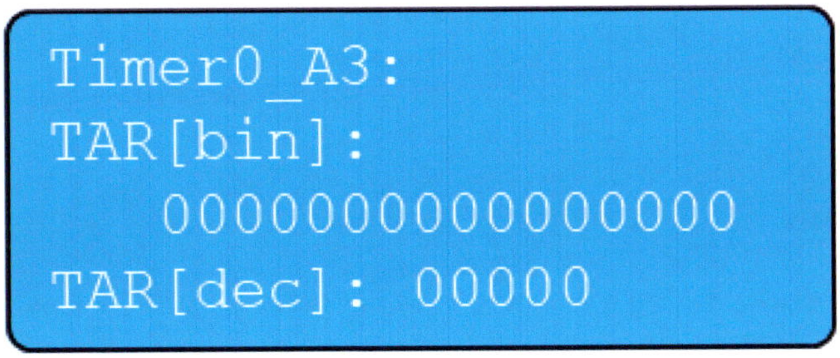

The counter then counts immediately.

There are two possibilities for counting: the first one is to count up from 00.000 to 65.535; overflow will lead to setting the counter back to zero and counting up again - option #1.

The second option is to count up from 00.000 to 65.535 and back down to 00.000 and then up again etc. - option #2.

There are two buttons available on the demo hardware - a button connected to P2.0 and another connected to P2.2.

Let's say, that if button P2.0 is pressed, the counter will be cleared (set to zero). When the other button (P2.2) is pressed, the counter will be set to the half of maximum value: 32.768 (or 8000h or 1000 0000 0000 0000b).

3.4.1.1 ● Hardware

We will reuse the hardware described in 3.1.4. (connecting an LCD)." (just remove the last part of the sentence please, as there is no other version of the firmware – only CCS version).

3.4.1.2 ● CCS Firmware

This firmware is written and tested using CCS Version: 10.1.1.00004.

The firmware is simple and the majority of the code lines are comments.

```
// ---------------------------------------------------------------------------------------
// ---------------------------------------------------------------------------------------
#include <msp430.h>                     //(1) including MSP430 library
#include <LCD4x20.h>                    //(2) including our own LCD library

void w_print(void);                     //(3) declaration of w_print function

double v_counter;                       //(4) main counter variable
// ---------------------------------------------------------------------------------------
// ---------------------------------------------------------------------------------------
int main(void) {
    WDTCTL = WDTPW | WDTHOLD;           //(5) Stop watchdog timer
    P1DIR = 0xFF;                       //(6a) Set P1.0 - P1.7 to output direction
    P1SEL = 0x00;                       //(6b) Set-up P1
    P2REN = 0b00000101;                 //(6c) Set-up buttons
    P2OUT = 0b00000101;                 //(6d) Set-up buttons

    lcd_init();                               //(7a) LCD initialization
    lcd_print_cc(0,0, "MSP430 Power Book");   //(7b) Welcome Screen
    lcd_print_cc(0,1, "MCU: MSP430G2553");    //(7c) Welcome Screen
    lcd_print_cc(0,2, "Chapter 3.4.1.");      //(7d) Welcome Screen
    lcd_print_cc(0,3, "01.01.2021");          //(7e) Welcome Screen

    wait_1ms(3000);                     //(8) wait 3 seconds
    lcd_clear();                        //(9) clear the screen

    // --------------------------------------------------------------------------------
    // ----- Set-Up for: Clock Source  [b9-b8]: 01 = ACLK
    // -----            Input Divider [b7-b6]: 11 = :8
    // -----            Mode          [b5-b4]: 10 = incremental counter ("continuous mode")
    // -----            Interrupt     [b1]   :  0 = Interrupt disabled
    // --------------------------------------------------------------------------------
    //        bbbbbbbbbbbbbbbb
    //        FEDCBA9876543210
    TA0CTL = 0b0000000111100100;              //(10-1) Timer_A control register - settings for option #1
```

```
    // -------------------------------------------------------------------------------

    // -------------------------------------------------------------------------------
    // ----- Set-Up for: Clock Source  [b9-b8]: 01 = ACLK
    // -----            Input Divider [b7-b6]: 11 = :8
    // -----            Mode          [b5-b4]: 11 = up/down mode
    // -----            Interrupt     [b1]   :  0 = Interrupt disabled
    // -------------------------------------------------------------------------------
    //       bbbbbbbbbbbbbbbb
    //       FEDCBA9876543210
    TA0CTL = 0b0000011111010O;               //(10-2) Timer_A control register - settings for option #2
    TACCR0 = 0xFFFF;
    // -------------------------------------------------------------------------------

    for(;;)                                  //(11) endless loop
    {
        if((P2IN & 0x01) == 0) TA0CTL |= BIT2;  //(12) P2.0 = 0 => clear the counter
        if((P2IN & 0x04) == 0) TA0R = 0x8000;   //(13) P2.2 = 0 => set the counter to 0x8000
                                                //                 direction is not changed
        v_counter = TA0R;                       //(14) copy counter to the counter-variable
        w_print();                              //(15) show the counter on LCD
    }
}
// -----------------------------------------------------------------------------------
// -----------------------------------------------------------------------------------
void w_print(void)                           //(16) build-up the main screen
{
    lcd_print_cc(0,0, "Timer0_A3: ");
//    lcd_print_cc(0,0, "x: ");
//    w_bin16(TA0CTL);

    lcd_print_cc(0,1, "TAR[bin]:");
    lcd_setcursor(3,2);
    w_bin16(v_counter);

    lcd_print_cc(0,3, "TAR[dec]:");
    lcd_print_ic(10,3,v_counter);
}
// -----------------------------------------------------------------------------------
// -----------------------------------------------------------------------------------
```

Just a small remark: Instead of TA0CTL, the short form TACTL can be used in CCS. Instead of TA0R, the short form TAR can be used.

The First 4 steps are just declarations, and we can see that variable v_counter has been defined (4) to store (a copy) the value from Timer register TAR.

In steps (5) to (9), we perform the required initialisations of the ports and display a "welcome screen" for 3 seconds.

Step (10-1) will set up option #1 mentioned earlier regarding Timer behaviour and step (10-2) will go for option #2. There will always be one of these steps commented out i.e. the one not to be used.

Step (11) is the start of the main endless loop of the demo software.

Steps (12) and (13) take care of buttons (as mentioned earlier). Step (14) takes care of the value of the timer register TAR and stores it to counter variable v_counter. This will be shown on the LCD using function w_print (15).

The function itself (16) is displaying all information we defined earlier.

3.5 • USCI

What do these four letters stay for? Well - USCI = Universal Serial Communication Interface - and it is a very useful hardware module. It opens the door to a nearly endless world of GPIO extensions, sensors, and other modules/slave chips available for the collection or distribution of any kind of information.

Our microcontroller MSP430G2553 provides two different USCI modules: the USCI_A0 and USCI_B0. The difference between "A" and "B" is the different support of serial communication protocols.

USCI_A0 module supports the following protocols:

- UART mode
- Pulse shaping for IrDA communication
- Automatic baud rate detection for LIN communications
- SPI mode

The USCI_B0 module supports the following protocols:

- I^2C mode
- SPI mode

Nevertheless, I decided to provide a simple example of I^2C communication without utilising the USCI module.

IDE Energia provides a library for I^2C communication, and we will write I^2C communication for the CCS IDE. This allows the use of these communication routines even with MSP430 microcontrollers which do not have a USCI-module.

Besides this, It is important to keep in mind that the USCI module uses (in I^2C mode) the following I/O to connect to the I²C-bus:

P1.6 = SCL
P1.7 = SDA

If we go for Energia, another two pins are utilised to define the I²C-bus:

P2.1 = SCL
P2.2 = SDA

Additionally in this chapter, we will look at "custom serial communication" - We investigate how a OneWire device can be connected to the MSP430G2553.

I do not want to describe the I²C protocol itself, even though we need this for the CCS implementation. It is still possible to do "reverse engineering" from the listing of the CCS firmware - if you are interested in the flows and "bits" of the communication itself.

Of course for Energia, we do not need to know anything about the flows, as we will use the standard Energia-I²C library.

Let's make a summary of the communication puzzles of the I²C protocol:

Step ("puzzle piece")	**Name of the function in CCS firmware**	**usage**
I²C Start	i2c_start()	Start of the I²C communication
I²C Stop	i2c_stop()	Finish of the I²C communication
I²C Send	i2c_send()	Send a byte through the I²C bus
I²C Receive	--	Receive a byte from slave through I²C bus; not implemented in our example, as we are not using this functionality here
I²C Send ACK	--	Send ACK (Acknowledgement) to slave; not implemented in our example, as we are not using this functionality here
I²C Send NOT ACK	--	Send NOT ACK (Not Acknowledgement) to slave; not implemented in our example, as we are not using this functionality here

Besides the listed function, we will use i2c_init() for the initialisation of the I²C bus.

3.5.1 • I²C communication by software / CCS

My favourite GPIO (General Purpose Input Output) chip, the PCF8574 will be used with I²C communication.

Working with the chip is very easy and we can quickly see whether communication via the I²C bus is successful.

A Description of the chip can be found in chapter "5.2.1. GPIO - PCF8574A", later in the book.

We will start with a description of the hardware and corresponding simple demo software for CCS and IDE Energia IDEs.

Here we will let the firmware count a counter variable from 255 backwards to 0, and send these values to the LEDs connected to the 8-bit PCF8574 GPIO driver. The LEDs will show the complement of the counter value as a binary number. Why complement? Because we will connect the LEDs with a common anode meaning, logical 1 will switch an LED off and logical zero will switch the corresponding LED on.

If we try to imagine only 4 bits displayed with LEDs with a common anode, we can see 16 different values (24). We can then easily understand the dependence between counter values and LEDs using the following table:

4-bit „complement counter“

counter	P3	P2	P1	P0	LEDs	„number on LEDs“
15	1	1	1	1	○○○○	0000 = 0
14	1	1	1	0	○○○●	0001 = 1
13	1	1	0	1	○○●○	0010 = 2
12	1	1	0	0	○○●●	0011 = 3
11	1	0	1	1	○●○○	0100 = 4
10	1	0	1	0	○●○●	0101 = 5
9	1	0	0	1	○●●○	0110 = 6
8	1	0	0	0	○●●●	0111 = 7
7	0	1	1	1	●○○○	1000 = 8
6	0	1	1	0	●○○●	1001 = 9
5	0	1	0	1	●○●○	1010 = 10
4	0	1	0	0	●○●●	1011 = 11
3	0	0	1	1	●●○○	1100 = 12
2	0	0	1	0	●●○●	1101 = 13
1	0	0	0	1	●●●○	1110 = 14
0	0	0	0	0	●●●●	1111 = 15

3.5.1.1 • Hardware

For our two examples, we will use the board from chapter 3.1.4, 'Connecting an LCD'. We will just add the I^2C bus. Here's a hint for the very beginning: if you intend to extend the construction by adding an I^2C port as described here, it is of course possible, and the firmware will work with the bus. Just consider that for the Energia-based example shown later, the I^2C bus is connected to different I/Os. The CCS version of the firmware can work with both connections.

The CCS extension of the hardware, conforming with USCI usage of the I/Os for I^2C looks like this:

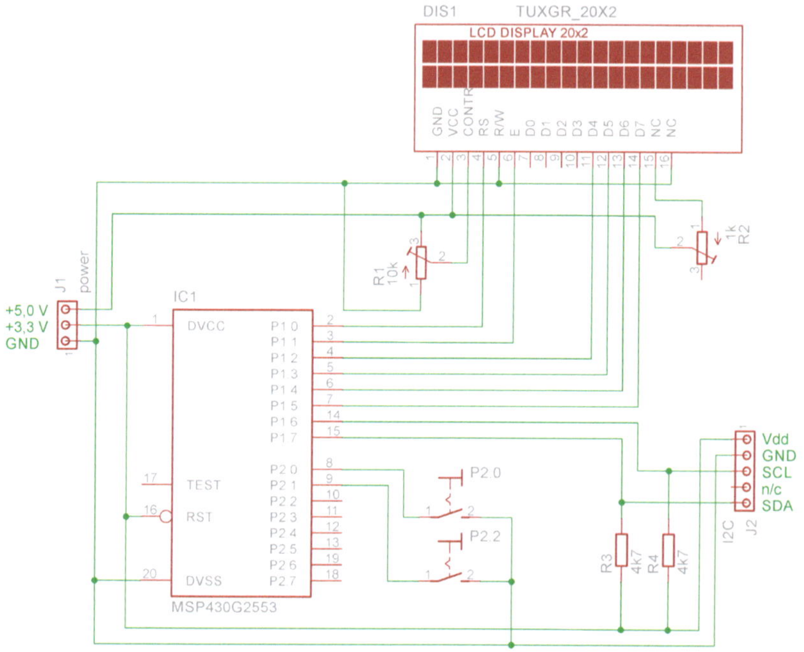

We can see that we need two additional resistors (R3 and R4) used as pull-ups for the SCL and SDA lines.

The periphery based on the PCF8574 and LEDs can be built as shown in the following schematics:

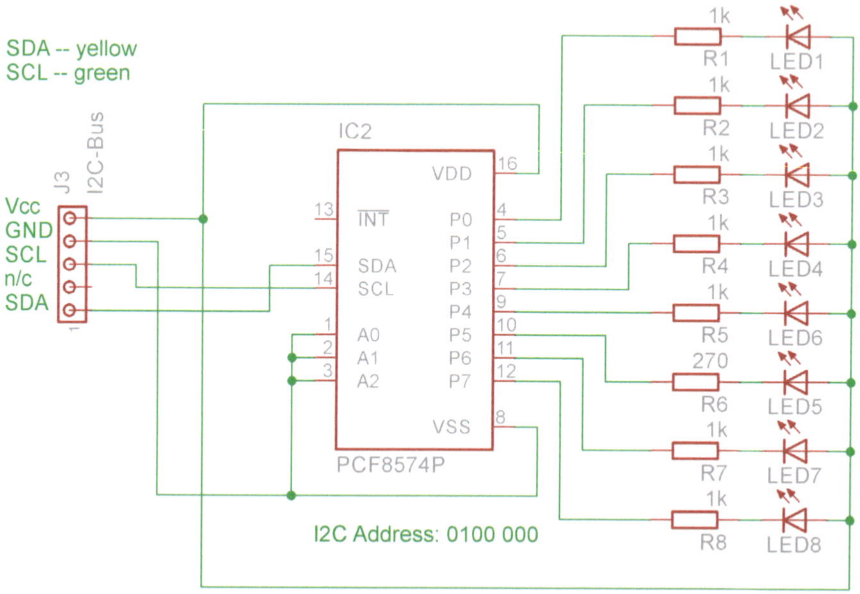

As we can see, you do not need anything besides the PCF8574 chip itself and LEDs with resistors.

The resistors used for LEDs need to be picked up based on the LEDs themselves. It is important to consider that the output current for one single I/O must not exceed 20mA and the total current for all LEDs must not exceed 100mA. Otherwise, the chip may become damaged.

3.5.1.2 • CCS Firmware

This firmware is written and tested with CCS Version: 10.1.1.00004.

Firmware written using IDE CCS is a bit more complex because we first need to implement the whole I²C communication, and only then we can start using it within our own logic. First, let's have a short look at the declaration and initialisation part of the firmware.

```
// -----------------------------------------------------------------------------------
// -----------------------------------------------------------------------------------
#include <msp430.h>                   //(1) including MSP430 library
#include <LCD4x20.h>                  //(2) including our own LCD library
// -----------------------------------------------------------------------------------
// -----------------------------------------------------------------------------------
#define byte    unsigned short        //(3) here we define, what it is “byte”

#define SCL  BIT6                     //(4a) definition of SCL for USCI-mode
#define SDA  BIT7                     //(4b) definition of SDA for USCI-mode

#define SCL_E  BIT1                   //(5a) definition of SCL for Energia-mode
#define SDA_E  BIT2                   //(5b) definition of SDA for Energia-mode

#define Energia 0                     //(6a) define switch value for Energia-mode
#define USCI_E  1                     //(6b) define switch value for USCI-mode
// -----------------------------------------------------------------------------------
// -----------------------------------------------------------------------------------
short gv_i2c_active;                  //(7) swtich for choosing Energia or USCI mode
// -----------------------------------------------------------------------------------
// -----------------------------------------------------------------------------------
void i2c_init();                     //(8a) declaration of I2C function i2c_init()
void i2c_start();                    //(8b) declaration of I2C function i2c_start()
void i2c_stop();                     //(8c) declaration of I2C function i2c_stop()
void i2c_send_b0();                  //(8d) declaration of I2C function i2c_send_b0()
void i2c_send_b1();                  //(8e) declaration of I2C function i2c_send_b1()
byte i2c_send(byte iv_byte);         //(8f) declaration of I2C function i2c_send()
byte i2c_ack_rq();                   //(8g) declaration of I2C function i2c_ack_rq()

void i2c_e_init();                   //(9a) declaration of I2C functions for Energia-mode
void i2c_e_start();                  //(9b) declaration of I2C functions for Energia-mode
```

```
void i2c_e_stop();                     //(9c) declaration of I2C functions for Energia-mode
void i2c_e_send_b0();                  //(9d) declaration of I2C functions for Energia-mode
void i2c_e_send_b1();                  //(9e) declaration of I2C functions for Energia-mode
byte i2c_e_ack_rq();                   //(9f) declaration of I2C functions for Energia-mode

void i2c_u_init();                     //(10a) declaration of I2C functions for USCI-mode
void i2c_u_start();                    //(10b) declaration of I2C functions for USCI-mode
void i2c_u_stop();                     //(10c) declaration of I2C functions for USCI-mode
void i2c_u_send_b0();                  //(10d) declaration of I2C functions for USCI-mode
void i2c_u_send_b1();                  //(10e) declaration of I2C functions for USCI-mode
byte i2c_u_ack_rq();                   //(10f) declaration of I2C functions for USCI-mode
// ----------------------------------------------------------------------------------------
void lcd_print_b8c(byte iv_row, byte iv_col, byte iv_bin8);
                                       //(11) LCD additional function
// ----------------------------------------------------------------------------------------
// ----------------------------------------------------------------------------------------
int main(void)                         //(12) start of the main program
{
    gv_i2c_active = Energia;           //(13) select Energia mode for I2C
//    gv_i2c_active = USCI_E;          //(14) select USCI mode for I2C

    int i;                             //(15) declaration of counter variable ("i")
    byte lv_ack;                       //(16) declaration of ACK-variable

    WDTCTL = WDTPW | WDTHOLD;          //(17) Stop watchdog timer
    P1DIR = 0xFF;                      //(18a) Set P1.0 - P1.7 to output direction
    P1SEL = 0x00;                      //(18b) Additional Port 1 settings
    P2SEL = 0x00;                      //(18c) Additional Port 2 settings

    lcd_init();                        //(19) Initialization of LCD

    lcd_print_cc(0,0, "MSP430 DemoBoard");      //(20a) show firmware version
    lcd_print_cc(0,1, "CCS Version v1.01.16"); //(20b) show firmware version
    lcd_print_cc(0,2, "01.05.2021");            //(20c) show firmware version
    lcd_print_cc(0,3, "SW I2C PCF8574");        //(20d) show firmware version

    wait_1ms(3000);                             //(21) wait 3 seconds
    lcd_clear();                                //(22) clear LCD

    i2c_init();                                 //(23) execute initialization of I2C bus
    i = 255;                                    //(24) counter start value: 255 = all LEDs off
    lcd_print_cc(0,0, "First I2C project");     //(25a) write static texts to LCD
    lcd_print_cc(0,1, "PCF8574 with LEDs");     //(25b) write static texts to LCD
    lcd_print_cc(0,2, "Counter:");              //(25c) write static texts to LCD
    lcd_print_cc(0,3, "Ad:no ack  D:no ack");   //(25d) write static texts to LCD
// ----------------------------------------------------------------------------------------
```

Steps (1) to (11) are declarations of libraries, variables, and functions implemented later in the coding. Even our LCD library will be in this example extended by 1 function - step (11). With step (12), the main program is started - with initialisations.

By activating step (13) and commenting out step (14) we select the Energia-variant of the code using P2.1 and P2.2 for communication. Doing it the other way around (commenting out step (13) and activating step (14)) we will choose the USCI-version - using P1.6 and P1.7.

Our counter variable here is called "i" and is declared in step (15). We want to show if we got an answer from the PCF8574 later. This answer will be during communication stored to the variable declared in step (16) - lv_ack. Step (17) will stop (finally) the watch-dog timer and in steps (18x) we undertake the P1.x and P2.x settings.

Now it is time to initialise LCD (19) so that we can show "a welcome note" (20x). After 3 seconds of waiting time (21) the LCD will be cleared (22).

In step (23) we are calling the function to initialise the I²C bus, and then (24) we set up the initial value of our counter to 255 as this value means all LEDs will be off.

The last part of preparation is to print the static texts to the LCD (25x), and the main loop of the code can be entered.

```
// ------------------------------------------------------------------------------------
    for(;;)                                     //(26) start of main (endless) loop
    {
        i--;                                    //(27) decrement main counter
        if (i < 0) i = 255;                     //(28) handle counter overflow
        lcd_print_b8c(9,2, i);                  //(29) show value of the counter on LCD

        i2c_start();                            //(30) start I2C communication
        lv_ack = i2c_send(0b01000000);          //(31) send the I2C address of PCF8574
        if(lv_ack == 0) lcd_print_cc(3,3,"ACK   ");  //(32a) show ACK / not ACK - based on the response
        if(lv_ack == 1) lcd_print_cc(3,3,"no ack");  //(32b) show ACK / not ACK - based on the response
        lv_ack = i2c_send(i);                   //(33) send the I2C address of PCF8574
        if(lv_ack == 0) lcd_print_cc(13,3,"ACK   ");  //(34a) show ACK / not ACK - based on the response
        if(lv_ack == 1) lcd_print_cc(13,3,"no ack");  //(34b) show ACK / not ACK - based on the response
        i2c_stop();                             //(35) finish the I2C communication

        wait_1ms(100);                          //(36) wait 0,1 sec - and the loop can start again
    }
}
// ------------------------------------------------------------------------------------
```

At the beginning of the main endless loop of the application, we decrement the value of the counter by 1 (27); and once it reaches 0, the counter will be put back to the initial value - 255 (28).

We then show the binary value of the counter on LCD (29) with the extension of our LCD library, and we initiate I^2C communication (30). We then have to address our PCF8574 chip by sending the I^2C address to the bus (31). Function i2c_send() will return zero if the send command has been acknowledged, and will return one if there was no acknowledgment. We will get NOT ACK if the PCF8574 is not connected at all.

Based on the response, we will show on LCD (32x) if the address has been confirmed. Based on the schematic, the I^2C address of our chip is 40h (0100 000xb). The last zero in the I^2C address byte is the indication of a write request (we want to write something to the chip, not read).

In the next step (33) we send the content of the counter variable "i" and again display the ACK information on the LCD (34x).

After this, we can stop I^2C communication (35). Wait 0.1 seconds and start the endless loop again.

Let's have a look now at the I^2C communication routines themselves. We can start with the very easy part - support of the two different modes - Energia and USCI.

```
// ---------------------------------------------------------------------------
// ---------------------------------------------------------------------------
// ---------------------------------------------------------------------------
// Software I2C communication routines
// Energia conform or
// USCI conform
// ---------------------------------------------------------------------------
// ---------------------------------------------------------------------------
// ---------------------------------------------------------------------------
void i2c_init()
{
    if (gv_i2c_active == Energia) i2c_e_init();
    else                          i2c_u_init();
}
// ---------------------------------------------------------------------------
// ---------------------------------------------------------------------------
void i2c_start()
{
    if (gv_i2c_active == Energia) i2c_e_start();
    else                          i2c_u_start();
}
// ---------------------------------------------------------------------------
```

```
// ------------------------------------------------------------------------------------------
void i2c_stop()
{
    if (gv_i2c_active == Energia) i2c_e_stop();
    else                          i2c_u_stop();
}
// ------------------------------------------------------------------------------------------
// ------------------------------------------------------------------------------------------
void i2c_send_b1()
{
    if (gv_i2c_active == Energia) i2c_e_send_b1();
    else                          i2c_u_send_b1();
}
// ------------------------------------------------------------------------------------------
// ------------------------------------------------------------------------------------------
void i2c_send_b0()
{
    if (gv_i2c_active == Energia) i2c_e_send_b0();
    else                          i2c_u_send_b0();
}
// ------------------------------------------------------------------------------------------
// ------------------------------------------------------------------------------------------
byte i2c_ack_rq()
{
    if (gv_i2c_active == Energia) return(i2c_e_ack_rq());
    else                          return(i2c_u_ack_rq());
}
// ------------------------------------------------------------------------------------------
// ------------------------------------------------------------------------------------------
```

Now we can have a closer look at the implementation for Energia-version of the I²C communication routines.

```
// ------------------------------------------------------------------------------------------
// ------------------------------------------------------------------------------------------
// ------------------------------------------------------------------------------------------
// Software I2C communication routines [Energia-like]
// SCL = P2.1
// SDA = P2.2
// ------------------------------------------------------------------------------------------
// ------------------------------------------------------------------------------------------
// ------------------------------------------------------------------------------------------
void i2c_e_init()                //(Init-1)
{
    P2DIR &= ~SCL_E;             //(Init-2a) SCL = High (disconnect)
    P2DIR &= ~SDA_E;             //(Init-2b) SDA = High (disconnect)
```

```
    P2OUT &= ~SCL_E;            //(Init-3a) prepare zero for SCL line
    P2OUT &= ~SDA_E;            //(Init-3b) prepare zero for SDA line
}
// ---------------------------------------------------------------------------
```

The initialization (starting at (Init-1)) of the bus is quite easy. As the I²C SCL and SDA lines are always built as open-drain connections, they are never actively pulled up on V_{cc}, not with master or slave chips. Therefore, we disconnect the outputs (Init-2x) and the external pull-up resistors take care of logical level 1 on both lines.

In addition, as we act only to push the lines down if required, we prepare to the output buffers logical zero (Init-3x).

Initialization of the bus can be described by the following signal diagram:

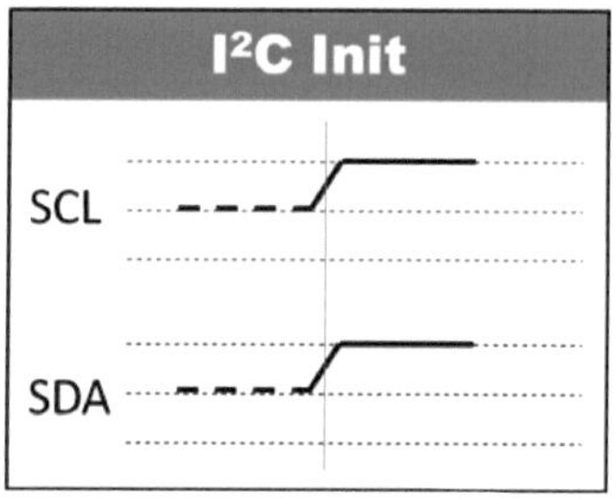

The generation of the start condition is the task of the function i2c_e_start():

```
// ---------------------------------------------------------------------------
void i2c_e_start()              //(S-1)
{
    P2DIR &= ~SCL_E;            //(S-2a) SCL = High
    P2DIR |= SDA_E;             //(S-2b) SDA = Low

    P2DIR |= SCL_E;             //(S-3a) SCL = Low
    P2DIR |= SDA_E;             //(S-3b) SDA = Low
}
// ---------------------------------------------------------------------------
```

As we can see, the generation of the start condition is quite easy and is following the definition of this sequence for the I²C bus.

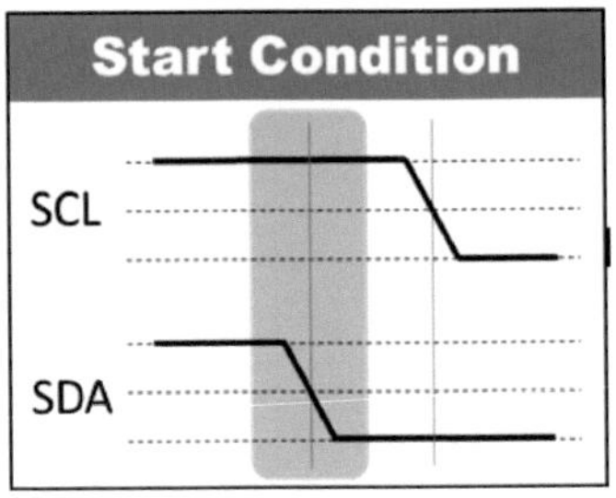

Stop condition generation is similar to the start condition, of course following the corresponding definition:

```
// ---------------------------------------------------------------------------------
void i2c_e_stop()              //(P-1)
{
    P2DIR |= SCL_E;            //(P-2a) SCL = Low
    P2DIR |= SDA_E;            //(P-2b) SDA = Low

    P2DIR &= ~SCL_E;           //(P-3a) SCL = High
    P2DIR |= SDA_E;            //(P-3a) SDA = Low

    P2DIR &= ~SCL_E;           //SCL = High
    P2DIR &= ~SDA_E;           //SDA = High
}
// ---------------------------------------------------------------------------------
```

A stop condition can be with a flow described like this:

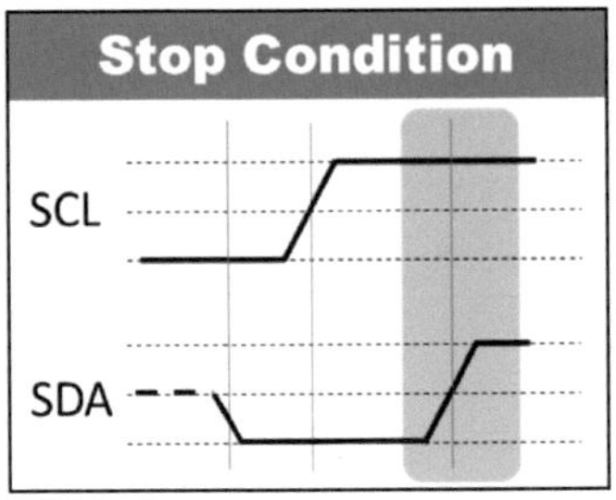

We can now initiate and finalise I²C communication with start and stop conditions. It is now important to send data over the bus. Therefore we first have to be able to send a logical one and zero.

Sending a logical One can be implemented as seen in the function i2c_e_send_b1():

```
// -------------------------------------------------------------------------------------
void i2c_e_send_b1()
{
    P2DIR |= SCL_E;             //SCL = Low
    P2DIR &= ~SDA_E;            //SDA = High

    P2DIR &= ~SCL_E;            //SCL = High
    P2DIR &= ~SDA_E;            //SDA = High

    P2DIR |= SCL_E;             //SCL = Low
    P2DIR &= ~SDA_E;            //SDA = High
}
// -------------------------------------------------------------------------------------
```

It is nothing else as the implementation of the following chart:

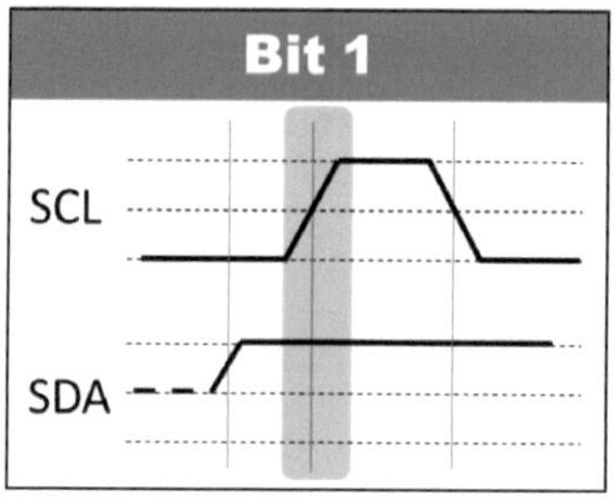

The next piece of communication is to send a logical Zero:

```
// -------------------------------------------------------------------------------------
void i2c_e_send_b0()
{
    P2DIR |= SCL_E;             //SCL = Low
    P2DIR |= SDA_E;             //SDA = Low

    P2DIR &= ~SCL_E;            //SCL = High

    P2DIR |= SCL_E;             //SCL = Low
}
// -------------------------------------------------------------------------------------
```

The corresponding flow is defined like this:

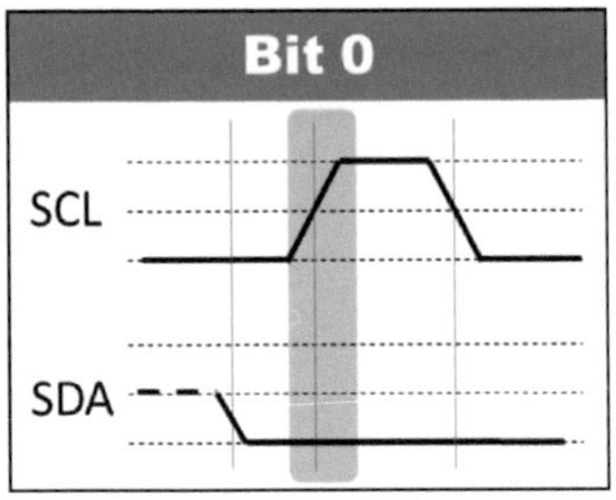

The last problem we need to tackle is the confirmation step. In the firmware, we have to be able to receive an ACK or NOT ACK from the slave. For this, we have to issue an additional "tik" on the clock line and test the level of the SDA line. The implementation has been made in the i2ce_ack_rqg() function:

```
// -----------------------------------------------------------------------------
byte i2c_e_ack_rq()
{
    byte lv_ack;

    lv_ack = 1;

    P2DIR |= SCL_E;            //SCL = Low
    P2DIR &= ~SDA_E;           //SDA = High

    P2DIR &= ~SCL_E;           //SCL = High
    //ACK -> return(0) - NOT_ACK -> return(1)
    if((P2IN & SDA_E) == 0) lv_ack = 0;
    return(lv_ack);
}
// -----------------------------------------------------------------------------
```

The ACK and NOT ACK flows can be described like this:

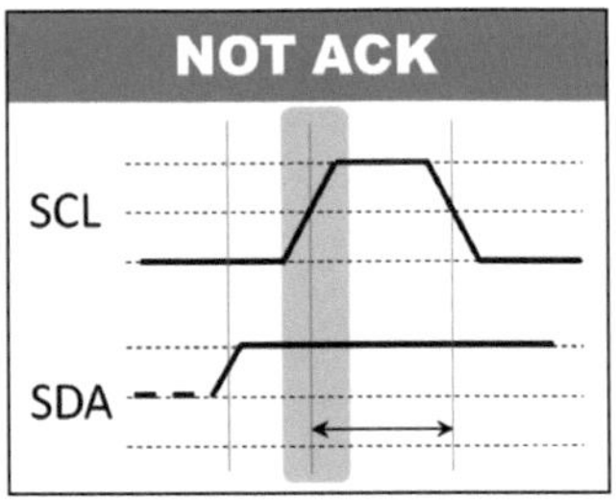

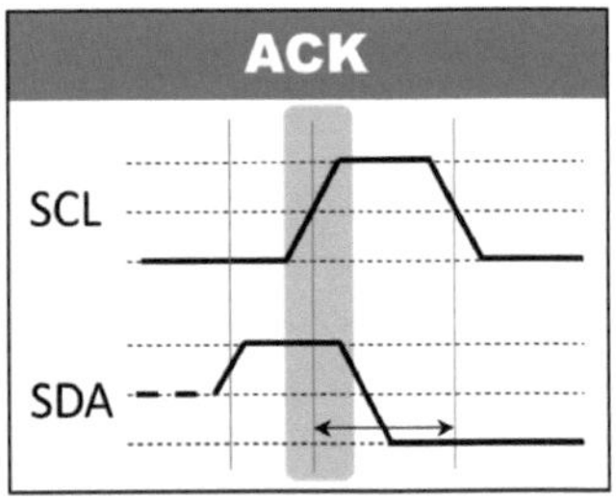

All pieces of communication have been discovered. We can put the puzzle into a picture now.

Just to have everything in one place, here are the routines for the USCI-like connection of SCL and SDA lines. We can see the code is nearly the same, we are just talking to P1.6 and P1.7 instead of P2.1 and P2.2:

```
// ---------------------------------------------------------------------------
// ---------------------------------------------------------------------------
// Software I2C communication routines [USCI-like}
// SCL = P1.6
// SDA = P1.7
// ---------------------------------------------------------------------------
// ---------------------------------------------------------------------------
void i2c_u_init()
{
    P1DIR &= ~SCL;          //SCL = High (disconnect)
    P1DIR &= ~SDA;          //SDA = High (disconnect)

    P1OUT &= ~SCL;          //prepare zero for SCL line
    P1OUT &= ~SDA;          //prepare zero for SDA line
}
// ---------------------------------------------------------------------------
// ---------------------------------------------------------------------------
void i2c_u_start()
{
    P1DIR &= ~SCL;          //SCL = High
    P1DIR |= SDA;           //SDA = Low

    P1DIR |= SCL;           //SCL = Low
    P1DIR |= SDA;           //SDA = Low
}
// ---------------------------------------------------------------------------
// ---------------------------------------------------------------------------
void i2c_u_stop()
{
    P1DIR |= SCL;           //SCL = Low
    P1DIR |= SDA;           //SDA = Low

    P1DIR &= ~SCL;          //SCL = High
    P1DIR |= SDA;           //SDA = Low

    P1DIR &= ~SCL;          //SCL = High
    P1DIR &= ~SDA;          //SDA = High
}
// ---------------------------------------------------------------------------
// ---------------------------------------------------------------------------
void i2c_u_send_b1()
{
```

```
    P1DIR |= SCL;           //SCL = Low
    P1DIR &= ~SDA;          //SDA = High

    P1DIR &= ~SCL;          //SCL = High
    P1DIR &= ~SDA;          //SDA = High

    P1DIR |= SCL;           //SCL = Low
    P1DIR &= ~SDA;          //SDA = High
}
// ---------------------------------------------------------------------------------
// ---------------------------------------------------------------------------------
void i2c_u_send_b0()
{
    P1DIR |= SCL;           //SCL = Low
    P1DIR |= SDA;           //SDA = Low

    P1DIR &= ~SCL;          //SCL = High

    P1DIR |= SCL;           //SCL = Low
}
// ---------------------------------------------------------------------------------
// ---------------------------------------------------------------------------------
byte i2c_u_ack_rq()
{
    byte lv_ack;

    lv_ack = 1;

    P1DIR |= SCL;           //SCL = Low
    P1DIR &= ~SDA;          //SDA = High

    P1DIR &= ~SCL;          //SCL = High
    //ACK -> return(0) - NOT_ACK -> return(1)
    if((P1IN & SDA) == 0) lv_ack = 0;
    return(lv_ack);
}
// ---------------------------------------------------------------------------------
// ---------------------------------------------------------------------------------
```

There is only more routine left that is independent of pins used, as these utilise our "bits" implemented earlier.

The routine sends a whole byte (8 bits) via I²C:

```
// ------------------------------------------------------------------------------------
byte i2c_send(byte iv_byte)                          //(I2CB-1)
{
    if((iv_byte & BIT7) != 0) i2c_send_b1();    //(I2CB-2-bit7-1)
    if((iv_byte & BIT7) == 0) i2c_send_b0();    //(I2CB-2-bit7-0)
    if((iv_byte & BIT6) != 0) i2c_send_b1();    //(I2CB-2-bit6-1)
    if((iv_byte & BIT6) == 0) i2c_send_b0();    //(I2CB-2-bit6-0)
    if((iv_byte & BIT5) != 0) i2c_send_b1();    //(I2CB-2-bit5-1)
    if((iv_byte & BIT5) == 0) i2c_send_b0();    //(I2CB-2-bit5-0)
    if((iv_byte & BIT4) != 0) i2c_send_b1();    //(I2CB-2-bit4-1)
    if((iv_byte & BIT4) == 0) i2c_send_b0();    //(I2CB-2-bit4-0)
    if((iv_byte & BIT3) != 0) i2c_send_b1();    //(I2CB-2-bit3-1)
    if((iv_byte & BIT3) == 0) i2c_send_b0();    //(I2CB-2-bit3-0)
    if((iv_byte & BIT2) != 0) i2c_send_b1();    //(I2CB-2-bit2-1)
    if((iv_byte & BIT2) == 0) i2c_send_b0();    //(I2CB-2-bit2-0)
    if((iv_byte & BIT1) != 0) i2c_send_b1();    //(I2CB-2-bit1-1)
    if((iv_byte & BIT1) == 0) i2c_send_b0();    //(I2CB-2-bit1-0)
    if((iv_byte & BIT0) != 0) i2c_send_b1();    //(I2CB-2-bit0-1)
    if((iv_byte & BIT0) == 0) i2c_send_b0();    //(I2CB-2-bit0-0)

    return(i2c_ack_rq());                            //(I2B-3)
}
// ------------------------------------------------------------------------------------
```

The last function we haven't touched upon is the LCD-library extension. This routine displays one byte - 8-bit - on the LCD in binary form; e.g. a byte 50h will be shown as 01010000.

```
// ------------------------------------------------------------------------------------
// ------------------------------------------------------------------------------------
void lcd_print_b8c(byte iv_row, byte iv_col, byte iv_bin8)
{
    lcd_setcursor(iv_row, iv_col);
    if((iv_bin8 & BIT7) != 0) lcd_print_c("1");
    if((iv_bin8 & BIT7) == 0) lcd_print_c("0");
    if((iv_bin8 & BIT6) != 0) lcd_print_c("1");
    if((iv_bin8 & BIT6) == 0) lcd_print_c("0");
    if((iv_bin8 & BIT5) != 0) lcd_print_c("1");
    if((iv_bin8 & BIT5) == 0) lcd_print_c("0");
    if((iv_bin8 & BIT4) != 0) lcd_print_c("1");
    if((iv_bin8 & BIT4) == 0) lcd_print_c("0");
    if((iv_bin8 & BIT3) != 0) lcd_print_c("1");
    if((iv_bin8 & BIT3) == 0) lcd_print_c("0");
    if((iv_bin8 & BIT2) != 0) lcd_print_c("1");
    if((iv_bin8 & BIT2) == 0) lcd_print_c("0");
    if((iv_bin8 & BIT1) != 0) lcd_print_c("1");
    if((iv_bin8 & BIT1) == 0) lcd_print_c("0");
```

```
    if((iv_bin8 & BIT0) != 0) lcd_print_c("1");
    if((iv_bin8 & BIT0) == 0) lcd_print_c("0");
}
// --------------------------------------------------------------------------------
// --------------------------------------------------------------------------------
```

We are done with the implementation of the software communication routines for the I²C protocol and the demo firmware "counter".

Let's continue now with the Energia example.

3.5.2 • I²C communication by software / Energia

Here the same example as in the previous chapter is described, but using Energia and Energia-conventions.

3.5.2.1 • Hardware

Energia-conventions denote the build-up of the I²C bus particularly. As mentioned, Energia uses P2.1 as SCL and P2.2 as SDA signals. Therefore the connection of the I²C bus is changed to meet the specification of the <Wire.h> library.

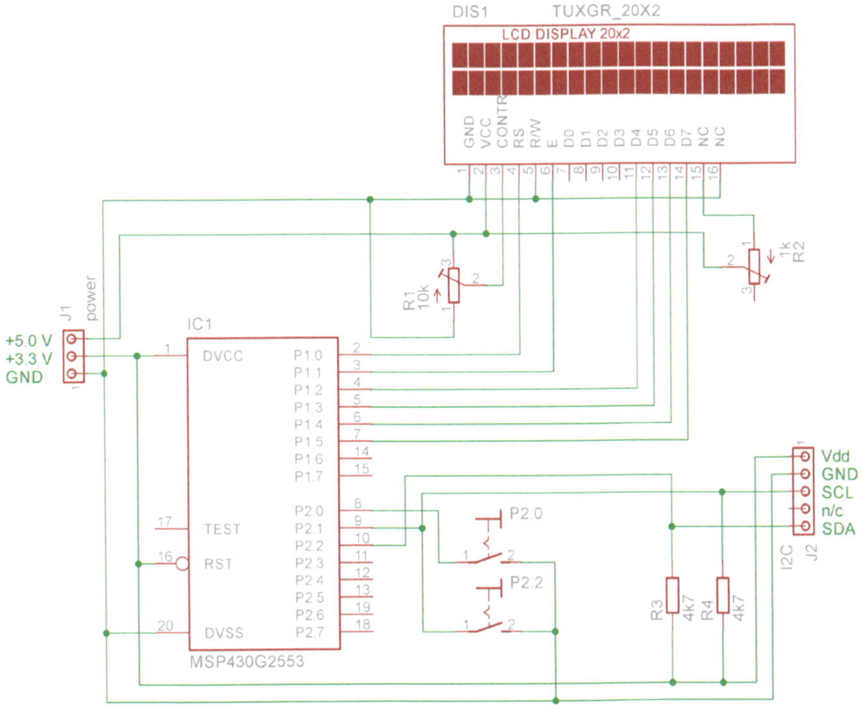

Of course, the same PCF8574-board can be used within this example as described earlier.

3.5.2.2 • Energia Firmware

This firmware is written and tested with Energia-1.8.7E21.

The Energia-version is much easier to compare to our example with CCS. There is a very simple reason for this. With CCS implementation we implemented the I²C communication itself, besides the "business functionality". In this version the <Wire.h> library is utilised.

```
//------------------------------------------------------------------------------
//------------------------------------------------------------------------------
// I2C communication with <Wire.h> library
// SCL = P2.1
// SDA = P2.2
//------------------------------------------------------------------------------
//------------------------------------------------------------------------------
#include <LiquidCrystal.h>                             //(1) LCD communication library
#include <Wire.h>                                      //(2) I2C communication library

LiquidCrystal lcd(P1_0, P1_1, P1_2, P1_3, P1_4, P1_5); //(3) define the connection to LCD
short v_counter = 0;                                   //(4) define counter variable
short i2c_trans_stat;                                  //(5) I2C communication result
// -----------------------------------------------------------------------------------------------------
// -----------------------------------------------------------------------------------------------------
void setup()                                           //(6) Setup function
{
  lcd.begin(20, 4);                                    //(7) set-up usage of 4 rows x 20 columns
  lcd.setCursor(0,0);                                  //(8) put cursor to position col:0 / row:0
  lcd.print("MSP430 Basics");                          //(9) write the text in quotes starting at 0,0
  lcd.setCursor(0,1);                                  //(10) put cursor to position col:0 / row:1
  lcd.print("MCU: MSP430G2553");                       //(11) write the text in quotes starting at 0,1
  lcd.setCursor(0,2);                                  //(12) put cursor to position col:0 / row:2
  lcd.print("Example    LCD+I2C");                     //(13) write the text in quotes starting at 0,2
  lcd.setCursor(0,3);                                  //(14) put cursor to position col:0 / row:3
  lcd.print("v1.03 / 27.03.2021");                     //(15) write the text in quotes starting at 0,3

  delay(3000);                                         //(16) wait 3 sec
  lcd.clear();                                         //(17) clear the content of the LCD
  Wire.begin();                                        //(18) I2C initialization
  v_counter = 255;                                     //(19) counter initialization
}
// -----------------------------------------------------------------------------------------------------
// -----------------------------------------------------------------------------------------------------
void loop()                                            //(20) main loop starts here
{
  write_texts();                                       //(21) write static texts
```

```
    pcf8574_send(v_counter);                     //(22) send value of the v_counter to PCF8574
    w_bin8(v_counter);                           //(23) show counter information
    w_ack_info();                                //(24) show result of I2C communication

    v_counter--;                                 //(25) decrement counter
    delay(200);                                  //(26) wait 0,2 sec
}
// -----------------------------------------------------------------------------------------
// -----------------------------------------------------------------------------------------
void write_texts()                               //(27) start of write_texts function
{
    lcd.setCursor(0,0);                          //(28) put cursor to position col:0 / row:0
    lcd.print("First I2C project");              //(29) write the text in quotes starting at 0,0
    lcd.setCursor(0,1);                          //(30) put cursor to position col:0 / row:1
    lcd.print("Energia: PCF8574+LCD");           //(31) write the text in quotes starting at 0,1
    lcd.setCursor(0,2);                          //(32) put cursor to position col:0 / row:2
    lcd.print("Counter:");                       //(33) write the text in quotes starting at 0,2
    lcd.setCursor(0,3);                          //(34) put cursor to position col:0 / row:3
    lcd.print("Ad:");                            //(35) write the text in quotes starting at 0,3
    lcd.setCursor(11,3);                         //(36) put cursor to position col:11 / row:3
    lcd.print("D:");                             //(37) write the text in quotes starting at 11,3
}
// -----------------------------------------------------------------------------------------
// -----------------------------------------------------------------------------------------
void w_bin8(short i_byte)                        //(38) writing counter stage - binary
{
    lcd.setCursor(9,2);                          //(39) put cursor to position col:9 / row:2
    if ((i_byte & 0x80) == 0) lcd.print("0");    //(40) if the corresponding bit is 0 -> write 0
    else                      lcd.print("1");    //(41) if the corresponding bit is not 0 -> write 1
    if ((i_byte & 0x40) == 0) lcd.print("0");    //(42) if the corresponding bit is 0 -> write 0
    else                      lcd.print("1");    //(43) if the corresponding bit is not 0 -> write 1
    if ((i_byte & 0x20) == 0) lcd.print("0");    //(44) if the corresponding bit is 0 -> write 0
    else                      lcd.print("1");    //(45) if the corresponding bit is not 0 -> write 1
    if ((i_byte & 0x10) == 0) lcd.print("0");    //(46) if the corresponding bit is 0 -> write 0
    else                      lcd.print("1");    //(47) if the corresponding bit is not 0 -> write 1
    if ((i_byte & 0x08) == 0) lcd.print("0");    //(48) if the corresponding bit is 0 -> write 0
    else                      lcd.print("1");    //(49) if the corresponding bit is not 0 -> write 1
    if ((i_byte & 0x04) == 0) lcd.print("0");    //(50) if the corresponding bit is 0 -> write 0
    else                      lcd.print("1");    //(51) if the corresponding bit is not 0 -> write 1
    if ((i_byte & 0x02) == 0) lcd.print("0");    //(52) if the corresponding bit is 0 -> write 0
    else                      lcd.print("1");    //(53) if the corresponding bit is not 0 -> write 1
    if ((i_byte & 0x01) == 0) lcd.print("0");    //(54) if the corresponding bit is 0 -> write 0
    else                      lcd.print("1");    //(55) if the corresponding bit is not 0 -> write 1
}
// -----------------------------------------------------------------------------------------
// -----------------------------------------------------------------------------------------
```

```
void w_ack_info()                          //(56) show info about the communication status
{
  switch(i2c_trans_stat)                   //(57) based on variable i2c_trans_stat we expect 3 options
  {
    case 0:                                //(58) everything went ok
       lcd.setCursor(3,3);                 //(59) set cursor to desired posiion on LCD
       lcd.print("ACK    ");               //(60) write text
       lcd.setCursor(13,3);                //(61) set cursor to desired posiion on LCD
       lcd.print("ACK    ");               //(62) write text
       break;                              //(63) done
    case 2:
       lcd.setCursor(3,3);                 //(64) set cursor to desired posiion on LCD
       lcd.print("not ack");               //(65) write text
       lcd.setCursor(13,3);                //(66) set cursor to desired posiion on LCD
       lcd.print("not ack");               //(67) write text
       break;                              //(68) done
    case 3:
       lcd.setCursor(3,3);                 //(69) set cursor to desired posiion on LCD
       lcd.print("ACK    ");               //(70) write text
       lcd.setCursor(13,3);                //(71) set cursor to desired posiion on LCD
       lcd.print("not ack");               //(72) write text
       break;                              //(73) done
  }
}
// -------------------------------------------------------------------------------------------
// -------------------------------------------------------------------------------------------
void pcf8574_send(short i_byte)            //(74) send data to PCF8574 via I2C
{
  Wire.beginTransmission(0b00100000);      //(75) start communication expecting the chip on address 40h
  Wire.write(i_byte);                      //(76) send the value of the counter
  i2c_trans_stat = Wire.endTransmission(); //(77) close communication and get the status
}
// -------------------------------------------------------------------------------------------
// -------------------------------------------------------------------------------------------
```

At the very beginning the libraries used are declared (1), (2), the initialisation of LCD is done (3) and the most important variable of the "business logic" is declared - the counter (4). The last global declaration belongs to the variable storing the result of the I²C communication (5).

In the setup() function (6) there is first the "welcome screen" implemented - in steps (7) to (16). This screen looks like we can see here:

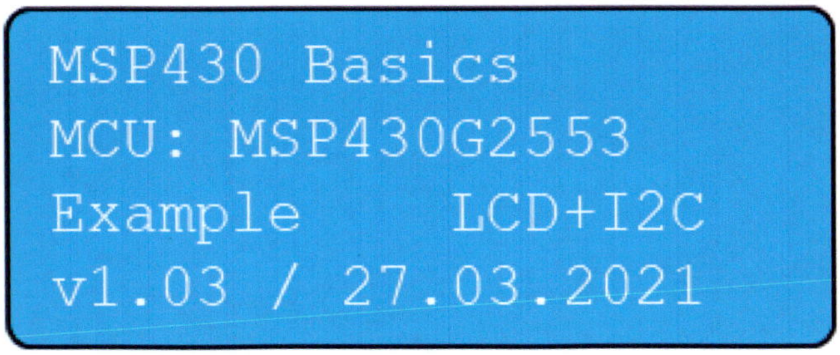

After this, we initialise everything possible (17) to (19). Please consider, that the counter is initialised with value FFh, meaning 1111 1111b. This is the first value to be sent to the PCF8574 which will switch off all the LEDs.

The detailed description of the firmware doesn't make much sense. The source code comment is quite detailed.

Let me just say that the whole I^2C communication with PCF8574 is "hidden" in function pcf8574_send() stating at line (74).

It is possible to find just 3 steps here: in step (75) the I^2C communication is initiated for the device on I^2C address 0100 000xb (in "Arduino-format" it is 0010 0000b). In the next step (76) the byte to be sent is put on the I^2C bus, and just afterwards the communication is finished (77). The Wire.endTransmission() function will return the status of the communication to the caller, where if the returned value is equal to 00h, everything was successful.

3.5.3 • OneWire Thermometer

This example doesn't have anything to do with USCI or a module integrated into the hardware of the MSP430G2553. However, it shows the potential of serial communication as a OneWire communication. And as OneWire Thermometer chips are widely used, I decided to include a "fast example" of utilising a DS18B20 Sensor from Maxim Integrated (sensor a lot of years ago developed by company Dallas - which was later included to Maxim Integrated).

We will build a simple Duo-Thermometer allowing us to measure temperature with two sensors in two different places - for example, "inside" and "outside".

We will of course use our MSP430G2553 microcontroller and to display the values 2x16 LCD. For this application, it doesn't make sense to go for a 4x20 display.

First of all, let's specify what the magic construction will do. We want to build a thermometer, which can measure internal and external temperature. Something like within the room and outside temperature. Therefore we will use the 2x16LCD, where on the first line the temperature within the room (described as "In") will be shown, and on the second line the temperature outside ("Out"). The temperature will be shown in °C and the range shall be appropriate for Europe, meaning -30°C to +60°C. We do not intend to go wireless between the thermometer and sensors, but on the other hand, we want to keep the amount of wires required as few as possible.

Last but not least, we want a kind of "still alive sign", to see that the thermometer is still working, even if the temperature is stable. Why? Well, on rare occasions it may happen, that the microcontroller "freezes" and we still have information displaying on the LCD. If on the LCD something is "flashing", we can be sure that the CPU is still alive, and the temperature is actual.

The LCD design looks like this:

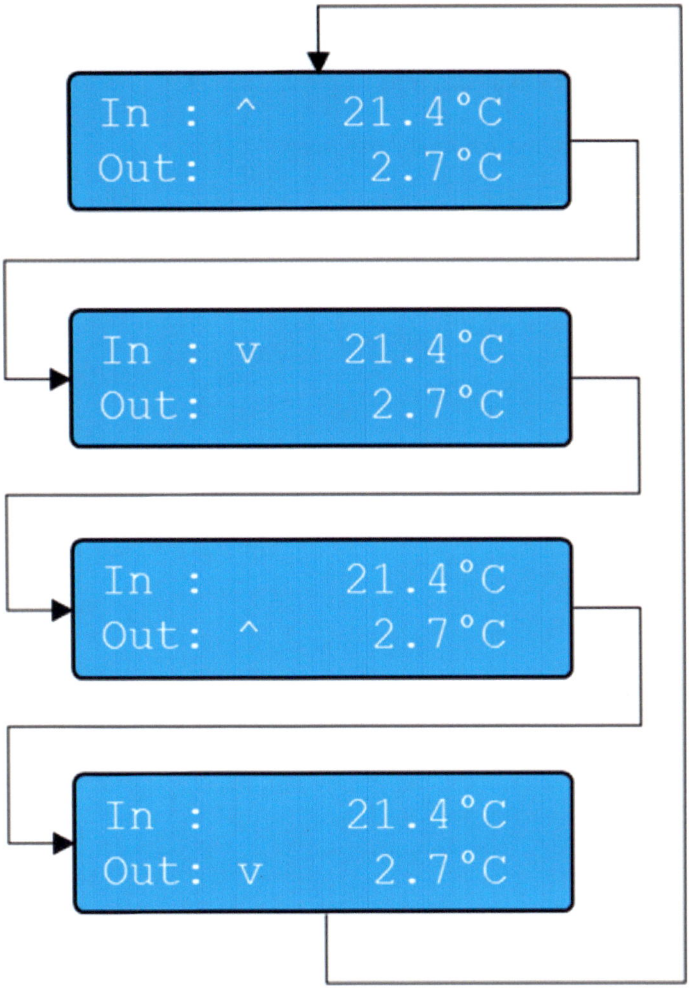

The "still alive sign" to be implemented is described here. We will have 4 different phases. At the beginning, an upside-down "v" will be displayed in the first row (sign "^"). After a while, this sign will be changed to real "v" - still in the first row. Then we repeat the same on the second line.

We specified everything we can - let's have a look at the implementation.

3.5.3.1 • Hardware

First, we have to define the "hardware implementation". We want to use two different temperature sensors to be able to measure the temperature in two different places (inside and outside). We want to use as few wires as possible to connect the sensors to the device itself. Therefore, we will use OneWire sensors.

As we want to make our software as simple as possible, we will want to avoid the need for OneWire-Search functionality. Therefore we will set up two independent OneWire buses, where exactly one sensor will be connected on each bus.

Under these assumptions, the schematic may look like this:

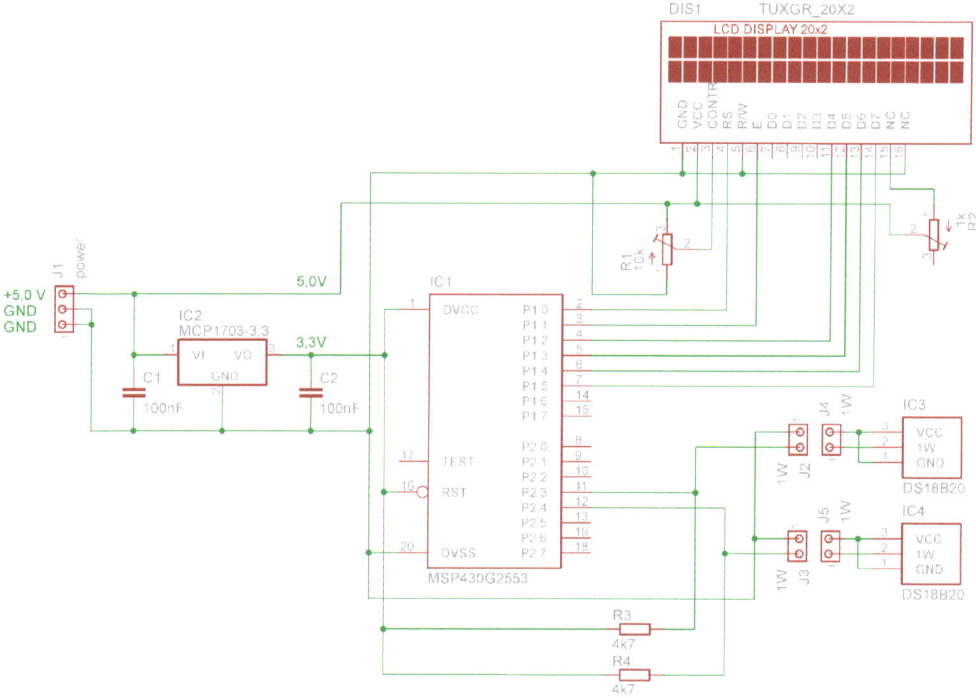

We are going to use the DS18B20 Maxim Integrated temperature sensor (former Dallas). We can see that IC3 is connected to P2.3. This will be shown on the first line of the LCD described as "In". IC4 will have the description "Out".

Four different types of sensors can be used: The DS18B20, DS18B20-PAR, DS1822, and DS1822-PAR. All of them can be connected without any need for software changes. If you connect the older DS18S20 version (or DS18S20-PAR), it will work, but the temperature shown will be wrong, as this sensor is using a slightly different coding. To be able to use this one, we need to adjust the firmware.

All sensors mentioned here are available in the transistor outline package TO-92.

Both of the sensors can be connected to the thermometer using just two wires over a distance of up to ten meters without any issues.

We are using an external power source of 5,0V and at least 100mA. The LCD is directly connected to 5,0V. For the MSP430G2553 we need a lower voltage and therefore we see the MCP1703-3,3 **LDO** taking care of producing 3,3V for the microcontroller. At this voltage level the temperature sensors are driven as well.

For this example, we will implement the firmware in Energia IDE.

3.5.3.2 • Energia Firmware

This firmware is written and tested with Energia-1.8.7E21.

Besides the LCD-library we already know, we use the OneWire library here to provide all necessary OneWire communication routines: <OneWire.h>. Therefore the work with OneWire devices is very easy.

Now we can have a closer look at the firmware. And of course, we start with the initialisation part.

```
// -----------------------------------------------------------------
// -----------------------------------------------------------------
// OneWire DS18B20, DS1822 Temperature Example
// -----------------------------------------------------------------
// -----------------------------------------------------------------
#include <LiquidCrystal.h>          //(1) LCD library
#include <OneWire.h>                //(2) OneWire library
// -----------------------------------------------------------------
LiquidCrystal lcd(P1_0, P1_1, P1_2, P1_3, P1_4, P1_5); //(3) LCD set-up
OneWire       ds18b20_1(11);       //(4) Set-up “in”  on pin 11 = P2.3
OneWire       ds18b20_2(12);       //(5) Set-up “out” on pin 12 = P2.4
// -----------------------------------------------------------------
byte ROM_ID1[8];                   //(6) ROM ID for in
byte ROM_ID2[8];                   //(7) ROM ID for out
byte data1[12];                    //(8) scratchpad data 1
byte data2[12];                    //(9) scratchpad data 2
byte i;                            //(10) vaiable i
int16_t t1_raw;                    //(11) help variable
int16_t t2_raw;                    //(12) help variable
float t1_in;                       //(13) help variable
float t2_out;                      //(14) help variable
byte v_data1_ok;                   //(15) help variable
byte v_data2_ok;                   //(16) help variable
byte v_index;                      //(17) help variable for “still alive”
// -----------------------------------------------------------------
// -----------------------------------------------------------------
void setup()
{
```

```
  lcd.begin(16, 2);                 //(18) LCD set-up
  lcd.setCursor(0, 0);              //(19) welcome screen
  lcd.print(“Duo-Thermometer”);     //(20) welcome screen
  lcd.setCursor(0, 1);              //(21) welcome screen
  lcd.print(“2.03/04.01.2021”);     //(22) welcome screen

  ds18b20_1.search(ROM_ID1);        //(23) find first sensor
  ds18b20_2.search(ROM_ID2);        //(24) find second sensor
  meassure_and_read_X(0);           //(25) meassure temperature
  convert_t1();                     //(26) calculate temperature
  convert_t2();                     //(27) calculate temperature

  delay(2000);                      //(28) wait 2 seconds
  lcd.clear();                      //(29) clear LCD
  v_index = 0;                      //(30) set index to zero
}
// -------------------------------------------------------------------
// -------------------------------------------------------------------
```

First (1) we declare the LCD and OneWire (2) libraries. Just after, the LCD to be used is defined (3) and which ports are used for the two OneWire buses (4) - (5).

In the next few steps, the important firmware variables are defined: ROM_ID1 (6) to store the ROM_ID of the first sensor and ROM_ID2 (7) for the next one. Buffers for scratch-pad reads are declared in steps (8) and (9).

The help variable “i” declared in step (10) is used to drive the cycles later within the firmware. The two t1_raw (11) and t2_raw (12) variables will be used to store the temperature obtained from the sensors.

The calculated temperature will be stored in variables t1_in (13) and t1_out (14).

The next two declared variables - v_data1_ok (15) and v_data2_ok (16) will be used as “quality managers” to maintain the information, if the data captured from the sensors is usable. e.g. to store the information, that there was no answer from the sensor and no temperature can be displayed etc.

Last but not least the v_index (17) variable is used to drive the “still alive sign”.

At the very beginning of the setup() function the LCD will be initialised (18) and the “welcome screen” displayed - in steps (19) to (22). The screen will look like this:

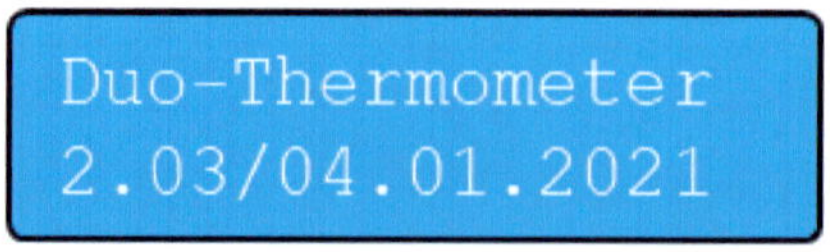

Now we are going to use OneWire search - because it is too easy in IDE Energia. We will get the ROM_ID of the first temperature sensor in step (23) and the second one in step (24). We then run the temperature measurement (25) and do a first pre-calculation of the results of the temperature measurement for both sensors in steps (26) - (27).

After a short delay (28) we clear the display (29), initialise the v_index variable to 0 (30), and with this step, successfully finished the setup() procedure.

The main endless loop of the firmware is very simple. It is just a collection of calls of "the real" routines:

```
// ------------------------------------------------------------
// ------------------------------------------------------------
void loop()
{
  t1_in  = (float)t1_raw / 16.0;    //(31) calculate temperature
  t2_out = (float)t2_raw / 16.0;    //(32) calculate temperature

  lcd_print_temp_duo();             //(33) show the temperature

  ds18b20_1.search(ROM_ID1);        //(34) update sensor 1 ID
  ds18b20_2.search(ROM_ID2);        //(35) update sensor 2 ID
  meassure_and_read_X(1);           //(36) meassure temperature
  convert_t1();                     //(37) calculate temperature
  convert_t2();                     //(38) calculate temperature
}
// -------------------------------------------------------
// -------------------------------------------------------
```

As the first measurement has been already made in the setup() part, the main loop starts with the calculation of the temperatures in steps (31) and (32).

In the next step (33) the results will be displayed. Afterwards will firmware has a look for the IDs of the connected temperature sensors in steps (34) and (35). The last three steps regard triggering the temperature measurement (36) and preparing data for conversion in steps (37) and (38).

The first step of conversion is performed in functions convert_t1() and convert_t2(). This is a very simple process step:

```
// -------------------------------------------------------------
// -------------------------------------------------------------
void convert_t1()
{
  v_data1_ok = 0x00;
  if ( data1[7] == 0x10 )
  {
    v_data1_ok = 0x01;
    // Convert the data to actual temperature
    // because the result is a 16 bit signed integer, it should
    // be stored to an "int16_t" type, which is always 16 bits
    // even when compiled on a 32 bit processor.
    t1_raw = (data1[1] << 8) | data1[0];
  }
}
// -------------------------------------------------------------
// -------------------------------------------------------------
void convert_t2()
{
  v_data2_ok = 0x00;
  if ( data2[7] == 0x10 )
  {
    v_data2_ok = 0x01;
    // Convert the data to actual temperature
    // because the result is a 16 bit signed integer, it should
    // be stored to an "int16_t" type, which is always 16 bits
    // even when compiled on a 32 bit processor.
    t2_raw = (data2[1] << 8) | data2[0];
  }
}
// -------------------------------------------------------------
// -------------------------------------------------------------
```

Those routines do two simple tasks. First - based on byte 8 of the content of scratchpad data will be decided. Whether the information obtained from the sensor is considered correct or not the byte will always be 10h.

The second task is to combine the two bytes of the temperature register to one common variable.

The functionality of both subroutines is the same just there is one separate function for each sensor.

The whole OneWire communication with the temperature sensors is implemented in the following function:

```
// ------------------------------------------------------------
// ------------------------------------------------------------
void meassure_and_read_X(byte i_style)
{
  ds18b20_1.reset();                //(MR-01) OneWire Reset on Bus 1
  ds18b20_1.select(ROM_ID1);        //(MR-02) OneWire Match ROM
  ds18b20_1.write(0x44, 1);         //(MR-03) start conversion, with parasite power

  ds18b20_2.reset();                //(MR-04) OneWire Reset on Bus 2
  ds18b20_2.select(ROM_ID2);        //(MR-05) OneWire Match ROM
  ds18b20_2.write(0x44, 1);         //(MR-06) start conversion, with parasite power

  if (i_style == 1) alive_sign();   //(MR-07) Still alive handling
  delay(750);                       //(MR-08) wait until meassurement is done

  ds18b20_1.reset();                //(MR-09) OneWire Reset on Bus 1
  ds18b20_1.select(ROM_ID1);        //(MR-10) OneWire Match ROM
  ds18b20_1.write(0xBE);            //(MR-11) Function Command Read Scratchpad
  for (i = 0; i < 9; i++)           //(MR-12) Loop to get all bytes from Scratchpad
     data1[i] = ds18b20_1.read();   //(MR-13) Read byte from Scratchpad
  ds18b20_1.reset();                //(MR-14) OneWire Reset on Bus 1

  ds18b20_2.reset();                //(MR-15) OneWire Reset on Bus 2
  ds18b20_2.select(ROM_ID2);        //(MR-16) OneWire Match ROM
  ds18b20_2.write(0xBE);            //(MR-17) Function Command Read Scratchpad
  for (i = 0; i < 9; i++)           //(MR-18) Loop to get all bytes from Scratchpad
     data2[i] = ds18b20_2.read();   //(MR-19) Read byte from Scratchpad
  ds18b20_2.reset();                //(MR-20) OneWire Reset on Bus 2
}
// ------------------------------------------------------------
// ------------------------------------------------------------
```

At the beginning, communication with the first sensor is initiated using OneWire reset (MR-01). After that, the sensor address is published (MR-02) and requested to start the temperature measurement and conversion issued (MR-03). Subsequently the same sequence is started for the second sensor - see steps (MR-04) to (MR-06). This can be done, as the second sensor is connected to the second OneWire bus. In the next step (MR-07) the still-alive sign is maintained (MR-07) and a delay of 0,75 seconds is executed (MR-08) - as this is the time needed for the sensors to finish with measurement and hardware conversion of the temperature.

In steps (MR-09) to (MR-14), the scratchpad memory of the first sensor is obtained and the same is repeated in steps (MR-15) to (MR-20) for the second sensor.

The next two functions are to take care of writing all the required information to the LCD. lcd_print_duo() - is the main display procedure writing the information. If a sensor is not available the text "No Sensor" is written instead of the temperature) or "Bad Sensor" if there is some information, but the byte 8 of scratchpad was not equal to 10h. The function implementation is as follows:

```
// -------------------------------------------------------------
// -------------------------------------------------------------
void lcd_print_temp_duo()
{
  lcd.setCursor(0, 0);
  lcd.print("In :      ");
  if ( v_data1_ok == 0x01 )
  {
    lcd.setCursor(7, 0);
    lcd_print_spaces(t1_in, 1);
    lcd.print(char(223));
    lcd.print("C  ");
  }
  else if ( data1[7] = 0xFF )
  {
    lcd.setCursor(7, 0);
    lcd.print("No Sensor");
  }
  else
  {
    lcd.setCursor(7, 0);
    lcd.print("Bad Sensor");
  }
  // -------------------------------------------------------------
  lcd.setCursor(0, 1);
  lcd.print("Out:      ");
  if ( v_data2_ok == 0x01 )
  {
    lcd.setCursor(7, 1);
    lcd_print_spaces(t2_out, 1);
    lcd.print(char(223));
    lcd.print("C  ");
  }
  else if ( data2[7] = 0xFF )
  {
    lcd.setCursor(7, 1);
    lcd.print("No Sensor ");
  }
  else
  {
    lcd.setCursor(7, 1);
    lcd.print("Bad Sensor");
```

```
  }
}
// -----------------------------------------------------------------
// -----------------------------------------------------------------
```

The second function takes care of formatting the numbers written to the display:

```
// -----------------------------------------------------------------
// -----------------------------------------------------------------
void lcd_print_spaces(float i_value, byte w_dec)
{
  if ( i_value >=  0 )
  {
    lcd.print(" ");          //instead of "-" for negative values
    if ( i_value <  10 ) lcd.print(" ");          // 10
    if ( i_value < 100 ) lcd.print(" ");          //100
  }
  else
  {
    lcd.print(" ");
    if ( i_value > -10 ) lcd.print(" ");          // 10
  }
  lcd.print(i_value, w_dec);
}
// -----------------------------------------------------------------
// -----------------------------------------------------------------
```

The very last function takes care of providing the "still alive sign" and is very simple:

```
// -----------------------------------------------------------------
// -----------------------------------------------------------------
void alive_sign(void)
{
  if(v_index == 0) {lcd.setCursor(5,0); lcd.print("^");}
  if(v_index == 1) {lcd.setCursor(5,0); lcd.print("v");}
  if(v_index == 2) {lcd.setCursor(5,1); lcd.print("^");}
  if(v_index == 3) {lcd.setCursor(5,1); lcd.print("v");}
  v_index++;
  if ( v_index >= 4 ) v_index = 0;
}
// -----------------------------------------------------------------
// -----------------------------------------------------------------
```

3.6 • Comparator_A+

The Comparator module of the microcontroller can be used for several purposes. We will touch on the basic one - to compare two analog signals.

The modules compare voltages between +terminal and -terminal. There are a couple of additional features we can give reason for by using the comparator. For example, we can activate an RC-filter on the comparator output, and utilise interrupt functionalities in connection with the comparator. We can also use different voltage references, connecting the comparator with a timer, etc.

The Comparator_A+ module is described in the following figure:

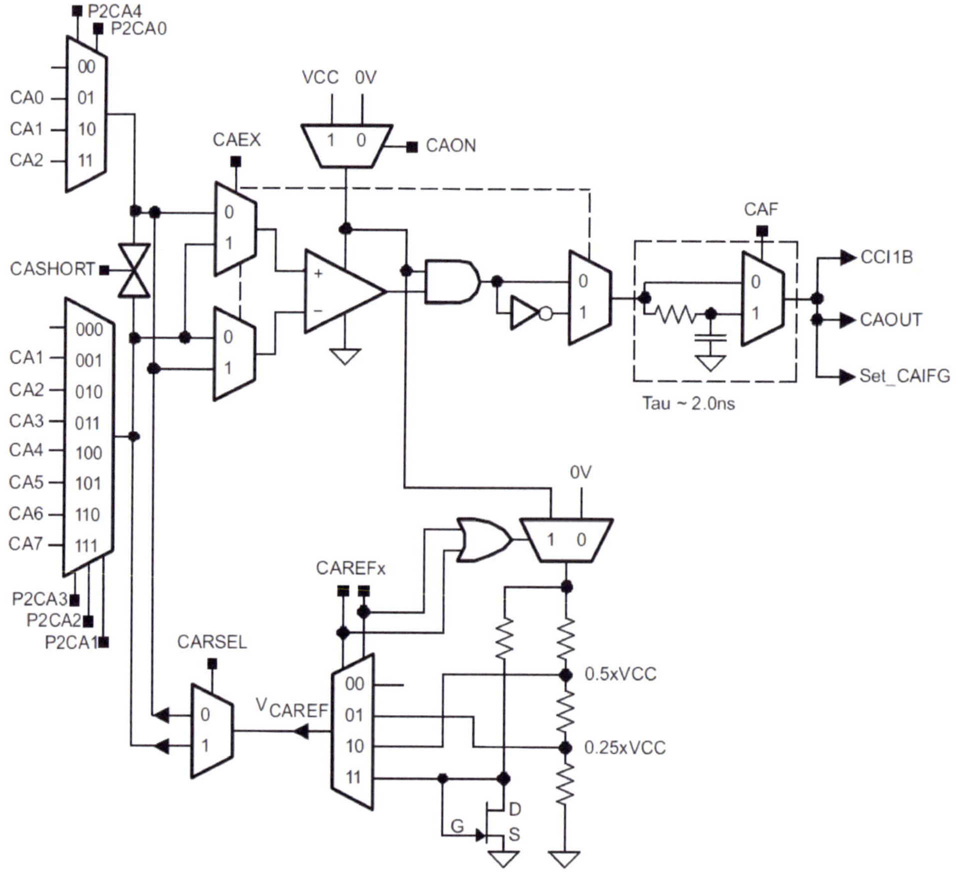

Figure 21-1. Comparator_A+ Block Diagram

In this table we can see where the assignment of the CAx inputs to the MSP430G2553 pins:

Comparator Input	MSP430G2553 Pin	Corresponding I/O
CA0	2	P1.0
CA1	3	P1.1
CA2	4	P1.2
CA3	5	P1.3
CA4	6	P1.4
CA5	7	P1.5
CA6	14	P1.6
CA7	15	P1.7

It doesn't make sense to walk through all the possibilities of the comparator module. Let's take a short look at the registers associated with the Comparator_A+ module - we only need to understand two control registers: CACTL1 and CACTL2.

Both registers are 8-bit width and allow us to switch on/off the comparator module completely and define what should be compared.

The CACTL1 register is defined like this:

CACTL1 - Control Register 1

bit 7	bit 6	bit 5	bit 4	bit 3	bit 2	bit 1	bit 0
CAEX	**CARSEL**	**CAREFx**		**CAON**	**CAIES**	**CAIE**	**CAIFG**
rw-0	rw-0	rw-0	rw-0	rw-0	rw-0	rw-0	rw-0

bit name	bit(s)	usage
CAEX	Bit 7	Comparator_A+ exchange. This bit exchanges the com-parator inputs and inverts the comparator output. 0 = normal operation 1 = inputs are exchanged, and output is inverted

CARSEL	Bit 6	When CAEX = 0 (default value): 0 - V_{CAREF} is applied to the +terminal 1 - V_{CAREF} is applied to the -terminal When CAEX = 1 - the V_{CAREF} is applied oppositely, meaning: 0 - V_{CAREF} is applied to the -terminal 1 - V_{CAREF} is applied to the +terminal
CAREFx	Bits 5 - 4	Selection of reference voltage V_{CAREF} 00 - internal reference is not used 01 - reference = 0,25 x V_{cc} (with ~3,3V it is around 0,825V) 10 - reference = 0,50 x V_{cc} (with ~3,3V it is around 1,650V) 11 - diode reference is used (around 0,550V - independent of V_{cc})
CAON	Bit 3	Switch on / off the whole comparator module: 0 - Comparator_A+ module is switched off and consumes no power 1 - Comparator_A+ module is switched on
CAIES	Bit 2	Comparator_A+ interrupt edge select 0 - rising edge 1 - falling edge
CAIE	Bit 1	Comparator_A+ module Interrupt Enable: 0 - interrupt from comparator is disabled 1 - interrupt is enabled
CAIFG	Bit 0	Comparator_A+ module Interrupt Flag: 0 - no interrupt is pending 1 - there is a pending interrupt

Control register 2 defines the inputs for +terminal and -terminal, and provides the result of the comparison.

CACTL2 - Control Register 2

bit 7	bit 6	bit 5	bit 4	bit 3	bit 2	bit 1	bit 0
CASHORT	**P2CA4**	**P2CA3**	**P2CA2**	**P2CA1**	**P2CA0**	**CAF**	**CAOUT**
rw-0	rw-0	rw-0	rw-0	rw-0	rw-0	rw-0	r-(0)

bit name	**bit(s)**	**usage**
CASHORT	Bit 7	Short +terminal and -terminal inputs: 0 - inputs are not shorted 1 - inputs are shorted
P2CA4:P2CA0	Bit 6 and Bit 2	Input selection; when CACTL1.CAEX = 0 (default value) input for +terminal definition when CACTL1.CAEX = 1 input for -terminal definition Input is selected like this: 00 - no connection 01 - CA0 10 - CA1 11 - CA2
P2CA3-P2CA1	Bits 5 - 3	Input selection; when CACTL1.CAEX = 0 (default value) input for -terminal definition when CACTL1.CAEX = 1 input for +terminal definition Input is selected like this: 000 - no connection 001 - CA1 010 - CA2 011 - CA3 100 - CA4 101 - CA5 110 - CA6 111 - CA7
CAF	Bit 1	Output filter on / off: 0 - Comparator_A+ output is not filtered 1 - Comparator_A+ output is filtered

CAOUT	Bit 0	Output - result of the comparison: 0 - the -terminal is more positive than the +terminal 1 - the +terminal is more positive than the -terminal Always 0, when the comparator is switched off

As mentioned earlier, the comparator module allows us to use a built-in filter to get a more stable output, when the compared values are "about to cross".

Let's take a short look at the filtering capabilities of this module.

The most simple way to understand the purposes of the filter is by using the following graphics:

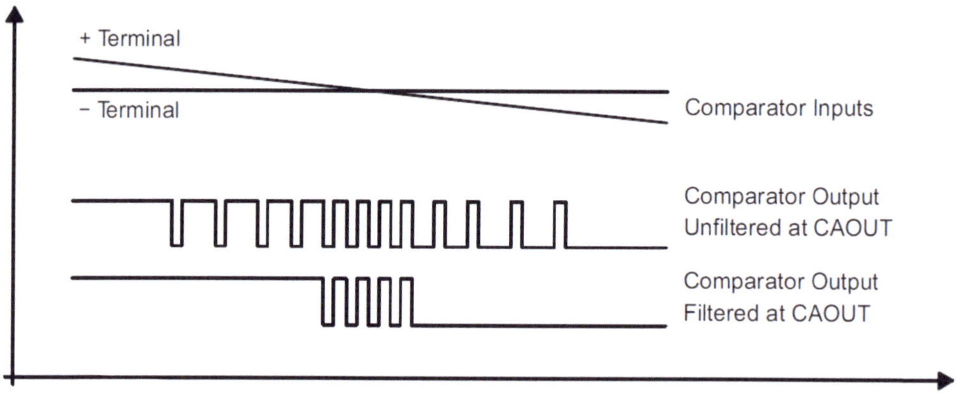

There is one more register associated with the analogue and digital capabilities of the MCU; especially regarding current consumption. With the single bits of the CAPD register, it is possible to disable corresponding input and output buffers of the single digital I/O - to reduce power consumption. If the power consumption is critical for an application, all ports connected to the digital signal will be the digital buffers disabled. If current consumption is not very critical, we do not need to take care of this register, as the buffers for all selected inputs - currently associated with the P2CAx bits are automatically disabled (independent of the corresponding bit of the CAPD register.

The **CAPD register** is defined like shown here:

bit 7	bit 6	bit 5	bit 4	bit 3	bit 2	bit 1	bit 0
CAPD7	**CAPD6**	**CAPD5**	**CAPD4**	**CAPD3**	**CAPD2**	**CAPD1**	**CAPD0**
rw-0	rw-0	rw-0	rw-0	rw-0	rw-0	rw-0	rw-0

When the CAPDx bit is equal to 0 (default value), the corresponding digital buffer is enabled. To disable the buffer, the corresponding bits have to be set to 1. CAPD7 corresponds to CA7, CAPD6 to CA6, etc.

The best way to copy the functionality (at least basic functionality) is to go for a simple example.

3.6.1 • Hit the reference

In this example we will compare the voltage on the potentiometer with a reference voltage of the Comparator_A+ module.

We will setup the module in the way, that we will compare the voltage from potentiometer with V_{CAREF}, where we will put V_{CAREF} to 0,5 x V_{cc}. The reference voltage shall be therefore reached roughly in the middle position of the potentiometer (assuming of course we are using linear potentiometer, not a logarithmic one).

To reach this settings, we will configure the Compare_A+ module using following settings for CACTL1 and CACTL2 registers:

CACTL1 - we will use the highlighted settings:

bit name	bit(s)	usage
CAEX	Bit 7	Comparator_A+ exchange. This bit exchanges the comparator inputs and inverts the comparator output. 0 = normal operation 1 = inputs are exchanged, and output is inverted
CARSEL	Bit 6	CAEX = 0: 0 - V_{CAREF} is applied to the +terminal 1 - V_{CAREF} is applied to the -terminal
CAREFx	Bits 5 - 4	Selection of reference voltage V_{CAREF} 00 - internal reference is not used 01 - reference = 0,25 x V_{cc} (with ~3,3V it is around 0,825V) 10 - reference = 0,50 x V_{cc} (with ~3,3V it is around 1,650V) 11 - diode reference is used (around 0,550V - independent of V_{cc})
CAON	Bit 3	Switch on / off the whole comparator module: 0 - Comparator_A+ module is switched off and consumes no power 1 - Comparator_A+ module is switched on
CAIES	Bit 2	Comparator_A+ interrupt edge select - actually doesn't matter, as we are not using it 0 - rising edge 1 - falling edge
CAIE	Bit 1	Comparator_A+ module Interrupt Enable: 0 - interrupt from comparator is disabled 1 - interrupt is enabled
CAIFG	Bit 0	Comparator_A+ module Interrupt Flag: - doesn't matter 0 - no interrupt is pending 1 - there is a pending interrupt

I guess the description is quite clear in the table. As we do not allow interrupt for this example, it doesn't matter, how we set the CAIES and CAIFG bits.

The settings of CACTL2 we be used like showed here - highlighted settings are used:

bit name	bit(s)	usage
CASHORT	*Bit 7*	Short +terminal and -terminal inputs: 0 - inputs are not shorted 1 - inputs are shorted
P2CA4:P2CA0	*Bit 6 and Bit 2*	Input selection; when CACTL1.CAEX = 0 (default value) input for +terminal definition when CACTL1.CAEX = 1 input for -terminal definition Input is selected like this: 00 - no connection 01 - CA0 10 - CA1 11 - CA2
P2CA3-P2CA1	*Bits 5 - 3*	Input selection; when CACTL1.CAEX = 0 (default value) input for -terminal definition when CACTL1.CAEX = 1 input for +terminal definition Input is selected like this: 000 - no connection 001 - CA1 010 - CA2 011 - CA3 100 - CA4 101 - CA5 110 - CA6 111 - CA7
CAF	*Bit 1*	Output filter on / off: 0 - Comparator_A+ output is not filtered 1 - Comparator_A+ output is filtered
CAOUT	*Bit 0*	Output - result of the comparison: 0 - the -terminal is more positive than the +terminal 1 - the +terminal is more positive than the -terminal Always 0, when the comparator is switched off This bit shows the outcome of our work; therefore the settings doesn't matter

3.6.1.1 • Hardware

We will reuse the shield we build for the Chapter 3.2.4. - experiment with a potentiometer. Nothing else is needed for this example.

3.6.1.2 • Energia Firmware

This firmware is written and tested with Energia-1.8.7E21.

The good thing about Energia is, that we do not necessarily need to know all the good and helpful libraries and commands to use different special parts of the environment. Of course it helps and make the coding easier a lot of times, but if we for example do not know, what library or commands can be used for the work with MSP430G2553 Comparator_A+ module - we can just simple work with registers based on the knowledge of the module.

We will undertake this example without any special library. One possible implementation can look like this:

```
//-----------------------------------------------------------------------------
//-----------------------------------------------------------------------------
//MSP430
//Chapter 3.6.1. - Hit the reference
//-----------------------------------------------------------------------------
//-----------------------------------------------------------------------------
void setup()                    //(1) set-up routine
{
  pinMode(P1_6, OUTPUT);        //(2) configure Pin 6 as digital output -> LED

  CACTL2 = 0b00000100;          //(3) set the config2 for Compare Module
  CACTL1 = 0b01101000;          //(4) set the config1 for Compare Module
}
//-----------------------------------------------------------------------------
void loop()                     //(5) main software loop
{
  if((CACTL2 & 0x01) == 0)      //(6) if CA0 <= Vcaref - blink slowly
  {
    digitalWrite(P1_6, HIGH);   //(7) switch the LED on
    delay(500);                 //(8) wait 0,5 sec
    digitalWrite(P1_6, LOW);    //(9) swtich the LED off
    delay(500);                 //(10) wait 0,5 sec
  }
  else
  {
    digitalWrite(P1_6, HIGH);   //(11) switch the LED on
    delay(100);                 //(12) wait 0,1 sec
    digitalWrite(P1_6, LOW);    //(13) swtich the LED off
    delay(100);                 //(14) wait 0,1 sec
```

```
  }
}
//---------------------------------------------------------------------------
//---------------------------------------------------------------------------
```

We do not have any library included in this code. The first line is the begining of the setup function (1). Here we just define P1.6 as digital output (2). And in next two steps we put earlier described values to the CACTL2 register (3) and to the CACTL2 register (4). We are going to use the order: first maintain CACTL2 and after that CACTL1 - because to put the value to the CACTL1 switched on the comparator module. With this step, all required settings has been done and the setup-function is finished.

Next one (5) is the start of the endless loop of the firmware. Here is more-less only one statement interesting in the context of the compare module - that's the step (6). Here we - as a part of "if-statement" read the result of the comparison and decide, if we go for slow blinking LED - steps (7) - (10); or for the fast blinking LED - steps (11) to (14).

The result of the comparison can be found in bit 0 of the CACTL2 register - therefore the result of the equation "CACTL2 & 0x01" is equal to 0, if the CA0 voltage is less as VCAREF, otherwise is the result 1.

3.6.1.3 • CCS Firmware

This firmware is written and tested with CCS Version: 10.1.1.00004.

The work with the comparator module within our use case (to see, if we cross the reference voltage or not) is actually very simple. We just need to set the control registers correctly and then observe the result.

One possible implementation in C-language in CCS may looks like this:

```
//--------------------------------------------------------------------
//--------------------------------------------------------------------
#include <msp430.h>                       //(1) include msp430 constants & declarations

void delay_ms(unsigned int iv_delay_ms);  //(2) definition of the delay routine
//--------------------------------------------------------------------
//--------------------------------------------------------------------
int main(void)                            //(3) main function starts here
{
    WDTCTL = WDTPW | WDTHOLD;             //(4) Stop watchdog timer
    P1DIR = 0b01000000;                   //(5) Set P1.6 to I/O output

    //          bbbbbbbb
    //          76543210
    CACTL2 = 0b00000100;                  //(6) set the config2 for Compare Module
```

```
    //          bbbbbbbb
    //          76543210
    CACTL1 = 0b01101000;                   //(7) set the config1 for Compare Module
    //----------------------------------------------------------------------
    for(;;)                                //(8) endless loop
    {
        if((CACTL2 & 0x01) == 0)           //(9) if CA0 <= Vcaref - blink slowly
        {
            P1OUT = 0b01000000;            //(10) switch on the LED on P1.0 (pin #2)
            delay_ms(500);                 //(11) wait 0,5 sec
            P1OUT = 0b00000000;            //(12) switch off the LED on P1.0 (pin #2)
            delay_ms(500);                 //(13) wait 0,5 sec
        } //if
        else                               //(14) if CA0 > Vcaref - blink fast
        {
            P1OUT = 0b01000000;            //(15) switch on the LED on P1.0 (pin #2)
            delay_ms(100);                 //(16) wait 0,1 sec
            P1OUT = 0b00000000;            //(17) switch off the LED on P1.0 (pin #2)
            delay_ms(100);                 //(18) wait 0,1 sec
        } //else
    } //for
}
//----------------------------------------------------------------------------
//----------------------------------------------------------------------------
void delay_ms(unsigned int iv_delay_ms)    //(19) delay routine
{
    while(iv_delay_ms--) __delay_cycles(1000);
}
//----------------------------------------------------------------------------
//----------------------------------------------------------------------------
```

As always, we first include the MSP430-library to the firmware (1). Then we pre-define a waiting routine (2) and the main function can start (3). As a part of preparation we deactivate the watch dog (4) and set P1.6 to output (5).

In steps (6) and (7) we write the values - as described in the tables earlier to registers CACTL2 (6) and CACTL1 (7) - exactly in this order, as pushing the value to CACTL1 will start the comparator module as well.

At this moment everything is prepared, and comparator module is already working; we can start the endless loop of the firmware (8).

At the begining we just check the comparison result (9) and if the voltage on P1.0 / CA0 is less then the half of the supply voltage, we let the LED blink slowly (with 0,5 sec break between switch on and switch off). This "blinks" are done in steps (10) through (13). If the voltage is higher (14), we let the LED blink quite fast (0,1 sec break) - steps (15) - (18) are taking care about.

And that's it - on line (19) is used delay routine implemented.

Chapter 4 • MSP430F2001 / MSP430F2012

In this chapter, we will make use of one of the simplest MSP430 family members. It will be quite a logical process to start with this and then continue in the next chapter with the more advanced version. The reason, why we proceed in this book the other way around for this is simple: The Energia IDE does not support the MSP430F2001 meaning that with this microcontroller we have to use the more advanced and more complicated CCS IDE.

For this simple microcontroller we will walk through those examples:

Example	Corresponding Periphery	Chapter	Short Description
Flashing Heart	GPIO	4.1	Very easy circuit; can be used for example as a (nice) gift for your girlfriend
Traffic Light	GPIO	4.2	very easy circuit; traffic light for two directions / 6 LEDs
Game Cube 2	GPIO	4.3	Game cube as in chapter 3 with the larger microcontroller
Game Cube 3	GPIO / ADC10	4.4	Game cube again, but let's say for demo purposes
Temperature measurement	GPIO / ADC10	4.5	Here we will measure the temperature in a living room with the usage of an analog temperature sensor.

All of them are simple examples using only digital I/O's. In these kinds of applications, is just important to consider that MSP430F2001 offers fewer Ports (10 instead of 16) and significantly less flash memory (1kB instead of 16kB) compared to the MSP430G2553.

In the last few examples, we will utilise an ADC module of the microcontroller. As the MSP430F2001 does not provide an ADC module, we will switch to the MSP430F2012: this is a bigger brother and includes an ADC module with more Flash memory (2kB).

4.1 • Flashing Heart

This is a very simple project involving flashing a couple of LEDs connecting to P1. It can be made as a gift for a beloved one, or just for fun.

In the picture is a very simple prototype on a universal board.

If we use low-power LEDs, we can even power the circuit from a CR2032 battery (3,0V).

Let's specify how the LEDs will work:

The LEDs will switch on / off in the following steps:

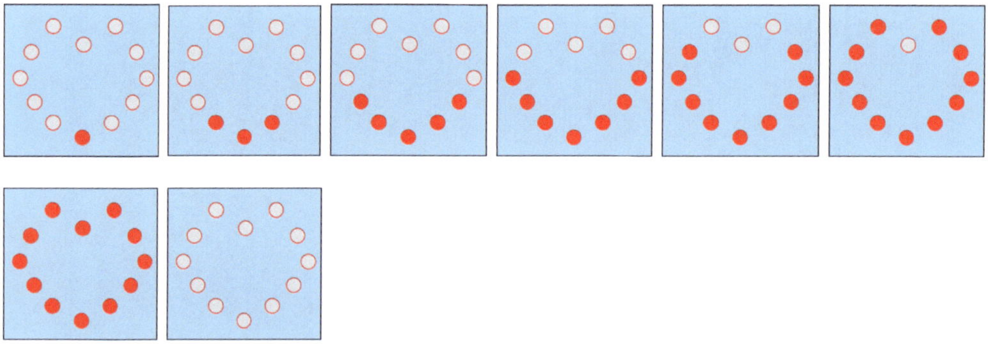

...and then again and again... in an endless loop.

4.1.1 • Hardware

Based on the specification, we can propose an appropriate hardware and software solution.

The schematic of the heart is very simple. We only need LEDs, a few resistors, and a microcontroller.

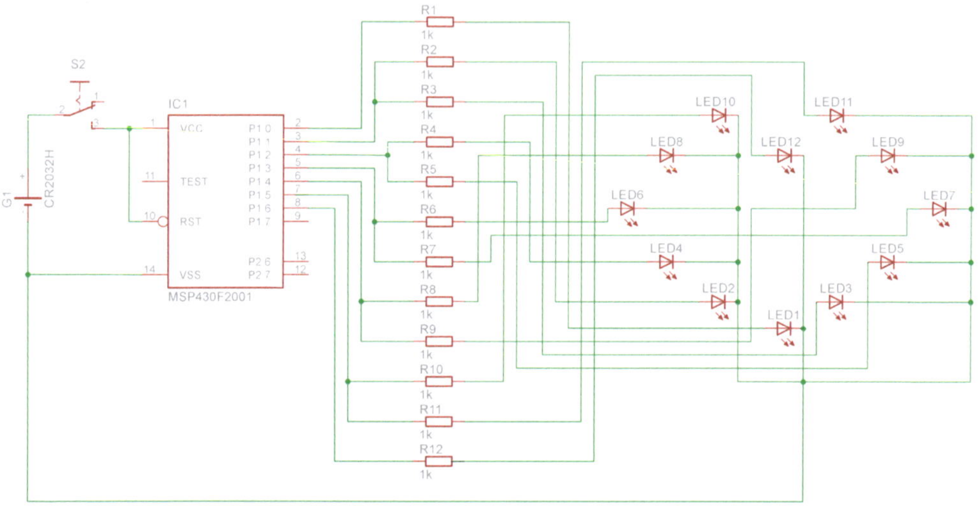

LEDs are connected based on the intended order of switching on and off of the LEDs. As we can see, two LEDs can be driven independently: LED1 (driven by P1.0) and LED12 (driven by P1.6). All other LEDs are connected in pairs:

LED2 and LED3 are both connected to P1.1
LED4 and LED5 are both connected to P1.2
LED6 and LED7 are both connected to P1.3
LED8 and LED9 are both connected to P1.4
LED10 and LED11 are both connected to P1.5

Naturally, the pairs can only be switched on and off together.

Regarding the microcontroller: we can use any of the 14-pin microcontrollers, like the MSP430F2001, MSP430F2002, and MSP430F2012. We do not use any special features of the microcontroller itself.

4.1.2 • CCS Firmware

This firmware is written and tested with CCS Version: 10.1.1.00004.

This firmware is very similar to our "Hello World" applications. We are only using digital outputs concerned with LEDs flashing.

```
//-----------------------------------------------------------------------------
#include <msp430.h>                          //(1) MSP430 library

void wait001(unsigned long int i_wt);        //(2) predefinition of wait routine
//-----------------------------------------------------------------------------
int main(void)                               //(3) start of main function
{
    unsigned long int wait_time = 25000;     //(4) definition of wait time value
    WDTCTL = WDTPW | WDTHOLD;                //(5) stop watchdog timer
    P1DIR = 0xFF;                            //(6) set P1.0 - P1.7 to output
    for(;;)                                  //(7) start of endless loop
    {
        P1OUT = 0x01;                        //(8.1-1) send 0b0000 0001 to output
        wait001(wait_time);                  //(8.1-2) wait predefined time

        P1OUT = 0x03;                        //(8.2-1) send 0b0000 0011 to output
        wait001(wait_time);                  //(8.2-2) wait predefined time

        P1OUT = 0x07;                        //(8.3-1) send 0b0000 0111 to output
        wait001(wait_time);                  //(8.3-2) wait predefined time

        P1OUT = 0x0F;                        //(8.4-1) send 0b0000 1111 to output
        wait001(wait_time);                  //(8.4-2) wait predefined time
```

```
        P1OUT = 0x1F;                         //(8.5-1) send 0b0001 1111 to output
        wait001(wait_time);                   //(8.5-2) wait predefined time

        P1OUT = 0x3F;                         //(8.6-1) send 0b0011 1111 to output
        wait001(wait_time);                   //(8.6-2) wait predefined time

        P1OUT = 0x7F;                         //(8.7-1) send 0b0111 1111 to output
        wait001(wait_time);                   //(8.7-2) wait predefined time

        P1OUT = 0xFF;                         //(8.8-1) send 0b1111 1111 to output
        wait001(wait_time);                   //(8.8-2) wait predefined time

        P1OUT = 0x00;                         //(8.9-1) send 0b0000 0000 to output
        wait001(wait_time);                   //(8.9-2) wait predefined time
    }
}
//-------------------------------------------------------------------------------
void wait001(unsigned long int i_wt           //(9) wait function
{
   volatile unsigned int i;
   i = i_wt;
   do i--;
   while(i != 0);
}
//-------------------------------------------------------------------------------
```

As we can see on line (1), the include <msp430.h> contains all required declarations for the MSP430F2001 microcontroller as well (until now we used this include for MSP430G2553).

I do not think we need a detailed description of the code as there is nothing new to compare with the examples we made for the MSP430G2553. There is no change in the syntax or code structure.

4.2 • Traffic Light

The traffic light is a very simple application from a hardware and software point of view. Let's start with the specification - what do we want to build? Let's say a simple traffic light for a "Y" cross - with one-way roads. Something like this:

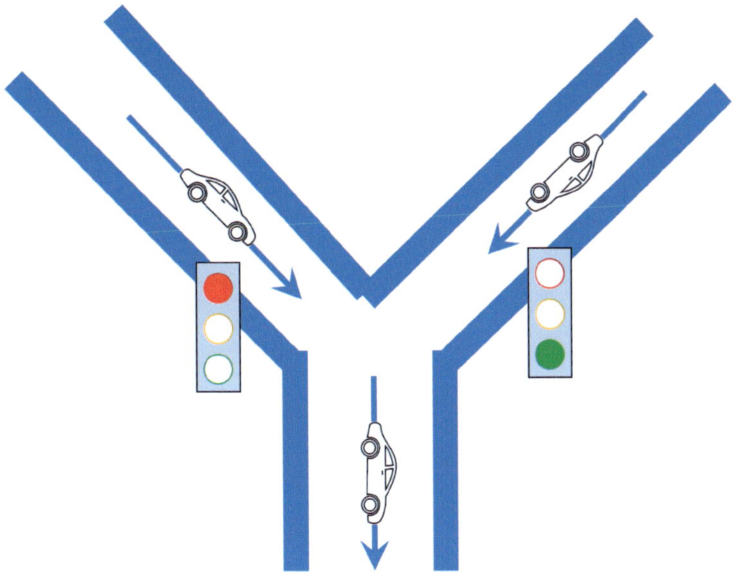

This means we have only two ways needing to be regulated, and no pedestrian lights. This is quite easy. Everybody knows, how the lights work.

To have at least one small "complication", let's define two different modes:

1. The standard one, taking care of traffic regulation - let's call this "active mode"
2. Passive mode, meaning only the yellow lights are flashing and there is no traffic control by the traffic light

When I started to design the code for the microcontroller, I realised that even for this simple task I have no clue how the transition between active and passive mode (and vice versa) is done.

Let's specify the modes themselves first. I would like to start with passive mode: Here it is quite easy: the only thing the lights have to do is flash with yellow lights. Let's flash them both together, meaning both yellow lights shall be on, off, and on again... etc.

Active mode is a bit more complex, but let's stick to the ordinary traffic lights with typically defined transitions between green, red and vice versa. We can describe the stages with the following graphic:

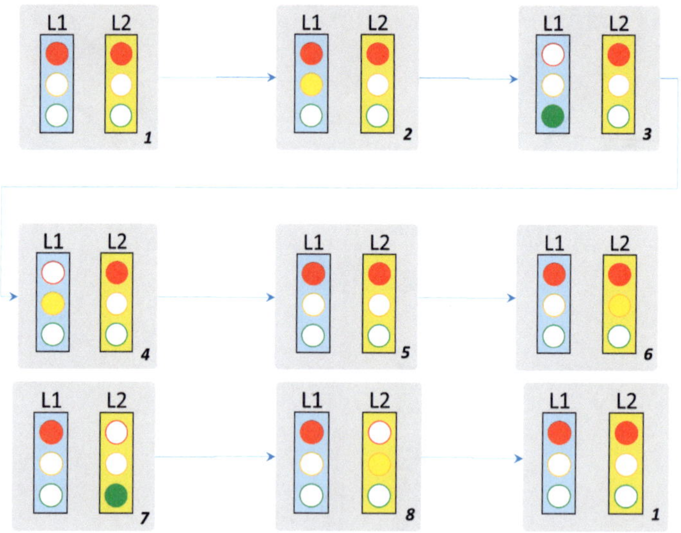

As we can see, the whole traffic light in our example in active mode is defined by 9 stages. Steps 3 and 7 are "stable once", where one way has the green light and the other stops on red. All other steps are transitions between steps 3 and 7, or between steps 7 and 3.

The last important part of the specification is the definition of transitions between passive and active mode, and between active and passive mode.

The transition from passive to active mode is more or less straightforward. From flashing yellow, we jump to step 1 of the procedure we defined for active mode (both directions get the red light).

The transition from active to passive mode is a bit more tricky. If we do not want cars to crash because of an odd traffic light situation, we have to clearly define this transition. Let's say the transition is allowed from only stages 1 or 5 - meaning only in a situation where there is a red light on both ways. In this case, we can always - for this transition - continue to stage 4 and start blinking with a yellow light in this direction, until the other direction is still red. After a few "blinks" we start blinking in the other direction as well.

We can now start with the execution:

4.2.1 • Hardware

The hardware itself is simple. It is just the microcontroller and LEDs we need to build the traffic light.

The traffic light LEDs for one direction are connected to P1.0 (yellow), P1.1 (green), and P1.2 (red). The second direction LEDs are connected to P1.3 (yellow), P1.4 (green), and P1.5 (red).

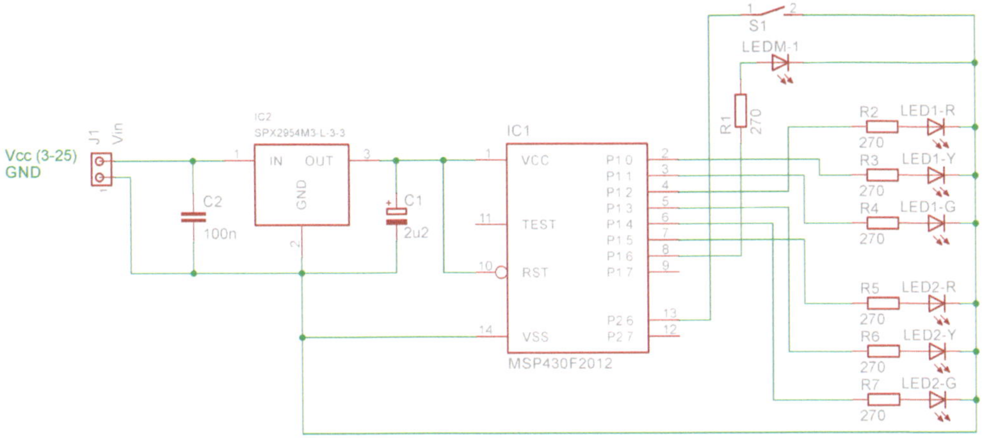

The S1 button initiates the transitions between passive and active modes and vice versa connected to P2.6. I added one more LED: LEDM-1 to P1.6. This LED indicates that a transition between active and passive (or the other way around) modes has been triggered. I added the LDO to provide 3,3V which allows us to use input voltage from let's say 4,0V to 25,0V - used with the SPX2954M3-L-3-3. We can also use any other kind of 3,3V LDO.

4.2.2 • CCS Firmware

This firmware is written and tested with CCS Version: 10.1.1.00004.

Let's have a look at the firmware in C. I'll assume that there is once more a surprise in code structure.

```
//---------------------------------------------------------------------------------
#include <msp430.h>                         //(1) MSP430 library

// P1.0 = L1-Yellow
// P1.1 = L1-Green
// P1.2 = L1-Red

// P1.3 = L2-Yellow
// P1.4 = L2-Green
// P1.5 = L2-Red

// P1.6 = board LED - signalization of change from operation to yellow-flash

// P2.6 = button (connected to GND)
//---------------------------------------------------------------------------------
//---------------------------------------------------------------------------------
void wait001(unsigned long int i_wt);       //(2) predefinition of wait routine
void m_loop();                              //(3) predefinition of m_loop routine
void i_loop();                              //(4) predefinition of i_loop routine
void post_i_loop();                         //(5) predefinition of post_i_loop routine

unsigned int butt_act;                      //(6) declaration of "button-variable"
//---------------------------------------------------------------------------------
void main(void)                             //(7) start of main function
{
    WDTCTL = WDTPW | WDTHOLD;               //(8) stop watchdog timer
    P1DIR = 0xFF;                           //(9) set P1.0 - P1.7 as outputs
    P2DIR = 0x00;                           //(10) set P2.x as inputs
    P2REN = 0x40;                           //(11-1) enable pull-up resistor for P2.6
    P2OUT = 0xFF;                           //(11-2) enable pull-up resistor for P2.6

    P1OUT = 0x00;                           //(12) all LEDs off
    for(;;)                                 //(13) start of endless loop
    {
        P1OUT &= 0b10111111;                //(14) transition LED off
        m_loop();                           //(15) execute main working loop - traffic light work
        P1OUT &= 0b10111111;                //(16) transition LED off
        i_loop();                           //(17) execute idle loop - yellow light is flashing
        post_i_loop();                      //(18) execute transition
    }
```

```
}
//-----------------------------------------------------------------------------------
//-----------------------------------------------------------------------------------
void post_i_loop()                          //(19) transition phase
{
   unsigned int i;                          //(20) help variable definition
// post "off" phase:
//       just wait a while to void switch to the i_loop by pressing the button too long

   i = 3;                                   //(21) 3x repeat the loop
   do {                                     //(22) inner loop
      i--;                                  //(23) decrease the help variable
      P1OUT |= 0b00001001;                  //(24) L1 & L2-Yellow on
      wait001(30000);                       //(25) wait a while
      P1OUT &= 0b11110110;                  //(26) L1 & L2-Yellow off
      wait001(30000);                       //(27) wait a while
     }
   while(i != 0);                           //(28) end of the inner loop
}
//-----------------------------------------------------------------------------------
//-----------------------------------------------------------------------------------
void i_loop()                               //(29) Idle loop - yellow blink
{
   unsigned int i;                          //(30) help variable definition
// first phase - keep the red on main road on first

   P1OUT &= 0b11011111;        //L2-Red off
   i = 5;
   do {
      i--;
      P1OUT |= 0b00001000;        //L2-Yellow on
      wait001(30000);
      P1OUT &= 0b11110111;        //L2-Yellow off
      wait001(30000);
     }
   while(i != 0);

// second / main phase - keep just the yellow lights flashing

   P1OUT = 0x00;                  //switch everything off
   butt_act = 0;                  // default - button is not active
   for(;;) {
      P1OUT |= 0b00001001;        //L1-Yellow on & L2-Yellow on
      wait001(30000);
      P1OUT = 0x00;               //switch all lights off
      wait001(30000);
```

```
        if (butt_act == 1) return;
    }
}
//-------------------------------------------------------------------------------------
//-------------------------------------------------------------------------------------
void m_loop()
{
    butt_act = 0;                   // default - button is not active
    P1OUT = 0x00;                   //switch all lights off
    for(;;) {
        P1OUT |= 0b00100100;        //L1-Red on & L2-Red on
        wait001(100000);
        if (butt_act == 1) return;
        P1OUT |= 0b00000001;        //L1-Yellow on
        wait001(100000);
        P1OUT &= 0b11111010;        //L1-Yellow off & L1-Red off
        P1OUT |= 0b00000010;        //L1-Green on
        wait001(400000);
        P1OUT &= 0b11111101;        //L1-Green off
        P1OUT |= 0b00000001;        //L1-Yellow on
        wait001(100000);
        P1OUT &= 0b11111110;        //L1-Yellow off
        P1OUT |= 0b00000100;        //L1-Red on
        wait001(100000);
        if (butt_act == 1) return;

        P1OUT |= 0b00001000;        //L2-Yellow on
        wait001(100000);
        P1OUT &= 0b11010111;        //L2-Yellow off & L2-Red off
        P1OUT |= 0b00010000;        //L2-Green on
        wait001(400000);
        P1OUT &= 0b11101111;        //L2-Green off
        P1OUT |= 0b00001000;        //L2-Yellow on
        wait001(100000);
        P1OUT &= 0b11110111;        //L2-Yellow off
    }
}
//-------------------------------------------------------------------------------------
//-------------------------------------------------------------------------------------
void wait001(unsigned long int i_wt)
{
    volatile unsigned long int i;
    i = i_wt;
    do {
        i--;
        if ((P2IN & 0x40) != 0x40)
```

```
            {
                butt_act = 1;
                P1OUT |= 0b01000000;        //switch the board LED on - transition active
            }
        }
    while(i != 0);
}
//--------------------------------------------------------------------------------
//--------------------------------------------------------------------------------
```

I will assume as in the previous example that you do not need a detailed description of the firmware. Just let's take a look at the firmware structure.
For every stage of the traffic light, we have a separate function. Therefore we have three major functions:

1. m_loop() is the "main loop" executed when the traffic lights are working ordinarily- - giving "go" and "stop" information.
2. 2. i_loop() is the "idle loop" - when only the yellow lights flash and there is no traffic control.
3. 3. post_i_loop() executes the transition stage between the idle and main loops.

Besides the three functions, there is the main() function coordinating the execution of the mentioned functions based on the button S1 which is used (by pressing) to switch between the main and idle loop. During the transition from main to idle and vice versa, the LEDM-1 is active to indicate that the request for transition (by pressing the button) has been acknowledged by the software. Once the transition is finished, LEDM-1 is switched off.

4.3 • Game Cube

We undertook this exercise earlier with the MSP430G2553. But for an application like this, it is enough to use a much smaller microcontroller, even just using 4x GPIOs. If we do not need the full flexibility of driving every LED independent of each other, we need only 4x Outputs, not 7. Why? Looking at the circuit (in chapter 4.3.1.) - for a real game cube, LED4 and LED5 are always on or off together. This is valid for LED3 and LED6 and LED2 and LED7. This means we can connect these pairs to 1x GPIO.

We will remake the example from chapter 3.1.3. but with the MSP430F2001. For this microcontroller, we do not need to combine the LEDs as we have 8 + 2 GPIOs even in this smaller version of the MCU.

4.3.1 • Hardware

The circuit is nearly the same as before, just the microcontroller is different.

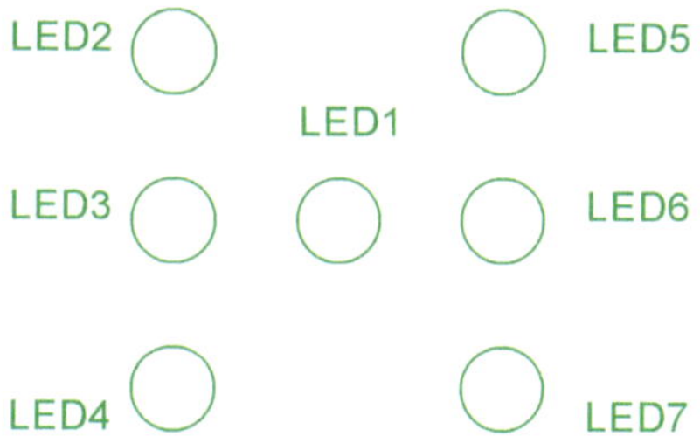

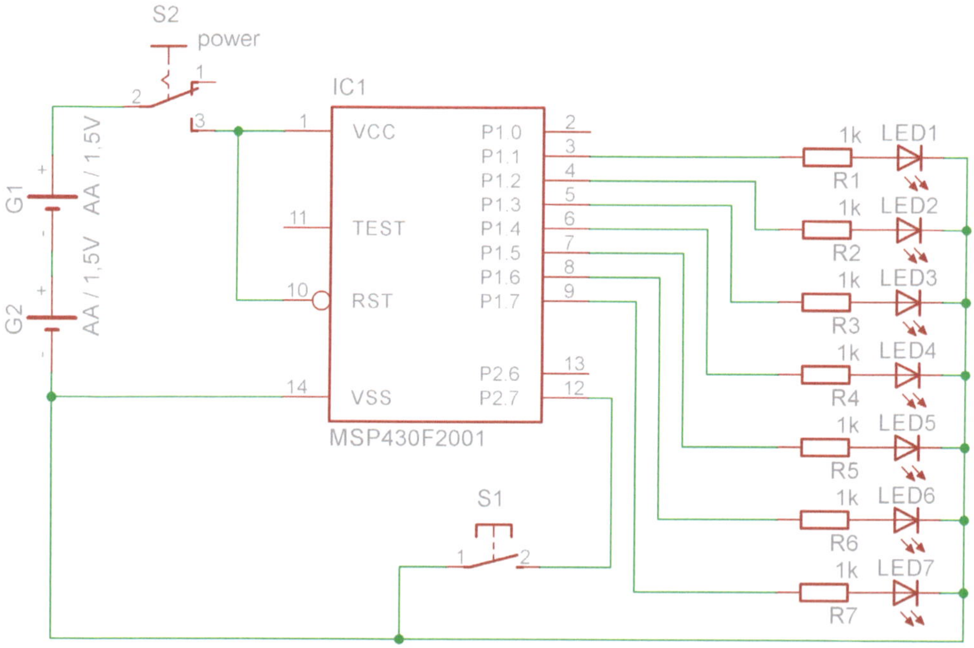

We can still use 2xAA (or 2xAAA) batteries to power the cube. Of course, we can also use another source of power providing let's say 2,7V - 3,3V.

4.3.2 • CCS Firmware

This firmware is written and tested with CCS Version: 10.1.1.00004.

For this example, we can completely skip the firmware listing and description. Why? Because the firmware is the same, as for the game cube described in chapter 3.1.3.3.

The firmware is not completely identical. The only difference is the different connections of LEDs and buttons. This means for example, that in our example from chapter 3.1.3. we tested "P1IN & BIT3" because the button was connected to port P1.3. Here we will test "P2IN & BIT7" because the button is connected to port P2.7.

4.4 • Game Cube / Demo

Let's do the cube again. Last time, I promise.

Now we will extend our last example; adding one potentiometer... Extending the firmware a bit... In doing this, we need a more powerful microcontroller - we will use the MSP430F2012. This provides 2kB Flash (instead of 1kB with the MSP430F2001). Furthermore, in addition to the ADC10 module - we will need to work with the potentiometer.

In our example, the potentiometer has two functions:

1. It will be possible to set the speed of changing numbers on the "display" - from: "all are lighting" - meaning very fast, up to I can pick-up what number I want - meaning changing slowly.
2. If the potentiometer is set to, or very close to V_{cc}, the cube will start a demo, changing numbers 1 to 6 without pressing the button.

4.4.1 • Hardware

The same connection of the LEDs as in our previous example, just we connect a potentiometer to P1.0. The resistance of the pot is not critical - I used 100k.

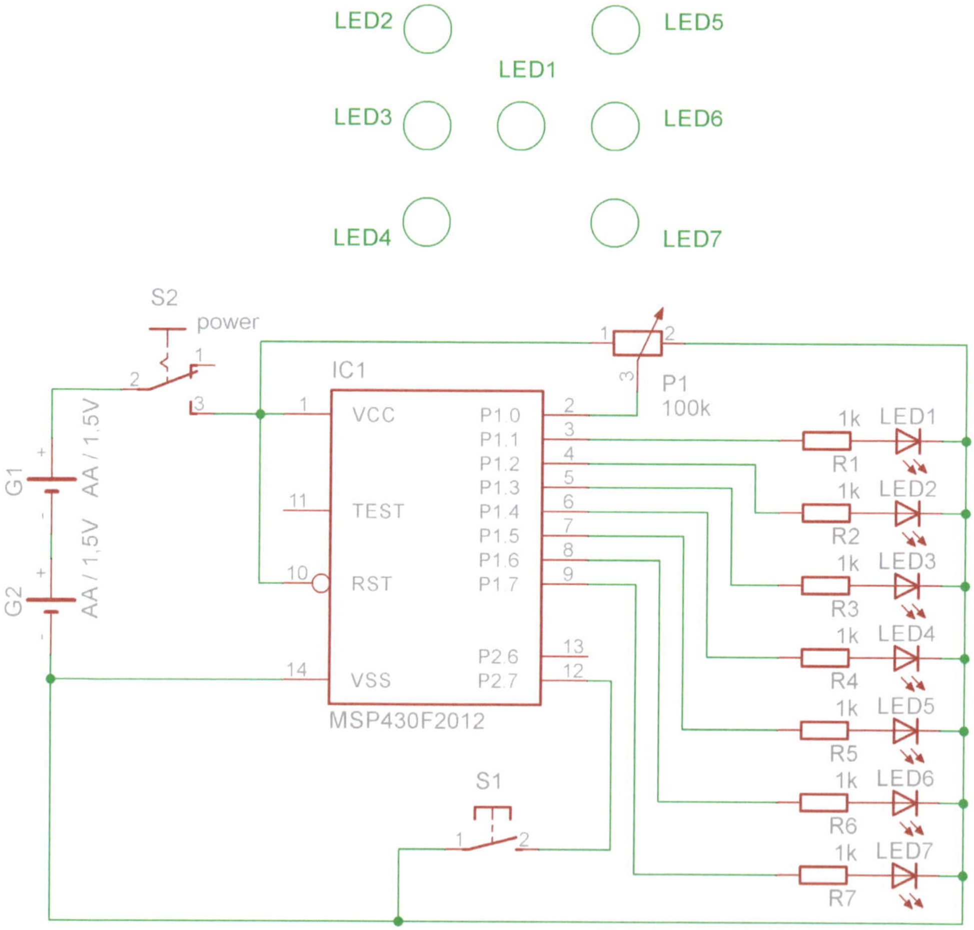

The difference to the last example is that here the microcontroller has to be the MSP430F2012. The reason is that other MCU's from the family either do not have the ADC10-module or contain another module (which will require changes in the firmware) or do not have enough Flash memory for the firmware.

4.4.2 • CCS Firmware

This firmware is written and tested with CCS Version: 10.1.1.00004.

We can now take a short look at the firmware for this special game cube. It is a kind of extended firmware used for "ordinary" cubes.

The firmware for our demo-cube looks like this:

```
//-------------------------------------------------------------------------
//-------------------------------------------------------------------------
#include <msp430.h>                             //(1) include msp430 constants & declarations

unsigned int wait_time = 500;                   //(2.1) define wait time between number changes
short v_act = 0x80;                             //(2.2) help variable for button
int adc10_read;                                 //(2.3) storage for date from ADC10

void wait001(unsigned long int i_wt);           //(3) there will be "wait001" function
void wm_01(void);                               //(4.1) character set: number 1
void wm_02(void);                               //(4.2) character set: number 2
void wm_03(void);                               //(4.3) character set: number 3
void wm_04(void);                               //(4.4) character set: number 4
void wm_05(void);                               //(4.5) character set: number 5
void wm_06(void);                               //(4.6) character set: number 6
void wm_x2(void);                               //(4.7) character set: number "strange 2"
void wm_space(void);                            //(4.8) character set: all off
void show_test(void);                           //(4.9) LED test for start-up
void read_adc10(void);
//-------------------------------------------------------------------------
//-------------------------------------------------------------------------
int main(void)                                  //(5) main function starts here
{
    WDTCTL = WDTPW | WDTHOLD;                   //(6) Stop watchdog timer
    P1DIR = 0b11111110;                         //(7) set-up I/O direction for P1
    P2SEL = 0x00;                               //(8.1) P2.7 setup / step 1
    P2DIR = 0b00000000;                         //(8.2) P2.7 setup / step 2
    P2REN = 0b11000000;                         //(8.3) enable resistor on P2.7
    P2OUT = 0b11000000;                         //(8.4) set up pull-up functionality for P2.7

    show_test();                                //(9) execute the LED test
    wm_x2();                                    //(10) show "strange 2"

    ADC10CTL1 = 0b0000000000000000;             //(11) set-up ADC10CTL1

    for(;;)                                     //(12) endless loop
    {
     read_adc10();                              //(13) read ADC10
     while((P2IN & BIT7) != v_act)              //(14) inner loop - when button is pressed
      {
         if ((P2IN & BIT7) != v_act) wm_01();   //(15.1a) change to 1 - if the button is still pressed
         wait001(wait_time);                    //(15.1b) wait a bit to make the LEDs flashing
         if ((P2IN & BIT7) != v_act) wm_02();   //(15.2a) change to 2 - if the button is still pressed
         wait001(wait_time);                    //(15.2b) wait a bit to make the LEDs flashing
         if ((P2IN & BIT7) != v_act) wm_03();   //(15.3a) change to 3 - if the button is still pressed
         wait001(wait_time);                    //(15.3b) wait a bit to make the LEDs flashing
```

```
            if ((P2IN & BIT7) != v_act) wm_04();   //(15.4a) change to 4 - if the button is still pressed
            wait001(wait_time);                    //(15.4b) wait a bit to make the LEDs flashing
            if ((P2IN & BIT7) != v_act) wm_05();   //(15.5a) change to 5 - if the button is still pressed
            wait001(wait_time);                    //(15.5b) wait a bit to make the LEDs flashing
            if ((P2IN & BIT7) != v_act) wm_06();   //(15.6a) change to 6 - if the button is still pressed
            wait001(wait_time);                    //(15.6b) wait a bit to make the LEDs flashing
        }
    }
}
//-----------------------------------------------------------------------
//-----------------------------------------------------------------------
void show_test(void)                           //(T-1) LED test for start-up
{
    wm_space();                                //(T-2) clear the display
    P1OUT = 0b10000001;                        //(T-3) switch on the P1.7 LED
    wait001(20000);                            //(T-4) wait a while
    P1OUT = 0b11000001;                        //(T-5) switch on the P1.6 LED
    wait001(20000);                            //(T-6) wait a while
    P1OUT = 0b11100001;                        //(T-7) switch on the P1.5 LED
    wait001(20000);                            //(T-8) wait a while
    P1OUT = 0b11110001;                        //(T-9) switch on the P1.4 LED
    wait001(20000);                            //(T-10) wait a while
    P1OUT = 0b11111001;                        //(T-11) switch on the P1.3 LED
    wait001(20000);                            //(T-12) wait a while
    P1OUT = 0b11111101;                        //(T-13) switch on the P1.2 LED
    wait001(20000);                            //(T-14) wait a while
    P1OUT = 0b11111111;                        //(T-15) switch on the P1.1 LED
    wait001(20000);                            //(T-16) wait a while
}
//-----------------------------------------------------------------------
//-----------------------------------------------------------------------
void wm_space(void)                            //(WM-S) switch off all LEDs
{
    P1OUT = 0x01;
}
//-----------------------------------------------------------------------
void wm_01(void)                               //(WM-1) show 1
{  P1OUT = 0b00000011; }
//-----------------------------------------------------------------------
void wm_02(void)                               //(WM-2) show 2
{  P1OUT = 0b00110001; }
//-----------------------------------------------------------------------
void wm_03(void)                               //(WM-3) show 3
{  P1OUT = 0b00110011; }
//-----------------------------------------------------------------------
void wm_04(void)                               //(WM-4) show 4
```

```
{  P1OUT = 0b10110101; }
//-----------------------------------------------------------------------
void wm_05(void)                              //(WM-5) show 5
{  P1OUT = 0b10110111; }
//-----------------------------------------------------------------------
void wm_06(void)                              //(WM-6) show 6
{  P1OUT = 0b11111101; }
//-----------------------------------------------------------------------
void wm_x2(void)                              //(WM-2x) show strange 2
{  P1OUT = 0b01001001; }
//-----------------------------------------------------------------------
//-----------------------------------------------------------------------
void wait001(unsigned long int i_wt)          //(D-1) delay routine
{
    volatile unsigned long int i;             //(D-2) volatile to prevent optimisation
    i = i_wt;                                 //(D-3) SW delay
    do i--;                                   //(D-4) delay loop
    while(i != 0);                            //(D-5) delay loop
    read_adc10();                             //(D-6) read the current position of potentiometer
}
//-----------------------------------------------------------------------
//-----------------------------------------------------------------------
void read_adc10(void)                         //(A-1) ADC10-read function
{
    adc10_read = ADC10MEM;                    //(A-2) get the result from ADC10MEM register
    ADC10CTL0 = 0b0001100001111011;           //(A-3) set up ADC10CTL0 and start conversion
    wait_time = 50 + adc10_read * 20;         //(A-4) calculate wait-time based on ADC10 value
    if (adc10_read > 1020)                    //(A-5.1) demo-mode
        {
            v_act = 0;                        //(A-5.2) demo-mode
            wait_time = 20000;                //(A-5.3) wait time for demo-mode
        }
    else v_act = 0x80;                        //(A-5.4) standard mode
}
// ------------------------------------------------------------------------------
// ------------------------------------------------------------------------------
```

At the very beginning, we can see that just one standard library is used (1).

In declarations (2.x) we define the variables used to control the behaviour of the cube - i.e the speed of changing the numbers and variable to store values coming from the ADC10. Steps (3) and (4.x) are declarations of later implemented functions and in step (5) the firmware main function implementation starts.

As we know, first we have to stop the watch-dog timer (6), and then set up the I/O ports as required for the application - steps (7) and (8.x). In step (9) we run a short "LED-test" and (10) show the "strange 2" to indicate the cube has been started and no valid value is provided yet.

In step (11) undertake the ADC10 settings necessary. Step (12) is the start of the main end-less loop of the application.

At the beginning of the main endless loop, we get the current value of the potentiometer through the ADC10 module (13). In step (14) we start the inner-loop. This runs until the button is pushed. All steps (15.x) are about taking care of controlling the button stage, displaying the current value of the cube, and executing wait cycles between numbers.

At the beginning, function show_test() executes "LED test" - we saw this already in another variation of the cube.

All wm_xx() functions display the required numbers using the cube LEDs.

We also saw the wait001()delay function. It is extended with the reading of the ADC10 module - the call of function read_adc10() in step (D-6).

Function read_adc10() reads the position of the potentiometer and based on this position calculates the new waiting time. If required this function activate demo mode (steps A-5.1 - A5.3).

4.5 • Temperature measurement

We will now measure the temperature with the help of the ADC10 module using the MSP430F2012 and an external analogue temperature sensor from Analog Devices called the TMP37.

The schematic is almost the same as in our example with Demo Game Cube from the last chapter (4.4.). Instead of a potentiometer we will connect an analogue temperature sensor and order the LEDs in a line (not as a cube) - and that's it. The firmware is a little different...

4.5.1 • Specification

We would like to construct a thermometer to measure indoor temperature from 18°C to 25°C using a scale built with LEDs. The lowest temperatures will be shown using yellow LEDs. The ambient temperature using green LEDs and the highest temperature with red LEDs as per below:

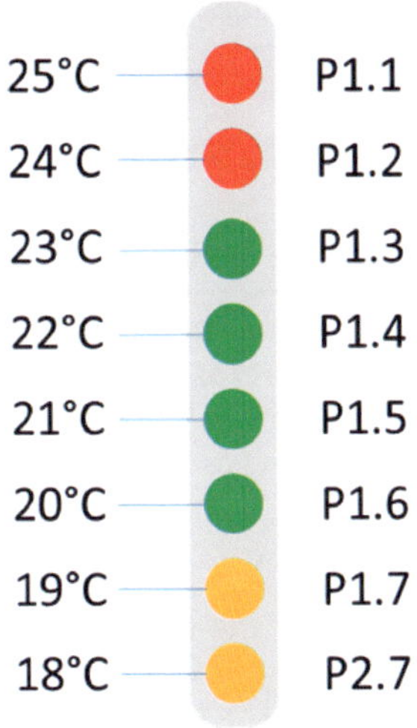

Should the temperature fall below 18°C, the two yellow LEDs will start to blink - as an indication that the temperature is below the lowest point that can be displayed. The same for high temperatures: if the temperature crosses 25°C, the two red LEDs start to blink. No interaction or setup or similar functionalities are required.

4.5.2 ● Hardware

Let's take a brief look at the components used. Besides the microcontroller, we are only using the aforementioned temperature sensor - the TMP37.

4.5.2.1 ● Temperature Sensor TMP37

The Temperature sensors used are available in SOT-23, SOIC-8, and TO-92 packages. The TO-92 package uses just three pins: V_{cc}, GND, and an analogue output. In the other two packages, there is a "shutdown" pin available. With this pin, it is possible to deactivate the sensor to save energy.

The pin assignment for the TO-92 package looks like this:

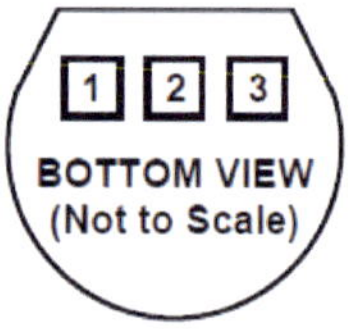

PIN 1, $+V_S$; PIN 2, V_{OUT}; PIN 3, GND

We can summarise the main attributes of the sensor in the following 4 lines:

Output voltage at 25°C = 500mV
Delta voltage per °C = 20mV
Power supply: 2,7V - 5,5V
Accuracy of the measurement: +/- 2°C

For our example, we do not need more information about the sensor.

4.5.2.2 • Schematic

As we can see, the whole construction is very simple. We need only the microcontroller and temperature sensor. Of course, in addition, we need a few LEDs and resistors.

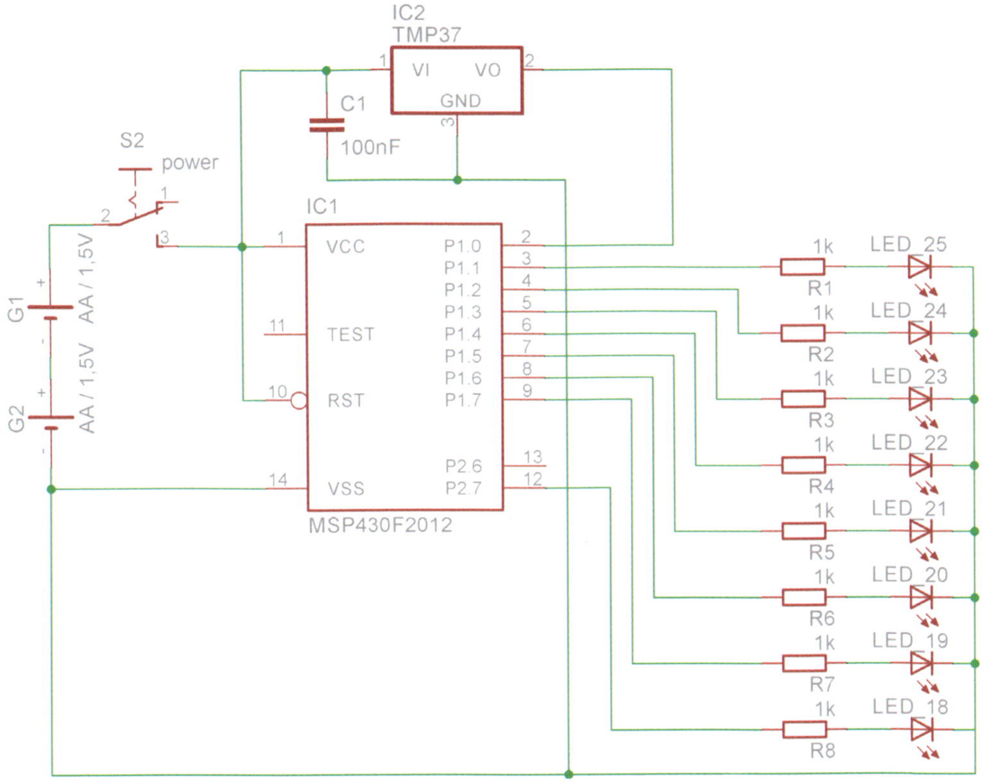

Regarding power supply, we can use either batteries (as shown in the circuit), or for example, a USB charger and 3,3V LDO - as mentioned at the beginning of chapter 3.

We will use P1.0 as input for the analogue temperature sensor. As we want to connect 8 LEDs, we will use P1.1 to P1.7 and port P2.7 to connect “the display”. Port 2.6 will be left unused. We could connect one more LED - to extend the range of temperatures shown, and adjust the firmware accordingly.

4.5.3 • Firmware

The software of the thermometer is quite simple and very similar to the one already mentioned in this chapter - the "demo playing cube". We have to drive 8 LEDs and use the ADC10 module. Nothing else. On the ADC10 module, we now connect the temperature sensor instead of the potentiometer for the game cube.

What is crucial for this firmware is the calculation of the temperature based on the sensor output voltage.

We can define an assignment of temperatures to the voltages and based on that calculate the result.

4.5.3.1 • Temperature Calculation

We know that our ADC10-module will give a digital result of 0 if the input voltage is 0V. We know that the result of the measurement will be 1.023. For ADC10 conversion we will use a built-in 1,5V reference voltage (as it is more precise than sticking to the power supply). We know, that the conversion is supposed to be linear and therefore we can say that a delta of 1 in the result means a delta of ~1,47mV on input (1,47mV x 1.023 = 1.504mV = ~1,50V). We also know that the output voltage of the sensor will be 500mV at a temperature of 25°C. We know additionally, that every 1°C more (than 25°C) will increase the output voltage of 20mV and every 1°C less will decrease the output of 20mV.

Based on this information, we can define a table of temperatures, voltages and ADC10 digital values:

Voltage [mV]	**Temperature [°C]**	**ADC10 result**
520	26	520mV / 1,47mV = 354
500	25	500mV / 1,47mV = 340
480	24	480mV / 1,47mV = 327
460	23	460mV / 1,47mV = 313
440	22	440mV / 1,47mV = 299
420	21	420mV / 1,47mV = 286
400	20	400mV / 1,47mV = 272
380	19	380mV / 1,47mV = 259
360	18	360mV / 1,47mV = 245
340	17	340mV / 1,47mV = 231
320	16	320mV / 1,47mV = 218

We can see from the table that the digital delta for the delta of 1°C is roughly 6.

The last step we need to define is to assign the LEDs to the intervals of the ADC10 result. We need to define, when and which LED will be active.

Voltage from [mV]	**voltage to [mV]**	**ADC10 result from**	**ADC10 result to**	**temp. from [°c]**	**temp. to [°C]**	**LED**	**Port**
	350		238		<17,5	/ blink	
351	370	239	251	17,5	18,4	18°C ( )	P2.7
371	390	252	265	18,5	19,4	19°C ( )	P1.7
391	410	266	279	19,5	20,4	20°C ( )	P1.6
411	430	280	292	20,5	21,4	21°C ( )	P1.5
431	450	293	306	21,5	22,4	22°C ( )	P1.4
451	470	307	319	22,5	23,4	23°C ( )	P1.3
471	490	320	333	23,5	24,4	24°C ( )	P1.2
491	510	334	347	24,5	25,4	25°C ( )	P1.1
511		348		>25,5		/ blink	

Based on the information summarised, we will implement the corresponding functions to calculate the temperature using the ADC10 in the firmware of our thermometer.

4.5.3.2 • ADC10 settings

We can have a look now at the settings used for the ADC10 for our thermometer construction. As the expected input voltage level is up to ~0,6V, we can use the internal microcontroller voltage reference 1,5V (see settings of bits SREFx, REF2_5, and REFON).

We will not use any interrupts and there is nothing particular in any other settings.

The **ADC10CTL0** register will be used like this:

bit name	bit(s)	usage
SREFx	15 - 13	Reference selection: 000: $V_{R+} = V_{CC}$ $V_{R-} = V_{SS}$ 001: $V_{R+} = V_{REF+}$ $VR- = V_{SS}$ 010: $V_{R+} = V_{eREF+}$ $VR- = V_{SS}$ 011: V_{R+} = buffered V_{eREF+} $VR- = V_{SS}$ 100: $V_{R+} = V_{CC}$ $VR- = V_{REF-} / V_{eREF-}$ 101: $V_{R+} = V_{REF+}$ $VR- = V_{REF-} / V_{eREF-}$ 110: $V_{R+} = V_{eREF+}$ $VR- = V_{REF-} / V_{eREF-}$ 111: V_{R+} = buffered V_{eREF+} $VR- = V_{REF-} / V_{eREF-}$
ADSC10SHTx	12 - 11	ADC10 sample and hold time: 00: 4 × ADC10CLKs (default value) 01: 8 × ADC10CLKs 10: 16 × ADC10CLKs 11: 64 × ADC10CLKs
ARC10SR	10	Default value used: 0
REFOUT	9	Default value used: 0
REFBURST	8	Default value used: 0
MSC	7	Default value used: 0
REF2_5V	6	If reference generator is active (on) - we can with this bit choose one of the possible reference voltages: 0: reference voltage is: 1,5V (default) 1: reference voltage is: 2,5V
REFON	5	Reference generator enable bit: 0: reference generator is off 1: reference generator is on
ADC10ON	4	ADC10 main switch - activate or deactivate ADC10 module: 0: ADC10 module is off (default value) 1: ADC10 is on
ADC10IE	3	ADC10 interrupt enable bit: 0 interrupt from ADC10 module is disabled (default value) 1 interrupt from ADC10 module is enabled

ADC10IFG	2	ADC10 interrupt flag; not relevant for configuration - set to 0
ENC	1	Enable conversion bit: 0 ADC10 conversion is disabled 1 ADC10 conversion is enabled
ADC10SC	0	Start of a conversion - this bit is cleared automatic. Writing 1 to this bit will trigger the conversion (of course, only if the ADC10 module is on and enabled): 0 no sample-and-conversion 1 trigger conversion

For the ADC10CTL1 register, it is only important to set up the correct input - port A0:

bit name	bit(s)	
INCHx	15 - 12	*Input channel select:* *0000: A0* *0001: A1* *0010: A2* *0011: A3* *0100: A4* *0101: A5* *0110: A6* *0111: A7* *1000: V_{eREF+}* *1001: V_{REF-} / V_{eREF-}* *1010: Internal Temperature Sensor* *1011: (V_{CC} - V_{SS}) / 2* *1100: (V_{CC} - V_{SS}) / 2 or A12 on devices with A12 input* *1101: (V_{CC} - V_{SS}) / 2 or A13 on devices with A13 input* *1110: (V_{CC} - V_{SS}) / 2 or A14 on devices with A14 input* *1111: (V_{CC} - V_{SS}) / 2 or A15 on devices with A15 input*
SHSx	11 - 10	Default value used: 00
ADC10DF	9	Default value used: 0
ISSH	8	Default value used: 0
ADC10DIVx	7 - 5	Default value used: 000
ADC10SSELx	4 - 3	Default value used: 00
CONSEQx	2 - 1	Default value used: 00
ADC10BUSY	0	Not relevant for the settings (set as 0)

4.5.3.3 • Firmware

We do not need to walk through all the code. I would however like to show the ADC10-related pieces of the code and the main loop of the software. The functions of driving LEDs, declarations, etc. we leave out as there is nothing that can be called "added value" to compare to examples we already sow.

Now let's have a look at the firmware - the main function first.

```
//--------------------------------------------------------------------------------------------
//--------------------------------------------------------------------------------------------
// MSP430F2020 + TMP37
//--------------------------------------------------------------------------------------------
//--------------------------------------------------------------------------------------------
...
//--------------------------------------------------------------------------------------------
void main(void)
{
    WDTCTL = WDTPW | WDTHOLD;                  //(1) stop watchdog timer

    P1DIR = 0b11111110;                        //(2) set-up I/O direction for P1
    P2SEL = 0x00;                              //(3) P2.7 setup
    P2DIR = 0b11000000;                        //(4) P2.7 setup

    ADC10CTL1 = 0b0000000000000000;            //(5) set-up ADC10CTL1

    show_test();                               //(6) execute LED test
    v_blink = 0;                               //(7) help variable for blinking - init

    for(;;)                                    //(8) start of main endless loop
    {
     read_adc10();                             //(9) read ADC10 - temperature from sensor
     temp_correction();                        //(10) execute correction

     v_temperature = 17;                       //(11) temperature bellow low border - “too cold”

     if(adc10_value > 239) v_temperature = 18; //(12a) set-up temperature based on ADC10 measurement
     if(adc10_value > 252) v_temperature = 19; //(12b) set-up temperature based on ADC10 measurement
     if(adc10_value > 266) v_temperature = 20; //(12c) set-up temperature based on ADC10 measurement
     if(adc10_value > 280) v_temperature = 21; //(12d) set-up temperature based on ADC10 measurement
     if(adc10_value > 293) v_temperature = 22; //(12e) set-up temperature based on ADC10 measurement
     if(adc10_value > 307) v_temperature = 23; //(12f) set-up temperature based on ADC10 measurement
     if(adc10_value > 320) v_temperature = 24; //(12g) set-up temperature based on ADC10 measurement
     if(adc10_value > 334) v_temperature = 25; //(12h) set-up temperature based on ADC10 measurement
     if(adc10_value > 348) v_temperature = 26; //(13)  temperature over hig border - “too hot”

     show_temp();                              //(14) show temperature
     delay_ms(100);                            //(15) wait 0,1 sec before next loop
    }
}
//--------------------------------------------------------------------------------------------
```

At the very beginning we stop the watchdog timer (1). In steps (2) - (4) we define P1.x and P2.7 as outputs to drive the LEDs and have an input (P1.0) for ADC10.

Step (5) will set up one part of ADC10 based on the description in the previous chapter. Before jumping to the main endless loop of the application, we will undertake a short LED test (6) and initialise a "blink variable" (7).

In step (8) we start the endless loop, where periodically the measurement and displaying of temperature is completed.

Step (9) calls the temperature measurement itself by working with ADC10. Afterwards (10) a very simple correction routine is executed to be able to adjust the temperature. Why? As we know already, the tolerance of the sensor used is +/- 2°C - which is quite a lot. Therefore we can - based on another reference thermometer, justify the temperature measured and correct the value if required in this routine. We will see it in a moment.

In step (11) we set up "too cold temperature". Our thermometer can show temperatures from 18°C to 25°C. All temperature values below 18°C will be shown as "too cold". This is the default value for the conversion. "Too cold" will be shown in a way, that the two "coldest" - yellow - LEDs will start to blink, as described in the specification part.

All steps (12*) are do the conversion of the ADC10 value to temperature based on the conversion table we saw at the beginning of this chapter.

Step (13) defines the "too hot" temperature i.e. the signal to start the blinking of the two red LEDs.

Step (14) will call the function to show the temperature. At the very end of the loop, we include a 0.1-second waiting time, before starting the next round.

We can now continue to the correction routine.

```
//------------------------------------------------------------------------------
void temp_correction(void)
{
    adc10_value = adc10_value - 0;
    adc10_value = adc10_value + 28;
}
//------------------------------------------------------------------------------
```

As we can see, it is very simple. We just subtract or add a constant value to the result of the measurement.

In the firmware is a digital delta of 14 equal to delta of 1°C. In the listing we can see that we increase the measurement value by 28 meaning the sensor used in my construction typically gives us 2°C less than the reference thermometer used. Therefore in the correction, the temperature will be corrected by +2°C.

The temperature measurement function is also quite simple. We just need to trigger ADC10 conversion.

```
//-----------------------------------------------------------------------------------------------
void read_adc10(void)
{
    ADC10CTL0 = 0b0011100000111011;        //(A-1) set up ADC10CTL0 and start conversion
                                           //interval: 0 <= adc10_read <= 1.023
                                           //reference 1,5V is used
    delay_ms(200);                         //(A-2) wait 0,2 sec
    adc10_value = ADC10MEM;                //(A-3) read the conversion result
}
//-----------------------------------------------------------------------------------------------
```

In the first step (A-1) we trigger the conversion using the settings described earlier. We then wait 0.2 seconds (A-2) and finally read the result of conversion to a global variable adc10_value (A-3). With this step, the measurement is finished.

The last function I would like to demonstrate is the display of the temperature.

```
//-----------------------------------------------------------------------------------------------
void show_temp(void)
{
    switch(v_temperature)                      //(D-1) start of the decision making
    {
        case 17: show_too_cold(); break;       //(D-2) execute blinking of "too cold" LEDs
        case 18: show_18(); break;             //(D-3a) switch on corresponding LED
        case 19: show_19(); break;             //(D-3b) switch on corresponding LED
        case 20: show_20(); break;             //(D-3c) switch on corresponding LED
        case 21: show_21(); break;             //(D-3d) switch on corresponding LED
        case 22: show_22(); break;             //(D-3e) switch on corresponding LED
        case 23: show_23(); break;             //(D-3f) switch on corresponding LED
        case 24: show_24(); break;             //(D-3g) switch on corresponding LED
        case 25: show_25(); break;             //(D-3h) switch on corresponding LED
        case 26: show_too_hot(); break;        //(D-4) execute blinking of "too hot" LEDs
    }
}
//-----------------------------------------------------------------------------------------------
//-----------------------------------------------------------------------------------------------
```

The "main display routine" uses other functions. Based on the temperature, we decide which function will be executed. Routines "show_18" to "show_25" switch the required LEDs on and off. Only one LED is switched on, and all others are switched off.

Two routines - "show_too_cold" and "show_too_hot" are responsible for the blinking of the corresponding doubles of LEDs.

To get the idea, here is the function showing 20°C:

```
//---------------------------------------------------------------------------------------
void show_20(void)
{
    P1OUT = 0b01000000;
    P2OUT = 0x00;
}
//---------------------------------------------------------------------------------------
```

And here we can see one (of the two) "border-routines" - this one is responsible for the blinking of the two red-LEDs to show "too hot-temperature":

```
//---------------------------------------------------------------------------------------
void show_too_hot(void)
{
    P2OUT = 0x00;
    if(v_blink == 1) P1OUT = 0b00000110;
    if(v_blink == 0) P1OUT = 0x00;
    v_blink++;
    if(v_blink == 2) v_blink = 0;
}
//---------------------------------------------------------------------------------------
```

These two examples of routines showing the results are quite self-explanatory.

Chapter 5 • The Application

I would like to describe a real application using the MSP430G2553 in this last chapter.

We will focus on I²C communication with the microcontroller and build a clock (calculate - based on the date - the day of the week) and thermometer showing humidity. All this information will be shown on the LCD at the same time.

Besides this, we will connect a 4x4 keypad to the application to be able to control required functions.

We will use a couple of different periphery chips to communicate with the microcontroller using the I²C interface.

We will use an RTC-chip and temperature/humidity sensors.

To connect the keyboard we will use a GPIO chip to communicate with the I²C protocol.

To be able to utilise the different function (e.g. to set the date and time) we will use a 4x4 keypad, with pre-defined symbols as seen here:

We can use simple buttons in a matrix or keypad module - it doesn't matter. We will use the symbols shown in the above picture to describe the behaviour of the construction.

We will first have a look at the possibilities and functionalities of this construction and then walk through the components used. The goal is not to describe the chips in details just to describe the practical functionalities used in the firmware.

5.1 • Specification

The main goal of this construction is to demonstrate the possibilities of I²C communication - utilising IDE Energia. Therefore we will connect all peripheries in this example to the I²C bus.

The main application is, as already mentioned the RTC-based clock showing the date, time and day of the week. The day of the week will be calculated and not based on the information provided by the RTC - we will touch this point later. Our application will inform us about temperature and air humidity. All sensors will be optional, meaning for exampe, if the humidity sensor is not connected, the information will not be available, but everything else works as expected.

5.1.1 • Behaviour

Here is a short summary of the desired behaviour of the construction.

After power-up, the device will come up with a "welcome screen" showing the firmware name and release - like this:

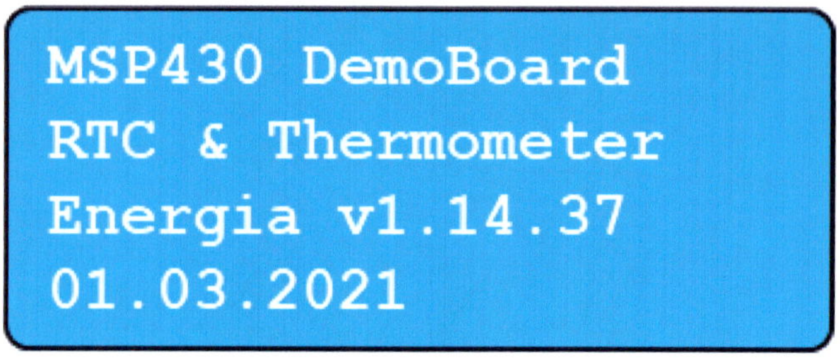

The information will stay on the screen for a couple of seconds, and then the main application will start. If all sensors and the RTC-chip are connected, you will see something like this:

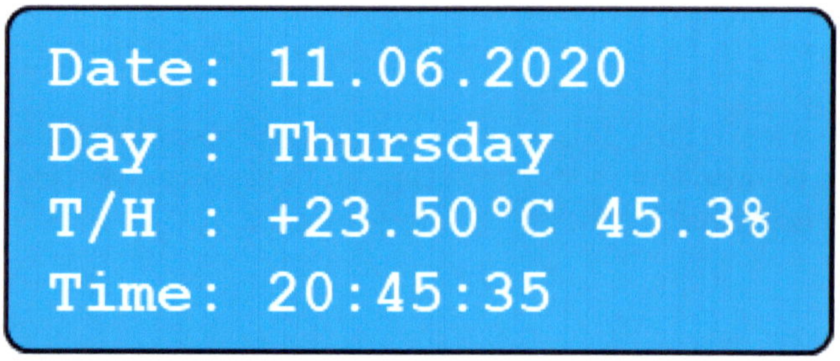

This screen will be the default one appearing after reset / power-up. This means that we will construct a real end product, something like clock plus temperature plus humidity meter providing additional information about the current day of the week based on the Gregorian calendar.

Additionally, there are a couple of additional functions, which will be available after exiting the main screen.

These functions will be accessible by pressing an assigned key from the selection screen:

If you would like extra temperature sensor functionality, jump there by pressing (1). Likewise, RTC (by pressing (2)) - clock settings (and date of course).

There is also the option to see more information regarding the humidity sensor.

5.1.2 • Operation

In this chapter, we will see how to operate the application, and how to switch between different functional areas and utilise implemented functions.

5.1.2.1 • Main Application / Main Menu

As mentioned, after start-up (and showing the release of firmware), the main application shows information like this:

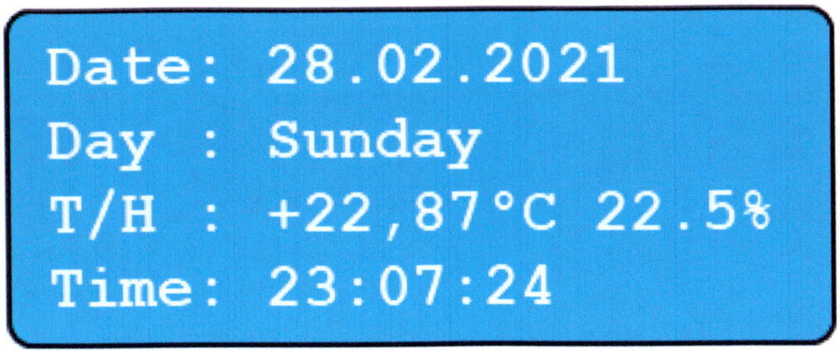

The date and time come from the DS1307 RTC-chip. "Day" is calculated by the firmware based on "date" data. If the DS1307 chip is not connected, we see the following info:

Date and Time information are not available, and therefore it is not possible to calculate the date of the week.

The temperature comes from the AT30TSE740. This sensor can be present on any of the pre-reserved I^2C addresses. The firmware will look up all 8 of them and where the first response comes, this sensor will be used for measurement.

If no temperature sensor is connected, the temperature sensor of the HYT939 humidity sensor will be used to show temperature.

If the humidity sensor is not connected (but the temperature sensor is present), the main screen will be adapted slightly:

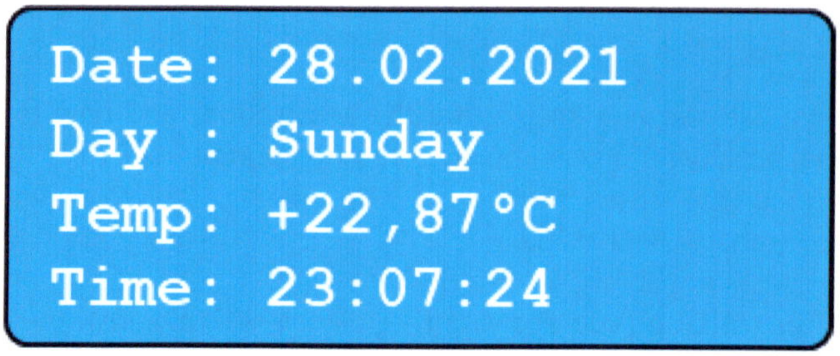

If there is no temperature or humidity sensor (but RTC connected) we will see the following screen:

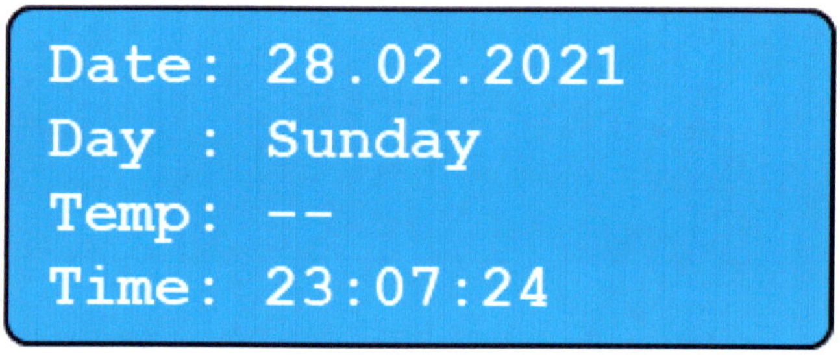

If there is no sensor or RTC connected, the screen will look quite simple:

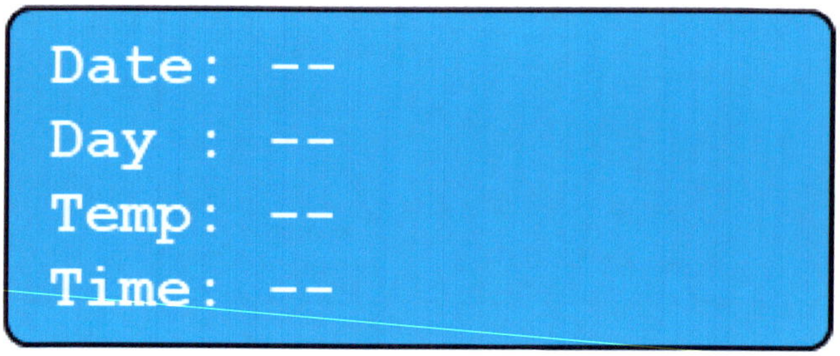

When the main screen is shown, there is no possibility to do anything.
We can only press the "*" (star) button to jump to the **main menu**:

5.1.2.2 • AT30TSE754

If we select the temperature sensor from the main menu, we have the following options:

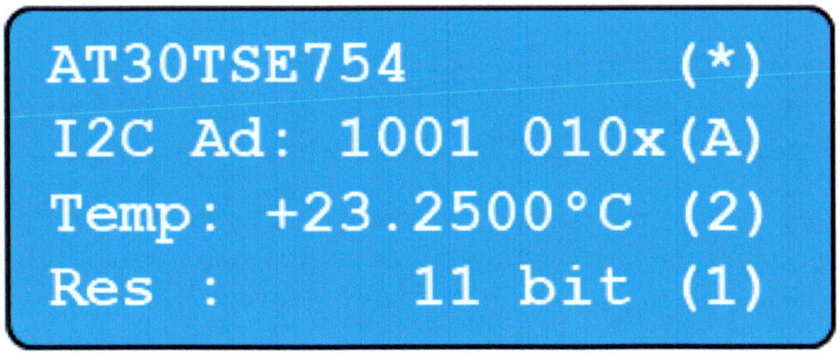

On the first line, we can see the name of the temperature sensor to be used. We can leave this sub-menu and go back to the main menu by pressing * (star button).
On the second line, we see the I²C address of the temperature sensor used for the communication. There is a range of I²C addresses we can use:

1001 000x
1001 001x
1001 010x
1001 011x
1001 100x
1001 101x
1001 110x
1001 111x

By pressing the "A" button, we can change the address used.

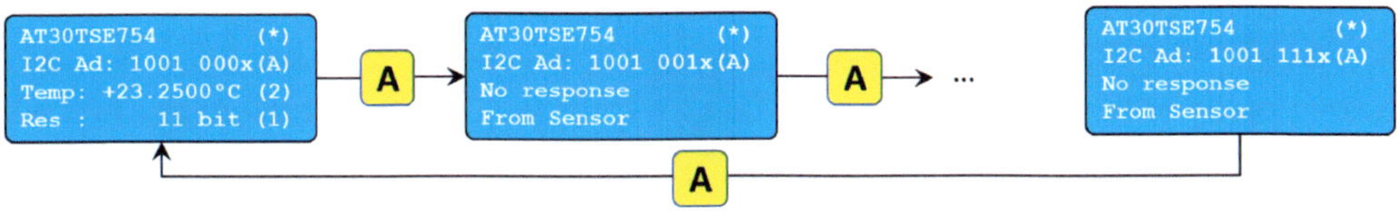

If we choose an address where no temperature sensor is connected, we will be informed by the firmware:

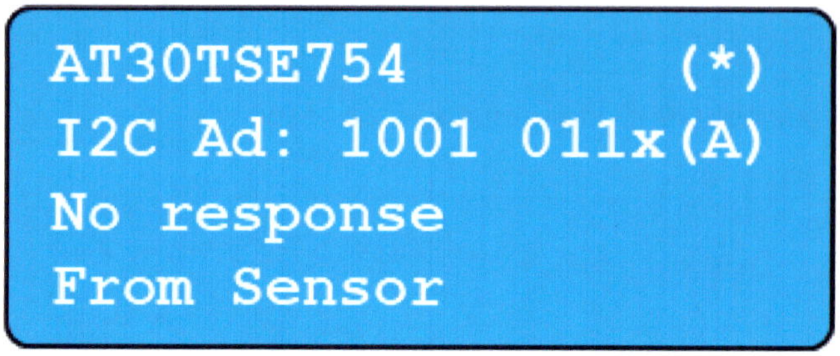

On the third line, we can see the temperature measured by the sensor. By pressing "2", we can change the format of the temperature on the display. We can use either 4 or 2 decimal places. Pressing 2 will change between these two formats:

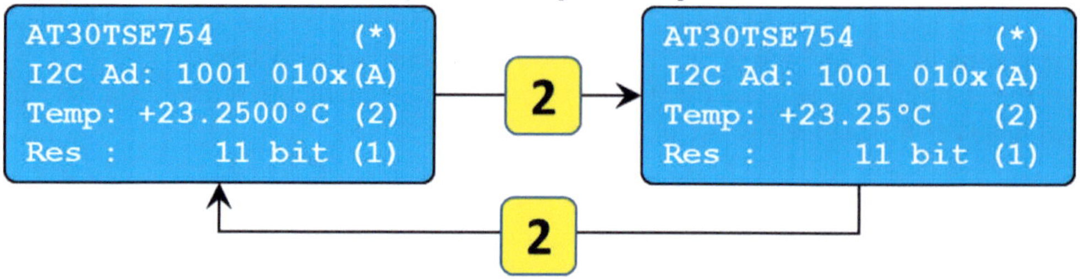

Last but not least: On the fourth line we see the selected resolution of the measurement. This can be 9, 10, 11, or 12 bits. Similar to switching the I²C address - by pressing the "1"-button we can change between the different resolutions:

9 -> 10 -> 11 -> 12...

5.1.2.3 • Real Time Clock

By pressing "2" in the main menu we jump to the RTC-functions. Here we can see the current date and time obtained from the DS1307-chip. We can also set the date and time.

The main screen of the RTC looks like this:

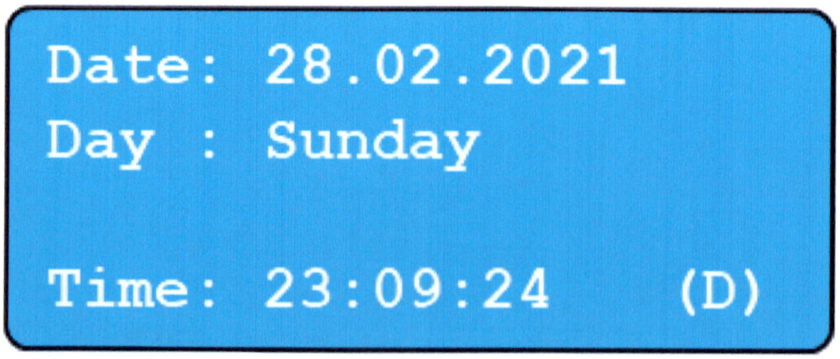

The first line shows the current date in the format: dd.mm.yyyy. The second line shows the calculated day of the week. The last line shows us the current time. By pressing "D" we can set the date and time:

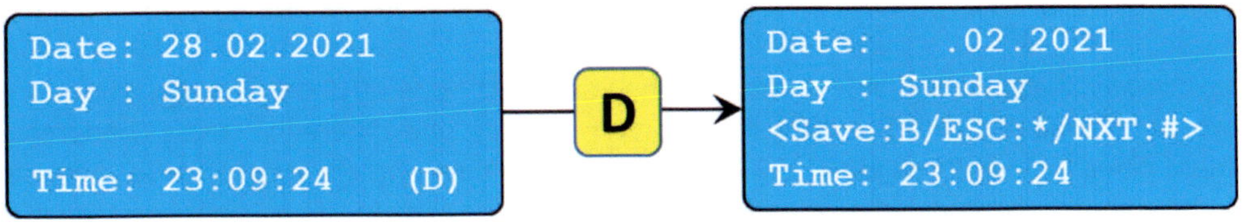

By activating the date/time set mode, we have the option of typing in the date and time using number buttons (0-9). The active position is blinking, and we can jump to the next position by pressing "#". If we want to save the entered date and time to the RTC chip, we have to press "B". If we want to discard the changes and leave setup mode without saving - we can press "*". The third line provides hints on which functions are available.

5.1.2.4 • Humidity Sensor

By pressing "3" on the main menu, we can activate the HYT-939 functionalities. There is nothing we can change here. We can just see the content of the humidity and temperature registers and the calculated humidity based on the humidity register:

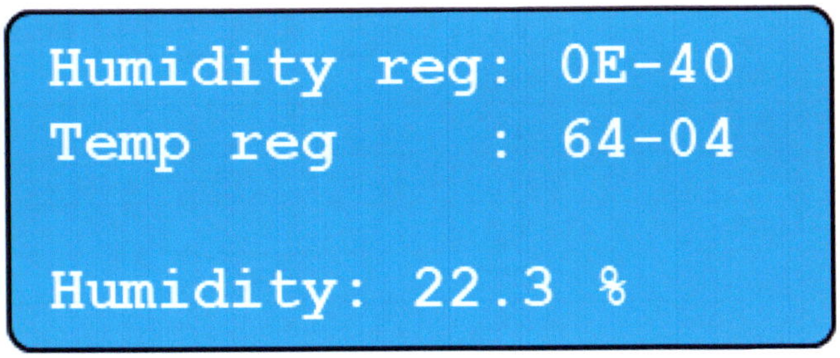

By pressing "*" we can return to the main menu.

Now we have seen what functionalities are available within this board, and we can take a look at the components used.

5.2 • Used Components

We will take a look at the I²C slave chips used in our construction without going into detail on the chips. We will describe the basics we need to understand and how the application/ software works.

5.2.1 • GPIO - PCF8574A

The PCF8574(A) is the most straightforward I^2C GPIO chip I am aware of. This chip does not use any configuration, and there are no settings registers. We have 8 I/O ports available, which can be used as outputs even to directly drive LEDs. They can also be used as inputs.

This chip is available in SOIC-16, and (in the year 2021) in a PDIP-16 package. There are two chips available that are almost identical with only one difference: the I^2C address. These chips provide three pins: A0, A1, and A2. Using these we can define the I^2C address of the chip. We can connect 16 identical chips at the same time to the I^2C bus. The available I^2C addresses of the PCF8574 and PCF8574A chips are summarised in the following table:

Chip	A2	A1	A0	I^2C Address (binary)
PCF8574	GND	GND	GND	0100 000x
PCF8574	GND	GND	V_{cc}	0100 001x
PCF8574	GND	V_{cc}	GND	0100 010x
PCF8574	GND	V_{cc}	V_{cc}	0100 011x
PCF8574	V_{cc}	GND	GND	0100 100x
PCF8574	V_{cc}	GND	V_{cc}	0100 101x
PCF8574	V_{cc}	V_{cc}	GND	0100 110x
PCF8574	V_{cc}	V_{cc}	V_{cc}	0100 111x
PCF8574A	GND	GND	GND	0111 000x
PCF8574A	GND	GND	V_{cc}	0111 001x
PCF8574A	GND	V_{cc}	GND	0111 010x
PCF8574A	GND	V_{cc}	V_{cc}	0111 011x
PCF8574A	V_{cc}	GND	GND	0111 100x
PCF8574A	V_{cc}	GND	V_{cc}	0111 101x
PCF8574A	V_{cc}	V_{cc}	GND	0111 110x
PCF8574A	V_{cc}	V_{cc}	V_{cc}	0111 111x

In our construction, we will use this chip to connect the 4x4 keypad.

The pins are connected for the DIP-16 package as shown here:

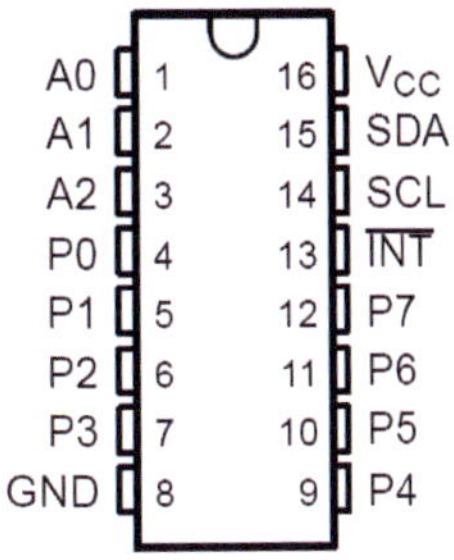

It is important to know is that the chip works with a power supply voltage in the range of 2,5V to 6,0V. This means we can use the chip with an MSP430G2553 with a power supply of 3,3V without any issues.

The I²C communication protocol of the chip is very, very simple.

We can describe writing to the PCF8574A with the following graphic:

Master	Master	Slave	Master	Slave	Master
Start	I²C Address + write: 0111 1110	ACK	byte for GPIO	ACK	Stop

After generation of a start condition, the master sends the I²C address (in our construction the I²C address 0111 111x is used) with indication, that we want to perform a write operation (LSb is set to zero), meaning the master sends 0111 1110. The I²C address is confirmed by the PCF8574A (slave) by sending ACK. After this, the master sends a byte, which is put to the 8-bit GPIO. The slave confirms with ACK again. In the last step of communication, the master will send the stop condition, and communication with the slave is finished.

We can sum it up in the following steps:

1. Master sends the start condition.
2. Master sends the I²C address and indicates a write operation (last bit is equal to zero) - in our case: 0111 1110b.
3. Slave (PCF8574A) confirms the I²C address with ACK.
4. Master sends the byte, which shall be put to the GPIO port
5. Slave confirms with ACK.
6. Master sends the stop condition and communication is finished.

As mentioned earlier, the PCF8574(A) does not provide any configuration registers. Therefore there are no settings possible to define a pin as input or output. Nevertheless, all I/O's can be used as input or output. It is given by the fact, that outputs are defined as outputs with an open collector. Logical one on the output can be considered as a weak pull-up. Logical zero means switching on an output MOS-FET transistor, meaning a real load (e.g. to drive a LED) can be made only with logical zero on the output. If a logical one is sent to the I/O, it can be used for input purposes. Therefore the I/O is called "quasi-bidirectional I/O".

The simplified architecture of the I/O can be described like this:

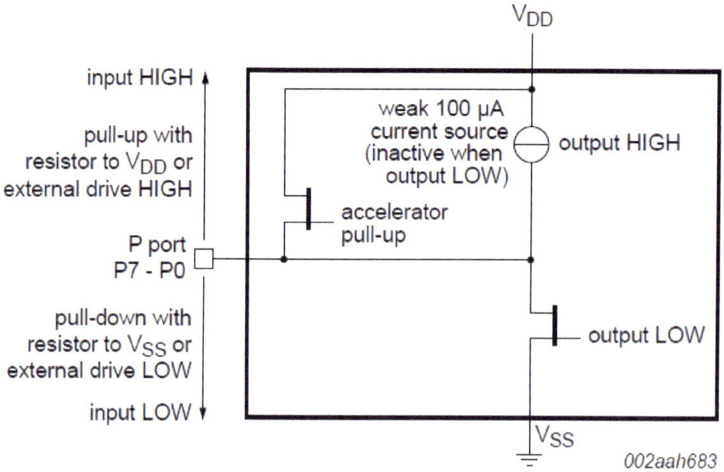

The read operation with PCF8574(A) is also very simple. Let's take a look at a similar graphical representation as we saw for write. GPIO Read looks like this:

Master	Master	Slave	Slave	Master	Master
Start	I²C Address + read: 0111 1111	ACK	byte from GPIO	NOT ACK	Stop

We can describe the read operation in steps (similar to write operation):

1. Master sends the start condition.
2. Master sends the I²C address and indicates read operation (last bit is equal to one) - in our case master sends: 0111 1111b.
3. Slave (PCF8574A) confirms the I²C address with ACK.
4. Slave sends the stage of GPIO port to the Master.
5. Master sends NOT ACK, as the communication is completed in the next step.
6. Master sends the stop condition and the communication is finished.

5.2.2 • RTC - DS1307

The DS1307 is a simple "classic" (meaning: "very old but still often used") RTC chip from former Dallas Semiconductor, now Maxim Integrated.

It is a simple RTC chip communicating with the I²C interface. This chip is available in a PDIP-8 package (and SOIC-8 package as well).

We can see the pin assignment for the DIP-8 package in the following picture:

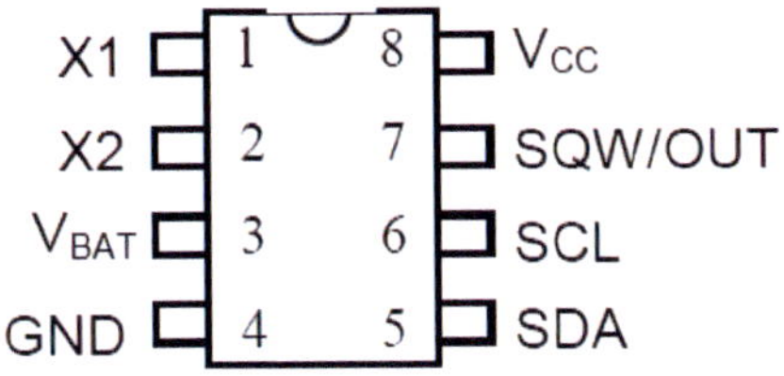

The issue with this chip and our construction is the power supply. The DS1307 works with a supply voltage of between 4,5V and 5,5V. Connecting this chip to 3,3V will not work. The DS1307 requires an external crystal 32.768 kHz / 12.5 pF connected to pins X1 and X2.

The Chip provides date and time information and it runs without a main power supply and instead a 3,0V backup battery. Typically is something like a CR2032 which can keep the clock running for a fairly long time with current consumption of around 500nA (0,5 µA).

I²C operation is quite easy with this RTC chip. The I²C address of the chip is 1101 000x.

How do we obtain the date and time information from the chip? Let's assume, we want to read date and time - meaning year, month, day, hours, minutes, and seconds. The RTC chip itself keeps the day of the week information, but this is just a counter with 7 values - independent of the current date. If the counter is updated correctly (from outside), the information is accurate, but there is no check within the chip if the day of the week fits the date. Therefore we will not use this information and will calculate the day of the week in the firmware.

We can describe the read operation with the following steps:

1. Master sends the start condition.
2. Master sends the I²C address and indicates write operation (last bit is equal to zero) - in our case master sends: 1101 0000b.
3. Slave (RTC) confirms the I²C address with ACK.
4. Master sends 00h (we will see, why this is required in next chapter describing communication with the temperature sensor, as the logic is the same)
5. Slave (RTC) confirms the I²C address with ACK.

6. Master sends the stop condition
7. Master sends the start condition (to start the communication again, but this time in read mode)
8. Master sends the I^2C address and indicates read operation (last bit is equal to one) - in our case master sends: 1101 0001b.
9. Slave (RTC) confirms the I^2C address with ACK.
10. Slave sends seconds to the Master.
11. Master confirms the reception of the byte with ACK
12. Slave sends minutes to the Master.
13. Master confirms the reception of the byte with ACK
14. Slave sends hours to the Master.
15. Master confirms the reception of the byte with ACK
16. Slave sends day of the week to the Master. We do not use this information, it is sent by RTC to this place.
17. Master confirms the reception of the byte with ACK
18. Slave sends date (day) to the Master.
19. Master confirms the reception of the byte with ACK
20. Slave sends month to the Master.
21. Master confirms the reception of the byte with ACK
22. Slave sends year to the Master.
23. Master confirms the reception of the byte with ACK
24. Master sends the stop condition and the communication is finished.

As we can see, communication itself is very easy - actually the same as with the PCF8574. We have many more steps but only because we want to read 8 bytes - instead of 1 from the PCF8574.

Later in firmware we have to consider that the information sent by the DS1307 contains some additional information we have to filter out during the evaluation of data obtained from the chip. We will touch on this topic later.

Write operation is again more-less the same and very easy:

1. Master sends the start condition.
2. Master sends the I^2C address and indicates write operation (last bit is equal to zero) - in our case master sends: 1101 0000b.
3. Slave (RTC) confirms the I^2C address with ACK.
4. Master sends 00h
5. Slave (RTC) confirms with ACK.
6. Master sends seconds to the RTC chip.
7. Slave (RTC) confirms with ACK.
8. Master sends minutes to the RTC chip.
9. Slave (RTC) confirms with ACK.
10. Master sends hours to the RTC chip.
11. Slave (RTC) confirms with ACK.
12. Master sends day of the week to the RTC chip.

13. Slave (RTC) confirms with ACK.
14. Master sends day to the RTC chip.
15. Slave (RTC) confirms with ACK.
16. Master sends month to the RTC chip.
17. Slave (RTC) confirms with ACK.
18. Master sends year to the RTC chip.
19. Slave (RTC) confirms with ACK.
20. Master sends the stop condition and the communication is finished.

5.2.3 • Temperature Sensor: AT30TSE754

The I²C temperature sensor produced by Microchip (actually comes from Atmel - a Microchip acquisition) is 9 to 12-bit resolution with ±0,5°C accuracy. The sensor operates with a single power supply of 1,7V to 5,5V meaning it can be powered directly with the same voltage as the MSP430G2553.

This chip contains 512 Bytes (4.096 bits) of EEPROM memory but we will not use this feature of the chip in our application.

The chip provides three inputs: A2, A1, A0 to set up the last part of the I²C address.

The I²C address of the temperature sensor is 1001 A2 A1 A0 x .

The EEPROM I²C address is 1010 A2 A1 A0 x .

The I²C addresses available for these temperature chips are summarised in the following table:

A2	**A1**	**A0**	**I²C Address (binary)**
GND	GND	GND	1001 000x
GND	GND	V_{cc}	1001 001x
GND	V_{cc}	GND	1001 010x
GND	V_{cc}	V_{cc}	1001 011x
V_{cc}	GND	GND	1001 100x
V_{cc}	GND	V_{cc}	1001 101x
V_{cc}	V_{cc}	GND	1001 110x
V_{cc}	V_{cc}	V_{cc}	1001 111x

The temperature sensor is available in for example a SOIC-8 package. Pin assignment for this package looks like this:

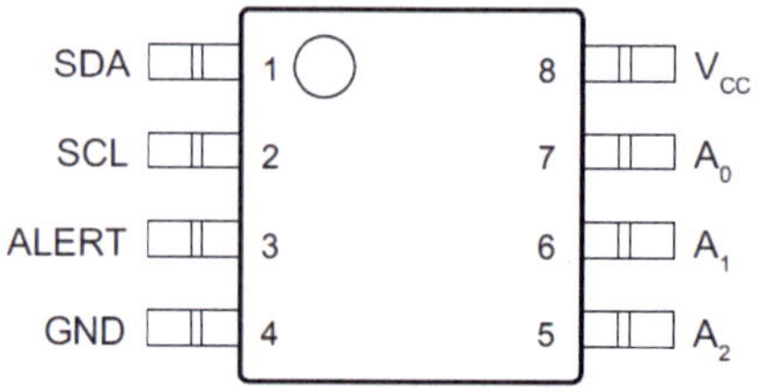

The pin names are self-explanatory, besides pin #3 - ALERT. This pin allows different applications to observe the measured temperature in different modes and for example if the temperature runs outside predefined + to provide direct "alarm on a pin" - not only through the I²C communication.

5.2.3.1 • Registers of the AT30TSE754

Let's get a little more familiar with the sensor registers. Firstly let's start with the register map of the AT30TSE754.

This sensor contains eight registers - actually seven, plus a Pointer Register. The task of the Pointer Register is to point to one of the seven registers defining, with which one the host wants to communicate (read or write).

The register map looks like this:

Register	Address	Read/ Write	Size	Power-on Default	Factory Default
Pointer Register	n/a	W	8-bit	00h	n/a
Temperature Register	00h	R	16-bit	0000h	n/a
Configuration Register	01h	R/W	16-bit	Copy of Nonvolatile Configuration Register	n/a
T_{LOW} Limit Register	02h	R/W	16-bit	Copy of Nonvolatile T_{LOW} Limit Register	n/a
T_{HIGH} Limit Register	03h	R/W	16-bit	Copy of Nonvolatile T_{HIGH} Limit Register	n/a
Nonvolatile Configuration Register	11h	R/W	16-bit	Last Programmed State	0000h
Nonvolatile T_{LOW} Limit Register	12h	R/W	16-bit	Last Programmed State	4B00h (75°C)
Nonvolatile T_{HIGH} Limit Register	13h	R/W	16-bit	Last Programmed State	5000h (80°C)

For us, only the first two + one registers are important. The first is the Temperature Register which is a 16-bit wide register containing measured temperature. It is not possible to write to this register (it actually will make no sense), thus it is a read-only register. The Temperature Register can be found at 00h. Please note, that this address does not have anything to do with the I²C address of the sensor. This is just the address of the register in the internal temperature sensor register map.

The second can be found on address 01h and is the 16-bit Configuration Register. From this we will use bits 14 and 13 to define the conversion resolution of the sensor. In the firmware we will set all other (writable) bits of the Configuration Register to zero, the default values after power-up.

The "plus one register" is the 8 bit Pointer Register. If we put the Pointer Register value to 00h, we will work with the Temperature Register. If we put to the Pointer the value to 01h we will work with the Configuration Register.

The registers on addresses 02h and 03h are important for the observation of the border and generation of ALARM-signal. Registers 11h - 13h provide the possibility of copying the values from registers 01h - 03h to the EEPROM area to be able to restore them after power-down and power-up conditions.

5.2.3.2 • I²C communication - Configuration Register

Let's have a look at the communication protocol of this temperature sensor. We can start with the Configuration Register but in point of fact, communication with any register is the same.

In the firmware, we need to be able to read the Configuration Register to show the currently active resolution on the display; and we will also need to write to the Configuration Register in case, we have to change the resolution.

In general, Read and write operations always contain two steps:

1. Set up the address of the register to operate with to the Pointer Register.
2. Execute required operation.

Please consider, that the Configuration Register is a 16-bit register meaning that during read and write operations, 2 bytes will always be transmitted. On the other hand, it is allowed to finish the operation after transmitting only the first byte. As the first transmitted byte (read and write operations) is always MSB (higher 8 bits), and we are interested only in the MSB of the Configuration Register, we can always "break up" the communication after the first byte is transmitted.

Read operation for the Configuration Register can be described in the following steps:

1. Master sends the start condition.
2. Master sends the I²C address of the temperature register with an indication of a write operation; if A2 = A1 = A0 = GND - master will send 1001 0000b.
3. Temperature sensor confirms the address with ACK.
4. Master sends the address to be written to the Pointer Register - here 01h.
5. Temperature sensor confirms the data with ACK.
6. Master sends stop condition.
7. Master sends the start condition.

8. Master sends the I²C address of the temperature register with an indication of a read operation; if A2 = A1 = A0 = GND - master will send 1001 0001b.
9. Master reads the MSB (higher 8 bits) of the Configuration Register from the sensor.
10. Master sends NOT ACK, as we are not interested in LSB.
11. Master finishes the communication by sending the stop condition.

Write operation is (as usual) a bit easier as we do not need to restart the communication in the middle (to change from write to read). We are just writing:

1. Master sends the start condition.
2. Master sends the I²C address of the temperature register with an indication of a write operation. If A2 = A1 = A0 = GND - the master will send 1001 0000b.
3. Temperature sensor confirms the address with ACK.
4. Master sends the address to be written to the Pointer Register - here 01h.
5. Temperature sensor confirms the data with ACK.
6. Master sends the MSB value for the Configuration Register.
7. Temperature sensor confirms the data with ACK.
8. Master ends the communication with a stop condition.

We will later see the implementation of the procedures in IDE Energia.

5.2.3.3 • I²C communication - Temperature Register

Now let's take a short look at the operation to read the content of the Temperature Register. The procedure is nearly the same as reading the Configuration Register. We are merely addressing another register and we will read both the MSB and LSB values of the 16-bit register.

Read operation for Temperature Register can be described in the following steps:

1. Master sends the start condition.
2. Master sends the I²C address of the temperature register with an indication of a write operation; if A2 = A1 = A0 = GND - master will send 1001 0000b.
3. Temperature sensor confirms the address with ACK.
4. Master sends the address to be written to the Pointer Register - here 00h.
5. Temperature sensor confirms the data with ACK.
6. Master sends stop condition.
7. Master sends the start condition.
8. Master sends the I²C address of the temperature register with an indication of a read operation; if A2 = A1 = A0 = GND - master will send 1001 0001b.
9. Master reads the MSB (higher 8 bits) of the Temperature Register from the sensor.
10. Master confirms with ACK, as we want to continue with reading
11. Master reads the LSB (lower 8 bits) of the Temperature Register from the sensor.
12. Master sends NOT ACK, as now we have the whole 16-bits and can now finish the communication
13. Master finishes the communication by sending the stop condition

5.2.4 • Humidity Sensor: HYT939

With help of this sensor, we can measure humidity from 0% to 100%, with a precision of 1.8%. We can also measure the temperature from -40°C to 125°C with the precision of 0,2°C.

The HYT939 works with a power supply from 2,7V to 5,5V. What is important and not mentioned yet is that it's a digital sensor communicating with a host via the I²C bus.

The sensor itself is available in a TO-39 package with four pins.

These four pins provide a power supply (V_{cc}, GND) and two necessary lines for the I²C bus (SDA and SCL):

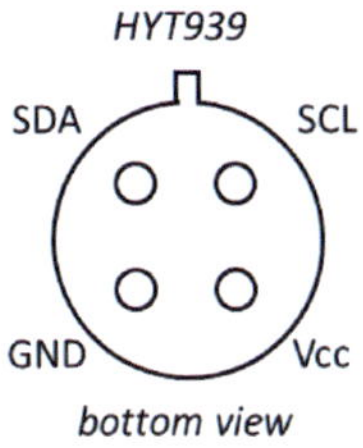

We have to be careful with the I²C address of the sensor - at least before the finalisation of the firmware. In the datasheet we can find the standard I²C address of the HYT939 is 28h (0010 1000b). Actually, all the sensors I tested on this address are not available. After a few tests, I got a response from address 50h (0101 0000b). This means even later in the firmware the address 0101 0000b is used.

The resolution of the humidity measurement is 14 bits, where the value 0000h means a humidity of 0% and 3FFFh stays for 100%.

I²C communication with the sensor is relatively simple. The sensor works with two "commands":

MR = Measurement Request
DF = Data Fetch

5.2.4.1 • I²C communication - Measurement Request

The HYT939 is always in sleep mode to save power. Therefore we have to trigger an explicit measurement if we want to have up-to-date values. Waking the device is achieved by sending the MR command. This one is very simple and is given by addressing the sensor in write mode.

The procedure looks like this:

1. Master sends start condition.
2. Master sends the I²C address of the sensor and indicates a write operation. The master sends 0101 0000b. The LSb of the value is the write indication.
3. Sensor answers with ACK. This means the sensor has recognised this communication as an MR-command and the measurement begins.
4. The Master ends communication with a stop condition.

5.2.4.2 • I²C communication - Data Fetch

Getting the data from the sensor is also relatively straightforward.

As previously mentioned - humidity and temperature data are stored in a 16-bit register. If we want to retrieve humidity and temperature data, we have to read 4 bytes from the HYT939.

Both of these values are stored as 14-bits. The first two highest bits from the humidity register are used for status information. We have to "filter them out" to calculate humidity. For temperature are the two low significant bits not used.

The procedure is described in the following steps:

1. Master sends start condition.
2. Master sends the I²C address of the sensor and indicates read operation; the master sends 0101 0001b. The LSb of the value is the read-indicator.
3. Sensor answers with ACK. This means the sensor has this communication as DF-command (based on read operation).
4. Master reads the MSB of the humidity register. (Master set bit 7 and bit 6 of the MSB to zero.)
5. Master sends ACK.
6. Master receives LSB of the humidity register.
7. Master sends ACK.
8. Master receives MSB of the temperature register.
9. Master sends ACK.
10. Master receives LSB of the temperature register. (Master set bit 1 and bit 0 of the LSB to zero.)
11. Master sends NOT ACK.
12. Master ends the communication with a stop condition.

5.2.4.3 • Calculation of humidity and temperature

We learned how to read data from the sensor. Now we need to know how to use them. Based on the datasheet, the temperature (in °C) can be calculated with the following equation:

$$T\ [°C] = 165 / 2\text{^}14 * T_{RAW} - 40$$

We will find a similar equation for the calculation of relative humidity:

$$rF\ [\%] = 100 / 2\text{^}14 * rF_{RAW}$$

We now know all that we need regarding the components used and we can now take a look at hardware schematics.

5.3 • Hardware

Now we are familiar with all components used, we can start with a definition of the schematic for our application.

We will define the construction as a collection of 4 modules:

- main module (microcontroller, LCD, power supply, and keyboard)
- RTC - module with DS1307
- temperature measurement - module with AT30TSE754
- humidity measurement - module with HYT939 (or similar)

We will assume an input voltage of 5,0V. Therefore we can use an ordinary smartphone charger or power bank to power the whole construction.

5.3.1 • Main Module

The main module contains the microcontroller itself, power management, a 4x20LCD, and keyboard. There exists the possibility to connect I^2C devices using connectors J2, J3, and J4.

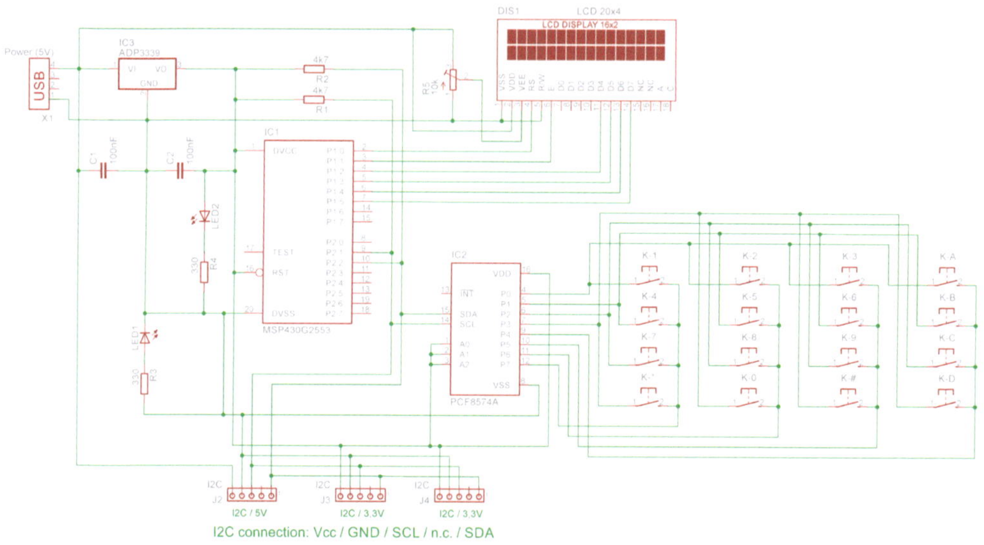

The I^{2}C bus is realized using P2.1 and P2.2. - because these ports are utilised by the IDE Energia when we use the library <wire.h> to drive I^{2}C communication. We will use 4k7 pull-up resistors for the SCL and SDA lines of the I^{2}C bus.

As we want to connect three different modules (RTC, temperature, humidity), we have three I^{2}C connectors on schematics: J2, J3, and J4. The power supply on J2 is 5,0V. To connect the RTC module, another two connectors have a power supply of 3,3V.

To get 3,3V out of the 5,0V input voltage I used the ADP3339 Analog Devices chip, but any LDO with a 3,3V output and at least 250mA current capability can be used.

The microcontroller with the internal PCF8574A chip and the two I^{2}C connectors are powered with 3,3V. The LCD module is powered by 5,0V.

The keyboard is connected in a 4x4 matrix with the help of the PCF8574A GPIO chip. Ports P4 - P7 are used as outputs to activate once at a time one column, and ports P0 - P3 are used as inputs to read which button has been pressed. A column is active by sending 0 to the corresponding port (all others have to be on 1). By sending logical 0 to one of the ports P4 - P7 (columns) and then reading the rows - ports P0 - P3, we can identify, which button is pressed. We will assume only one button is pressed at a time. If more buttons have been pressed, this will be either ignored by the firmware, or one of the pressed buttons will be picked up. No combinations are recognised later in the firmware.

We can see the keyboard connection in the following picture:

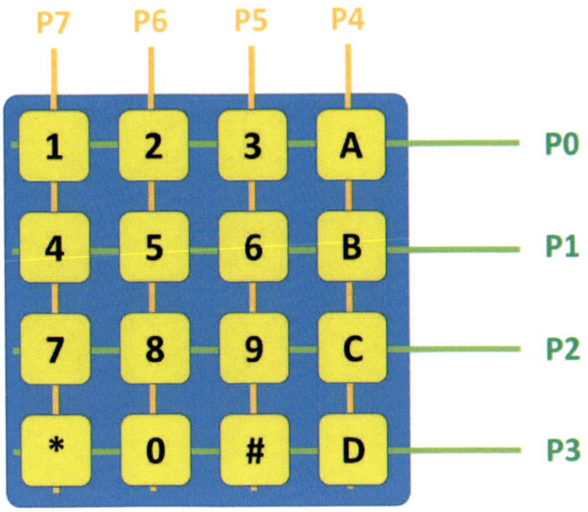

We can now have a look at the I²C modules.

5.3.2 • RTC I²C Module

The RTC module is very simple. This module can be easily constructed on a universal board.

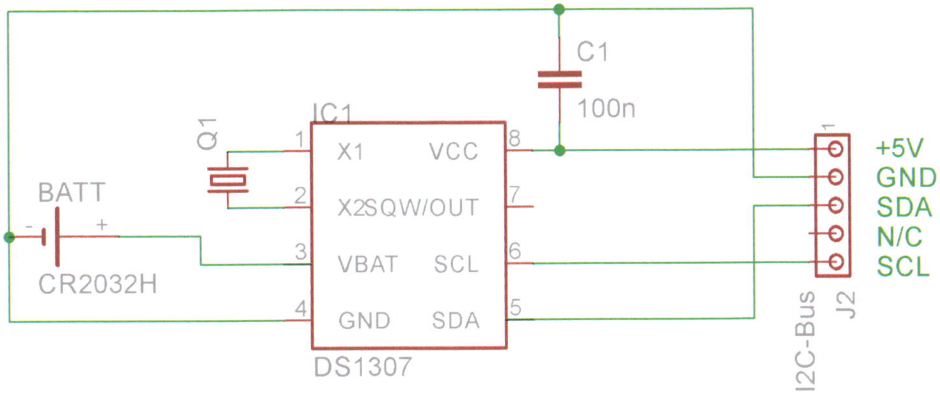

As we can see, besides the RTC-chip itself, we need just a few components. The Clock-crystal is important - 32,768 kHz with a load capacitance of 12,5pF.

It is important to consider that the RTC module needs to be powered with 5,0V. Using 3,3V, we will not be able to communicate with the chip.

5.3.3 ● Temperature I²C Module

The optional temperature measurement module is even more straightforward than the RTC module. This module is optional. If the firmware should not find this temperature sensor, the internal temperature sensor of the humidity module will be used for temperature measurement.

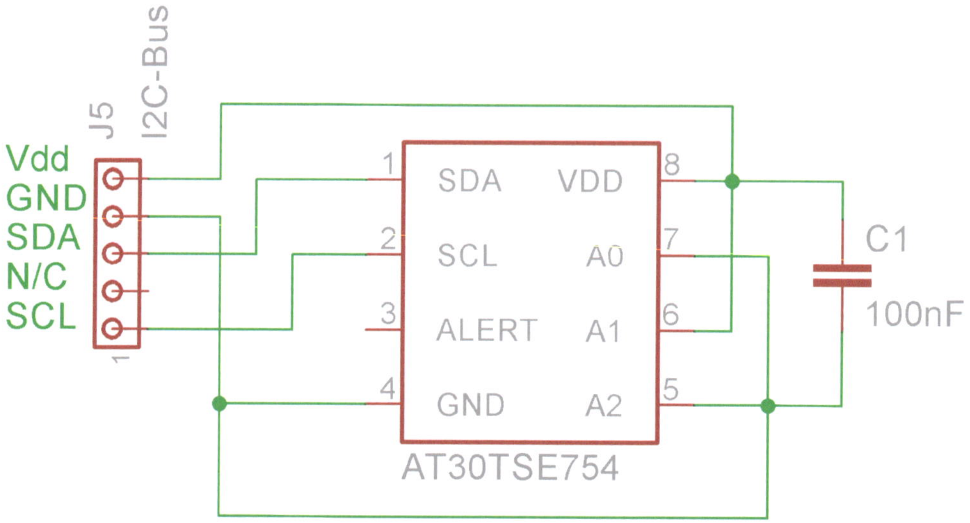

In this connection we choose the I²C address 1001 010x (A0 = A2 = GND and A1 = V_{cc}). For our application, we can pick up any of the 8 available addresses, as the firmware will scan the I²C bus and find any temperature sensors on available I²C addresses.

The temperature sensor module can be utilised on the universal board and for example, looks like this:

It doesn't matter if we use the AT30TSE754, AT30TSE752 AT30TSE758, or even AT30TSE750 for our application. The only difference between these sensors is the capacity of the EEPROM which is not used here anyway.

5.3.4 • Humidity I²C Module

The humidity module is very simple and besides the sensor itself, we need only a 100nF capacitor to make it stable.

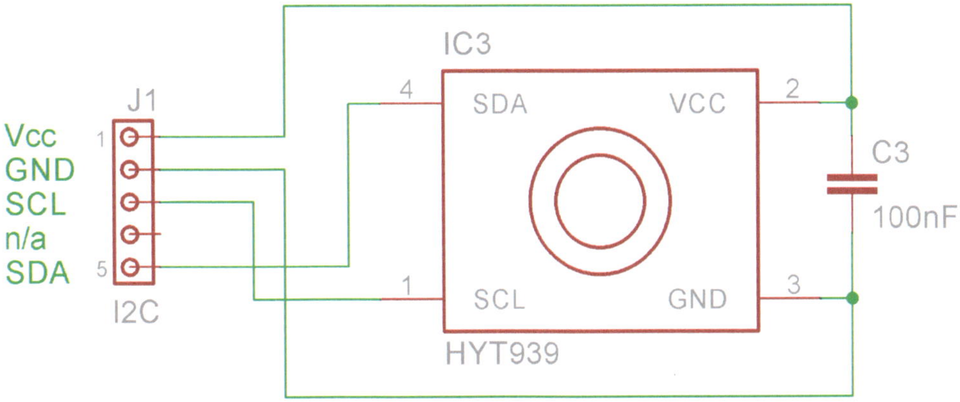

In the picture we can see an LED - this is just power-signalisation. We can connect it to an appropriate resistance with LED to V_{cc} and GND - but this is not necessary.

5.4 • Test-Firmware

We will start now with a test firmware. This piece of software can work with an RTC and temperature sensor. We will skip this functionality now and come back to it later with "real-firmware".

What is interesting is the keyboard driver. With the test firmware, we can see if the keyboard is working and if the keys are connected correctly.

5.4.1 • What we can see?

After start-up, we can see the test-firmware version.

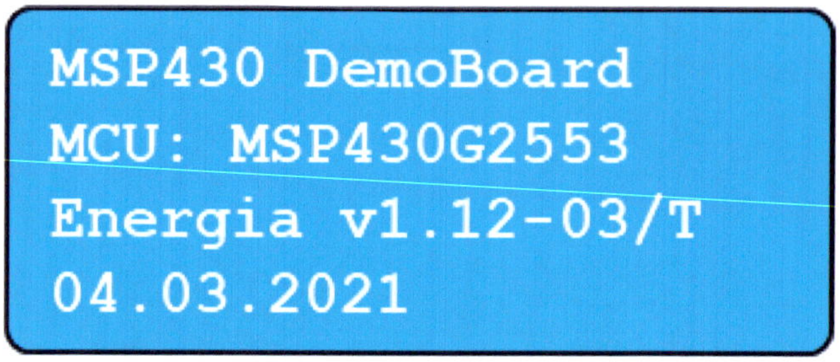

After 3 seconds we jump directly to the keyboard test function, and if we leave this, we get the selection screen, where we can choose option (1) - Keyboard Test and start the same test again.

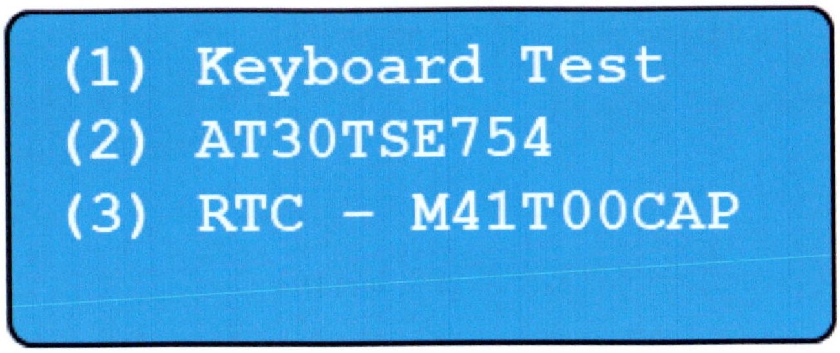

Once we select "Keyboard Test" we will see what happens on the keyboard interface.

If no buttons are pressed, we can see the "key code" is equal to FFh:

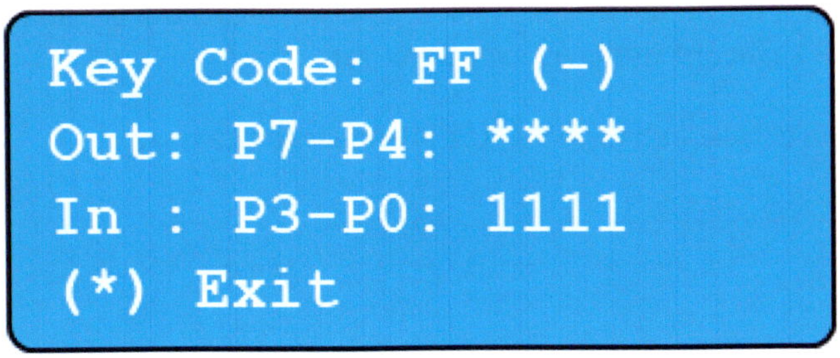

In the first column - on the left side, we have buttons 1, 4, 7, and star. We will never see the analysis for star, as this button is intended to leave the function., Using these four buttons we will see the following results on the LCD:

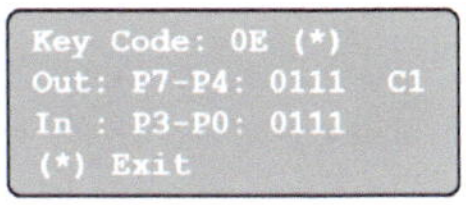

In the second column we have keys 2, 5, 8, and 0. By pressing one of the buttons, if everything is connected correctly, we will see the following results:

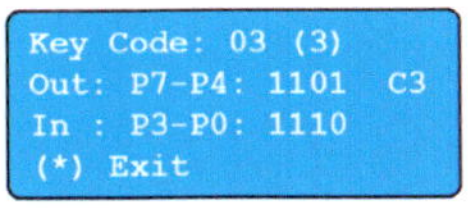

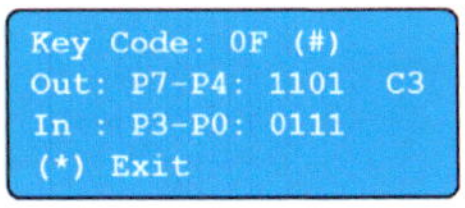

The next column contains the keys 3, 6, 9, and #:

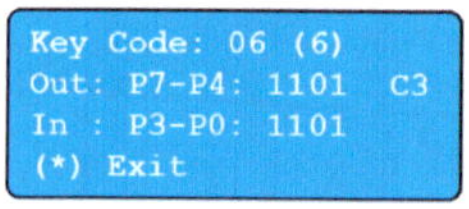

The last column (4) contains the keys: A, B, C, and D:

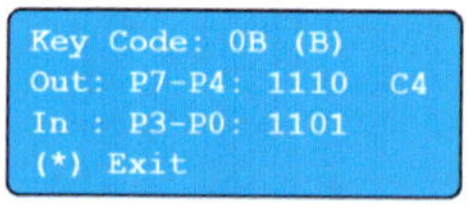

5.4.2 ● Firmware for keyboard test

How does the test firmware look? Let's look at the "keyboard-driver" and the tests helping us to check if the keyboard works as expected.

The main function is called kbd_smoke_test() and looks like this:

```
// -------------------------------------------------------------------
// -------------------------------------------------------------------
// ---- Keyboard Smoke Test
// -------------------------------------------------------------------
// -------------------------------------------------------------------
void kbd_smoke_test()
{
  active_key = 0xFF;            //(ST-1) per default - no button is pressed
  lcd.clear();                  //(ST-2) clear LCD
  lcd.setCursor(0,3);           //(ST-3a) write the hint how to leave this functionality
  lcd.print("(*) Exit");        //(ST-3b) write the hint how to leave this functionality
  while(active_key != 0x0E)     //(ST-4) main test loop; leave the loop, if star has been pressed
  {
    read_kbd();                 //(ST-5) read active key (pressed key)
    test_show_key_code();       //(ST-6) display active key (pressed key)
    delay(100);                 //(ST-7) wait 100ms
  }
  gv_refresh = 1;               //(ST-8) request LCD refresh after comming back to main firmware
loop
}
// -------------------------------------------------------------------
```

At the very beginning (ST-1) we set up the default value of the "active_key" variable to FFh - means: no button pressed.

After this (ST-2) we will clean up the display and then write the static test to the last line of the LCD (ST-3a + ST-3b) and start the main loop of this test function (ST-4). This is active until we press the "*" (star-button). This is the only button, where we will not see what has been pressed - but we will leave the test function and return to the upper-level menu.

The first function of the main loop is to read the keyboard (ST-5). After this, we will display the code of pressed button, or FFh, if no button is active (ST-6) and wait 0,1 seconds (ST-7).

That's all that happens in the main loop . Let's take a short look at the corresponding functions.

Before leaving the function, we indicate to the function maintaining the upper-level menu that the LCD will be cleared before "painting" the new menu (ST-8).

Here we can see the function taking care of showing the pressed button i.e the code, line, and column of the pressed button.

```
// ----------------------------------------------------------------------
void test_show_key_code()
{
  byte lv_in;
  byte lv_out;

  lcd.setCursor(0,0);
  lcd.print("Key Code: ");
  w_hex(active_key);
  lcd.print(" (");
  if (active_key == 0xFF) lcd.print("-");
  else lcd.print(char(act_key_ascii));
  lcd.print(")");

  lcd.setCursor(0,1);
  lcd.print("Out: P7-P4: ");
  if (active_key == 0xFF) lcd.print("****    ");
  else
  {
    if ((active_key == 0x01) || (active_key == 0x04) ||
        (active_key == 0x07) || (active_key == 0x0E)) lcd.print("0111  C1");
    if ((active_key == 0x02) || (active_key == 0x05) ||
        (active_key == 0x08) || (active_key == 0x00)) lcd.print("1011  C2");
    if ((active_key == 0x03) || (active_key == 0x06) ||
        (active_key == 0x09) || (active_key == 0x0F)) lcd.print("1101  C3");
    if ((active_key == 0x0A) || (active_key == 0x0B) ||
        (active_key == 0x0C) || (active_key == 0x0D)) lcd.print("1110  C4");
  }

  lv_in = in_kbd_7 & in_kbd_6 & in_kbd_5 & in_kbd_4;
```

```
  lcd.setCursor(0,2);
  lcd.print("In : P3-P0: ");
  w_in(lv_in);
}
// ----------------------------------------------------------------
```

It doesn't make sense to walk through the code line-by-line since it is fairly self-explanatory. In the following two functions, we can see how we can use the "bitRead" function to show "1" or "0" based on the value of the corresponding bit of a byte.

```
// ---------------------------------------------------------------------
void w_out(byte iv_byte)
{
  lcd.print(bitRead(iv_byte,7));
  lcd.print(bitRead(iv_byte,6));
  lcd.print(bitRead(iv_byte,5));
  lcd.print(bitRead(iv_byte,4));
}
// ---------------------------------------------------------------------
void w_in(byte iv_byte)
{
  lcd.print(bitRead(iv_byte,3));
  lcd.print(bitRead(iv_byte,2));
  lcd.print(bitRead(iv_byte,1));
  lcd.print(bitRead(iv_byte,0));
}
// ---------------------------------------------------------------------
```

We will skip the rest of the code now. We will see the functions as a part of the "real" firmware.

5.5 • Firmware

It's time to take a look at the firmware - the "real one" and not the support test software. The software is written in IDE Energia and occupies the whole Flash memory of the MSP430G2553.

We will not walk through it line by line as it's too big. We will skip some of the LCD-write and output formatting routines, but pick up the most important parts and take a closer look at them.

5.5.1 • Libraries

In the firmware, two libraries are used to drive the LCD and I^2C bus.

```
// ------------------------------------------------------------------
/*
1. LCD connection - library: LiquidCrystal.h
 Connection:
 ================================
 LCD pin                Connect to
 --------------------------------
 01 - GND               GND, pot
 02 - VCC               +5V, pot
 03 - Contrast          Pot wiper
 04 - RS                P1.0
 05 - R/W               GND
 06 - EN                P1.1
 07 - DB0               GND
 08 - DB1               GND
 09 - DB2               GND
 10 - DB3               GND
 11 - DB4               P1.2
 12 - DB5               P1.3
 13 - DB6               P1.4
 14 - DB7               P1.5
 15 - BL+               +5V
 16 - BL-               GND
 ================================
// ------------------------------------------------------------------
2. I2C Bus - Library: Wire.h
   Connection:
      SCL -> P2.1
      SDA -> P2.2
 */
// ------------------------------------------------------------------
#include <LiquidCrystal.h>
#include <Wire.h>
// ------------------------------------------------------------------
// initialize the library with the numbers of the interface pins
LiquidCrystal lcd(P1_0, P1_1, P1_2, P1_3, P1_4, P1_5);
// ------------------------------------------------------------------
```

We can see the assumed connection of LCD and I²C.

The last line is the initialisation command for the LCD, where our connections are inputs to the "LiquidCrystal" definition of "lcd".

We skip all the declarations of global variables and functions used and will continue with the next interesting part of the firmware. Let's continue with the setup function.

5.5.2 ● Setup function

The setup function is simple and has one task: to display the version of the Firmware and to initialise the I²C bus.

```
// -----------------------------------------------------------------------
void setup()
{
  lcd.begin(20, 4);                    //(SF-1) set up the LCD's number of columns and rows
  lcd.setCursor(0,0);                  //(SF-2a) Display Firmware version
  lcd.print("MSP430 DemoBoard");       //(SF-2b) Display Firmware version
  lcd.setCursor(0,1);                  //(SF-2c) Display Firmware version
  lcd.print("RTC & Thermometer");      //(SF-2d) Display Firmware version
  lcd.setCursor(0,2);                  //(SF-2e) Display Firmware version
  lcd.print("Energia v1.14.36");       //(SF-2f) Display Firmware version
  lcd.setCursor(0,3);                  //(SF-2g) Display Firmware version
  lcd.print("24.01.2021");             //(SF-2h) Display Firmware version

  delay(3000);                         //(SF-3) wait 3 seconds
  lcd.clear();                         //(SF-4) clear display

  Wire.begin();                        //(SF-5) Initialize I2C bus
}
// -----------------------------------------------------------------------
```

At the very beginning (SF-1) **it is defined, that** the LCD contains 20 columns and 4 rows. Then (SF-2a) to (SF2-h) display the firmware version. We wait 3 seconds (3.000 ms) in step (SF-3), clear the LCD (SF-4), and initialise the I²C bus (SF-5).

With the I²C bus initialisation, the setup function finished.

5.5.3 ● Main Loop

The main loop of the firmware is just two lines of code.

```
// -----------------------------------------------------------------------
void loop()
{
  i2c_add = 0b01001000;          //(ML-1) Set default I2C address for temperature sensor
  entry_main();                  //(ML-2) Start the main selection function
}
// -----------------------------------------------------------------------
```

In the first line (ML-1) we define the default I²C address for the temperature sensor. This is the "Arduino-Syntax". The default I²C is the most common address assuming A2 = A1 = A0 = GND: 1001 000x. It is only the default, as if the firmware does not get any response from this address, other I²C addresses will be checked.

After this (ML-2) we jump to the "function selection" function.

5.5.4 • Function Selection

Function selection - entry_main() - is the main selection screen that allows us to select one of the four possible functions of the board:

(1) temperature sensor functionalities
(2) RTC functionalities
(3) Humidity sensor functionalities
(9) Main Application

By default, the main application is always started without the need for any selection. Only when the main application is terminated, the selection screen will be shown. The numbers above are the keys to be pressed to initiate the functionalities.

```
// -------------------------------------------------------------------
// ----------- Main Selection Screen / Entry Screen -----------------
// -------------------------------------------------------------------
void entry_main()
{
  main_app();                         //(EM-1) as default selection start main
application immedaitely
  while(1)                            //(EM-2) enless-loop
  {
    lcd.clear();                      //(EM-3a) Function selection screen
    lcd.setCursor(0,0);               //(EM-3b) Function selection screen
    lcd.print("(1) AT30TSE754");      //(EM-3c) Function selection screen
    lcd.setCursor(0,1);               //(EM-3d) Function selection screen
    lcd.print("(2) RTC: DS1307");     //(EM-3e) Function selection screen
    lcd.setCursor(0,2);               //(EM-3f) Function selection screen
    lcd.print("(3) HYT939");          //(EM-3g) Function selection screen
    lcd.setCursor(0,3);               //(EM-3h) Function selection screen
    lcd.print("(9) Main Application"); //(EM-3i) Function selection screen

    gv_refresh = 0;                   //(EM-4) shall be the selection screen refreshed?
    while(gv_refresh == 0)            //(EM-5) keyboard-read loop
    {
      read_kbd();                     //(EM-6) read keyboard
      switch(active_key)              //(EM-7) select function based on key pressed
      {
        case 0x01: i2c_temp_1(); break;   //(EM-8) temperature functions
        case 0x02: i2c_datum_1(); break;  //(EM-9) RTC functions
        case 0x03: hyt939(); break;       //(EM-10) Humidity sensor functions
```

```
        case 0x09: main_app(); break;      //(EM-11) Main Application
      }
    }
  }
}
// -------------------------------------------------------------------
```

As already mentioned, at the very beginning (EM-1), the main application will be started - without the need to pick up any functionality. This allows the use of this construction as a stand-alone clock with thermometer and humidity measurement. Even after discontinuation and later restoration of power, the main application will begin.

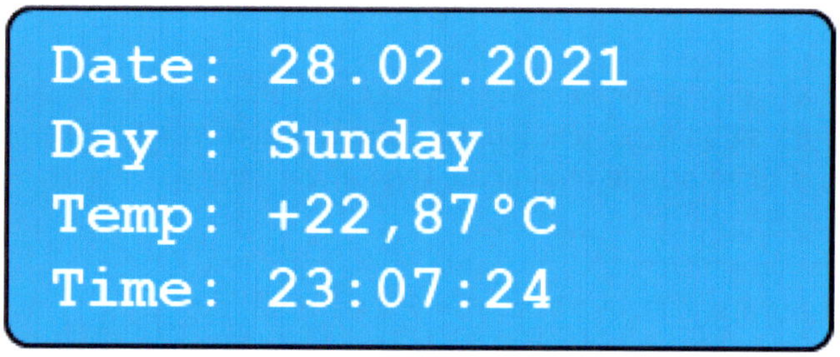

In case, the main application run is interrupted - by pressing the star-key (*), we will start an endless loop (EM-2). At the beginning of the loop, the selection screen is displayed (EM-3*).

Steps (EM-4) to (EM-11) take care of reading the keyboard and triggering the selected function if one of the four keys has been pressed. Here we take care of cleaning up the LCD if required (using variable gv_refresh, which can be set if it is important in the different function blocks).

5.5.5 ● The main application

Function main_app() is the implementation of the main functionality of the construction. Here, all data from sensors and RTC is collected and displayed on LCD.

Let's take a look at the first part of the function:

```
// ---------------------------------------------------------------------
// --- Main application: RTC + Temperature
// ---------------------------------------------------------------------
void main_app()
{
   byte temp_lsb_old = 0xFE;                //(MA-1)
   byte temp_lsb_new;                       //(MA-2)
   byte lv_c1;                              //(MA-3)

   lcd.clear();                             //(MA-4)
   w_rtc_txt(1);                            //(MA-5)

   gv_format = 1;                           //(MA-6) display 2 decimal places

   while(active_key != 0xFF) read_kbd();    //(MA-7)
   while(active_key != 0x0E)                //(MA-8)
   {
// ---------------------------------------------------------------------
```

At the beginning - steps (MA1) to (MA-3) a small number of help variables are initialised. Then we clean up the LCD (MA-4) and write the static texts around RTC and temperature measurement (MA-5). After this, we define that we want to display the temperature to two decimal places (MA-6) and start the main loop (MA-8). Before this (MA-7) we wait until all buttons are released just in case, something is (still) pressed during initialisation.

The main loop starts with the RTC-related functionalities:

```
// ---------------------------------------------------------------------
// ------------------------- RTC -------------------------------------
     i2c_rtc_read();                        //(MA-9)
     if (i2c_answer == 0)                   //(MA-10)
     {
       w_date_time(3);                      //(MA-11)
     }
     else                                   //(MA-12)
     {
       lcd.setCursor(6,0);                  //(MA-13a)
       lcd.print("--          ");           //(MA-13b)
       lcd.setCursor(6,1);                  //(MA-13c)
       lcd.print("--          ");           //(MA-13d)
       lcd.setCursor(6,3);                  //(MA-13e)
       lcd.print("--          ");           //(MA-13f)
     }
// ---------------------------------------------------------------------
```

We first read the current date & time from the RTC chip by calling the i2c_retc_read() function (MA-9). If we get the expected answer (MA-10), it means, the RTC module is connected and working and we will display obtained information (MA-11)
If there was no response from the RTC module (MA-12), we just show "minus minus" to indicate, there is no working RTC module connected (MA-13x).

We can now continue with the data processing from the humidity sensor.

```
// ---------------------------------------------------------------------
// ------------------------ HYT939 -----------------------------------
    gv_hyt939 = hyt939_start();              //(MA-14)
    lcd.setCursor(14,2);                     //(MA-15)
    if(gv_hyt939 == 0)                       //(MA-16)
    {
      hyt939_read();                         //(MA-17)
      lcd.setCursor(14,2);                   //(MA-18a)
      lcd.print(" ");                        //(MA-18b)
      if(h939_rf_result < 10) lcd.print(" "); //(MA-18c)
      lcd.print(h939_rf_result, 1);          //(MA-18d)
      lcd.print("%");                        //(MA-18e)
    }
    else lcd.print("      ");                //(MA-19)
    w_rtc_txt(1);                            //(MA-20)
// ---------------------------------------------------------------------
```

Here we first trigger the humidity measurement (MA-14) and write the results, positioning the beginning cursor at the LCD position, where we will start writing (MA-15).

If we get a response from HYT-939 during the triggering of the measurement (MA-16), we first read the results (MA-17) and write them to LCD (MA-18x).

If there is no response from the HYT-939 module, we just clean up the corresponding part of the display (MA-19), and re-write the static texts on LCD (MA-20).

The most complex part is temperature measurement.

```
// ----------------------------------------------------------------
// ------------------------ AT30TSE754 ------------------------------
    find_i2c_temp();                     //(MA-21) find attached I2C sensor
    temp_res = 1;                        //(MA-22a)
    t_change_res();                      //(MA-22b) set resolution to 11 bit
    Wire.beginTransmission(i2c_add);     //(MA-23-01)
    Wire.write(0x00);                    //(MA-23-02)
    i2c_answer = Wire.endTransmission(1); //(MA-23-03)
    if (i2c_answer == 0)                 //(MA-23-04)
    {
```

```
      Wire.requestFrom(i2c_add, 2, 1);      //(MA-23-05) I2C address / 2 bytes // stop
      v_temp_msb =  Wire.read();            //(MA-23-06) read MSB of the temperature
      temp_lsb_new =  Wire.read();          //(MA-23-07) read LSB of the temperature
      if(temp_lsb_old == 0xFE)              //(MA-23-08)
      {
        v_temp_lsb = temp_lsb_new;          //(MA-23-09)
        temp_lsb_old = temp_lsb_new;        //(MA-23-10)
        lv_c1 = 0;                          //(MA-23-11)
      }
      if(temp_lsb_new != temp_lsb_old) lv_c1++; //(MA-23-12)
      else lv_c1 = 0;                       //(MA-23-13)
      if(lv_c1 == 3)                        //(MA-23-14)
      {
        v_temp_lsb = temp_lsb_new;          //(MA-23-15)
        temp_lsb_old = temp_lsb_new;        //(MA-23-16)
        lv_c1 = 0;                          //(MA-23-17)
      }
      w_temp_ub(6,2,1);                     //(MA-23-18)
    }
    else                                    //(MA-24)
    {
      if(gv_hyt939 == 0)                    //(MA-25)
      {
        lcd.setCursor(6,2);                 //(MA-26a)
        if(h939_temp_result>=0)             //(MA-24b)
        {
          lcd.print("+");                   //(MA-24c)
          if(h939_temp_result < 10) lcd.print("0"); //(MA-24d)
        }
        lcd.print(h939_temp_result,2);      //(MA-24e)
        lcd.print(char(223));               //(MA-24f)
        lcd.print("C");                     //(MA-24g)
      }
      else                                  //(MA-25)
      {
        v_temp_lsb = 0xFF;                  //(MA-26a)
        w_temp_ub(6,2,1);                   //(MA-26b)
      }
    }
// -------------------------------------------------------------------
```

At the beginning of this block, we try to find the AT-temperature sensor (MA-2) connected. The I²C address of the sensor will be stored in the variable i2c_add. We then set the measurement resolution to 11-bit (MA-22x) as this has been chosen for the main application. After this, we attempt to communicate with the temperature sensor in steps (MA-23-01) to (MA-23-02). If the attempt is successful (MA-23-04) we will read and show the temperature using steps (MA-23-05) to (MA-23-18). Some of the steps ((MA-23-08) to (MA-23-17)) take care of the stability of the displayed information. This means that if the sensor returns after a 3rd read a different value, as in the two cycles before, we will not directly display the new information, and just wait for the next two read cycles to see if this was just a measurement error or the temperature has been changed. This makes the information shown more stable as to **display directly what we get**.

At the end we need to check the keyboard again and start from the beginning.

```
// ---------------------------------------------------------------------
      read_kbd();
      delay(100);
    }
    gv_refresh = 1;
}
// ---------------------------------------------------------------------
// ---------------------------------------------------------------------
```

We are finished with the main loop of the application and can now take a look at supporting functions.

5.5.6 • RTC

We can start for example with RTC-related functionality.

5.5.6.1 • RTC LCD-only related functions

This function concerns writing static texts if the RTC pure function is selected from the menu or the main application is running.

```
// ---------------------------------------------------------------------
// ---------------------------------------------------------------------
void w_rtc_txt(byte x1)
{
  lcd.setCursor(0,0);
  lcd.print("Date: ");
  lcd.setCursor(0,1);
  lcd.print("Day : ");
  lcd.setCursor(0,3);
  lcd.print("Time:");
  if(x1 == 0)
  {

    lcd.setCursor(17,3);
    lcd.print("(D)");
  }
```

```
  if(x1 == 1)
  {
    lcd.setCursor(0,2);
    if(gv_hyt939 == 0) lcd.print("T/H :");
    else lcd.print("Temp:");
  }
}
// --------------------------------------------------------------------
// --------------------------------------------------------------------
```

We do not need to go into the details of the function. It is worth mentioning that if the import variable x1 is set to 0, we assume that the RTC pure function is selected, and therefore the hit (D) is displayed - to say, by pressing "D" it is possible to set up date and time.

If x1 is equal to 1, we assume the main application is running, and will not display any "D". We will display either "T/H: " - if HYT 939 is present, or "Temp:" if the hygrometer is not included.

5.5.6.2 • RTC main functions

The following function is the main function for RTC pure functionality (from the main menu the point "(2) RTC: DS1307".

We are maintaining this screen with the functions described in this chapter:

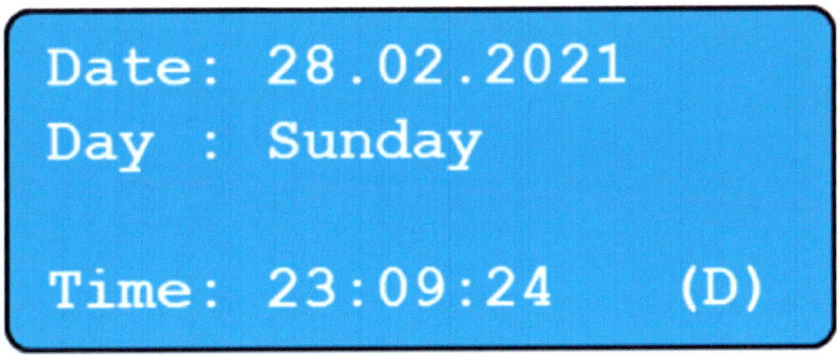


```
// --------------------------------------------------------------------
// --------------------------------------------------------------------
// ---- I2C RTC
// --------------------------------------------------------------------
// --------------------------------------------------------------------
void i2c_datum_1()                              //(RTC-1)
{
   lcd.clear();                                 //(RTC-2)
   w_rtc_txt(0);                                //(RTC-3)
   while(active_key != 0xFF) read_kbd();        //(RTC-4)
```

```
    while(active_key != 0x0E)                           //(RTC-5)
    {
       w_rtc_txt(0);                                    //(RTC-6)
       i2c_rtc_read();                                  //(RTC-7)
       if (i2c_answer == 0)                             //(RTC-8)
       {
         w_date_time(3);                                //(RTC-9)
       }
       else                                             //(RTC-10)
       {
         lcd.setCursor(0,0);                            //(RTC-11a)
         lcd.print("No answer             ");           //(RTC-11b)
         lcd.setCursor(0,1);                            //(RTC-11c)
         lcd.print("from RTC Chip         ");           //(RTC-11d)
         lcd.setCursor(0,3);                            //(RTC-11e)
         lcd.print("                      ");           //(RTC-11f)
       }
       read_kbd();                                      //(RTC-12)
       delay(100);                                      //(RTC-13)
       if (active_key == 0x0D && i2c_answer == 0) //(RTC-14)
       {
       rtc_setup();                                     //(RTC-15)
       lcd.setCursor(0,2);                              //(RTC-16a)
       lcd.print("                    ");               //(RTC-16b)
       lcd.setCursor(17,3);                             //(RTC-16c)
       lcd.print("(D)");                                //(RTC-16d)
       }
    }
    gv_refresh = 1;                                     //(RTC-17)
}
// -------------------------------------------------------------------
// -------------------------------------------------------------------
```

You can probably already recognise the same muster as the main application. At the beginning (RTC-1) to (RTC-3) clean up the display and show some static texts. Then two loops begin, waiting for button release (RTC-4). The main loop of the function runs until the star button is pressed (RTC-5). Let's mention step (RTC-7). This is a call of the function to read the date & time information from the DS1307 chip. We will see this function a bit later.

We can see again the provisioning of information to the LCD, and a call of function read_kbd() in step (RTC-12). This function will return the pressed button if any. We can see in (RTC-14), that if the code of the pressed button is 0x0D (the "D-button"), we will call the function rtc_setup() to allow the adjustment of date and time (RTC-15). We will see this function soon.

In the following function, the day, month, year, and time are calculated based on the specification of the date format of the DS1307 chip.

```
// ---------------------------------------------------------------------
// ---------------------------------------------------------------------
void w_date_time(byte w_col)
{
  rtc_day = ( ( rtc_day & 0b11110000 ) / 16 ) * 10 + ( rtc_day & 0b00001111 );
  rtc_mnt = ( ( rtc_mnt & 0b11110000 ) / 16 ) * 10 + ( rtc_mnt & 0b00001111 );
  rtc_year = ( ( rtc_year & 0b11110000 ) / 16 ) * 10 + ( rtc_year & 0b00001111 );
  rtc_year = rtc_year + 2000;

  lcd.setCursor(6,0);
  w_print_dec01_wlz(rtc_day);
  lcd.print(".");
  w_print_dec01_wlz(rtc_mnt);
  lcd.print(".");
  lcd.print(rtc_year);

  calc_day();

  lcd.setCursor(6,1);
  w_week_day(0);
  lcd.print("   ");

  lcd.setCursor(6,w_col);
  rtc_hrs = ( ( rtc_hrs & 0b00110000 ) / 16 ) * 10 + ( rtc_hrs & 0b00001111 );
  w_print_dec01_wlz(rtc_hrs);
  lcd.print(":");
  rtc_min = ( ( rtc_min & 0b01110000 ) / 16 ) * 10 + ( rtc_min & 0b00001111 );
  w_print_dec01_wlz(rtc_min);
  lcd.print(":");
  rtc_sec = ( ( rtc_sec & 0b01110000 ) / 16 ) * 10 + ( rtc_sec & 0b00001111 );
  w_print_dec01_wlz(rtc_sec);
}
// ---------------------------------------------------------------------
```

The next function is based on the variable rtc_wday ("real-time clock - day of the week") and will be the name of the day written.

```
// ------------------------------------------------------------------
// --- write day in a week
// ------------------------------------------------------------------
void w_week_day(byte i_language)
{
   switch(rtc_wday)
     {
      case 1:
         lcd.print("Monday");
         break;
      case 2:
         lcd.print("Tuesday");
         break;
      case 3:
         lcd.print("Wednesday");
         break;
      case 4:
         lcd.print("Thursday");
         break;
      case 5:
         lcd.print("Friday");
         break;
      case 6:
         lcd.print("Saturday");
         break;
      case 0:
         lcd.print("Sunday");
         break;
     }
}
// ------------------------------------------------------------------
```

5.5.6.3 • RTC I²C communication

In this chapter, we can find two I²C communication routines for the DS1307 chip. We can see, how the data is obtained from the RTC-chip, and how the data can be written to the chip via the I²C bus using the <Wire.h> library in IDE Energia.

The function i2c_rtc_read() will read the following data from DS1307:

- Time: Seconds (00 to 59)
- Time: Minutes (00 to 59)
- Time: Hours (00 to 23)
- Date: Day of a Week (0 to 6)
- Date: Day (calendar day in the month: 00 - 31)
- Date: Month (00 - 12)
- Date: Year (00 - 99)

```
// -------------------------------------------------------------------
// --- I2C RTC Read --------------------------------------------------
// -------------------------------------------------------------------
void i2c_rtc_read()                         //(RR-1)
{
   Wire.beginTransmission(0b01101000);      //(RR-2)
   Wire.write(0x00);                        //(RR-3)
   i2c_answer = Wire.endTransmission(1);    //(RR-4)

   Wire.requestFrom(0b01101000, 7, 1);     //(RR-5) I2C address / 2 bytes // stop
   rtc_sec = Wire.read();                  //(RR-6a) read seconds
   rtc_min = Wire.read();                  //(RR-6b) read minutes
   rtc_hrs = Wire.read();                  //(RR-6c) read hours
   rtc_day = Wire.read();                  //(RR-6d) dummy read (day of a week)
   rtc_day = Wire.read();                  //(RR-6e) read calendar day
   rtc_mnt = Wire.read();                  //(RR-6f) read month
   rtc_year = Wire.read();                 //(RR-6g) read year
}
// -------------------------------------------------------------------
```

In the function (RR-1) we follow the DS1306 protocol for I^2C communication with this chip. As every piece of data has its own address, and the time & date info starts at address 00h, if we first say to the chip we want to start the read operations with address 00h. This happens in the writing procedure in steps (RR-2) to (RR-4). We can also see that we expect the RTC-chip response from I^2C address 1101 000x (binary) - see step (RR-2).

Once we set the read pointer to 00h, we can start the read operation. This happens in step (RR-5), where we open the I^2C communication to read 7 bytes from the chip on address 1101 000x (binary), issuing a stop condition after the last byte has been received. In the following steps, we read single bytes from the RTC.

Please have especially a look at steps (RR-6d) and (RR-6e). It is not a or bug in the firmware or a typo, that the result of step (RR-6d) is overwritten in step (RR-6e) - both of them are stored to the same variable: rtc_day. The reason for this is that the firmware is not using the day of week information from the RTC chip. The day of the week is calculated by the firmware based on the date. Why? Because the day of a week in the RTC chip is just a simple counter from 0 to 6 and doesn't have anything to do with the date stored on the chip. If we store to the RTC, that 11th of April 2021 is Wednesday, then the chip will just take it, and continue counting. This means the chip will then say that the 12th of April 2021 is a Thursday, and the 13th of April 2021 will be Friday, etc. Not mentioning, that during set up we have to set the day of the week manually.

This function writes after set-up the date & time back to the DS1307 chip. Again just following the DS1307 protocol.

```
// ------------------------------------------------------------------
// --- I2C RTC Write ------------------------------------------------
// ------------------------------------------------------------------
void i2c_rtc_write()                                      //(RW-1)
{
   rtc_sec = (rtc_sec/10)*16 + (rtc_sec%10);              //(RW-2a)
   rtc_min = (rtc_min/10)*16 + (rtc_min%10);              //(RW-2b)
   rtc_hrs = (rtc_hrs/10)*16 + (rtc_hrs%10);              //(RW-2c)
   rtc_day = (rtc_day/10)*16 + (rtc_day%10);              //(RW-2d)
   rtc_mnt = (rtc_mnt/10)*16 + (rtc_mnt%10);              //(RW-2e)
   rtc_year = rtc_year - 2000;                            //(RW-2f)
   rtc_year = (rtc_year/10)*16 + (rtc_year%10);           //(RW-2g)

   Wire.beginTransmission(0b01101000);                    //(RW-3)
   Wire.write(0x00);                                      //(RW-4)
   Wire.write(rtc_sec);                                   //(RW-5a)
   Wire.write(rtc_min);                                   //(RW-5b)
   Wire.write(rtc_hrs);                                   //(RW-5c)
   Wire.write(rtc_wday);                                  //(RW-5d)
   Wire.write(rtc_day);                                   //(RW-5e)
   Wire.write(rtc_mnt);                                   //(RW-5f)
   Wire.write(rtc_year);                                  //(RW-5g)
   i2c_answer = Wire.endTransmission(1);                  //(RW-6)
}
// ------------------------------------------------------------------
```

After start (RW-1), we transform the date & time information first based on firmware internal variables into the DS1307-format (RW-2x). Then (RW-3) we start the I^2C communication in write mode for the device on address 1101 000x (binary). The first byte written to the device is again the address from which we want to operate (RW-4) - to store the following bytes. Then we just send the 7 bytes with time & date information to the chip (RW-5x) and finish the I^2C communication (RW-6).

5.5.7 • Calculation of a weekday

For this application, I decided to not use the functionality of the RTC chip for counting the day of a week. As mentioned already, in all RTC chips I know of (incl. DS1307), it is just a 3-bit counter keeping values from 0 to 6 (or from 1 to 7) incremented always on time change from 23:59:59 to 00:00:00. This counter needs to be set up manually meaning, as we have to set up the hours, minutes, seconds, day, month, and year, we need to set up the day of the week as well. The RTC hardware never checks if the day fits to the date or not.

Therefore I decided to not use this counter, and instead calculate the day of the week based on the date stored in the RTC chip. For the calculation I use formulas which can be found e.g. on this German wiki-page:

https://de.wikipedia.org/wiki/Wochentagsberechnung

Here we can find the following formula to calculate the day:

$$w = \left(d + \lfloor 2{,}6 \cdot m - 0{,}2 \rfloor + y + \left\lfloor \frac{y}{4} \right\rfloor + \left\lfloor \frac{c}{4} \right\rfloor - 2c\right) \bmod 7$$

We can rewrite the formula in slightly different format:

w = (d + (2,6 x m - 0,2) + y + (y / 4) + (c / 4) - 2 x c) mod 7

As we can see, we have 5 different variables in the equation:

1. w (result),
2. d (day within the month),
3. m (month variable),
4. y (year variable 1) and
5. c (year variable 2).

The meaning of the variables is following:

The resulting **variable "w"** is the day of the week - following coding in this table:

Value of "w"	0	1	2	3	4	5	6
Day of the week	Sunday	Monday	Tuesday	Wednesday	Thursday	Friday	Saturday

Variable "d" is just the day within the month. The value can be, like in a calendar in an interval from 1 to 31.

Variable "m" represents the month. Nevertheless, it is not directly the number of the month. "m" is coded as we can see here:

Month	March	April	Mai	June	July	August	September	October	November	December	January	February
Value of "m"	1	2	3	4	5	6	7	8	9	10	11	12

The reason for this strange coding is to get the month February to the end of the list - because February is a strange month. February has only 28 days, sometimes 29; but never 30 or 31 as with other months.

Variable "y" is defined as follows:

1. For all months March to December the last two numbers of the year;
2. For months January and February - the last two numbers of the previous year.

Variable "c" is defined as follows:

1. For all months March to December the first two numbers of the year;
2. For months January and February - the first two numbers of the previous year.

Let's take a look at the implementation in the firmware of our application. The corresponding function is called calc_day() and after execution, the global variable rtc_wday will be set to conform to the definition of variable "w" already described.

```
// ------------------------------------------------------------------
// ------------------------------------------------------------------
// --- Calculation of week day; only if date > 2000
//     https://de.wikipedia.org/wiki/Wochentagsberechnung
// ------------------------------------------------------------------
// ------------------------------------------------------------------
void calc_day()
{
  byte cd_d;                          //(DW-1a) - variable "d"
  byte cd_m;                          //(DW-1b) - variable "m"
  byte cd_y;                          //(DW-1c) - variable "y"
```

```
  byte cd_c;                     //(DW-1d) - variable "c"
  word cd_help1;                 //(DW-1e)
  byte cd_help2;                 //(DW-1f)
  byte cd_help3;                 //(DW-1g)
  float cd_w_w2;                 //(DW-1h) - variable "w"

  cd_d = rtc_day;                //(DW-2) - calculate variable "d"
  cd_m = rtc_mnt - 2;            //(DW-3a) - calculate variable "m"
  if (rtc_mnt == 1) cd_m = 11;   //(DW-3b) - calculate variable "m" - for January
  if (rtc_mnt == 2) cd_m = 12;   //(DW-3c) - calculate variable "m" - for February
  cd_y = rtc_year - 2000;        //(DW-4a) - calculate variable "y"
  if (rtc_mnt < 3) cd_y = cd_y - 1;  //(DW-4b) - adjust variable "y" - for January and February
  cd_c = 20;                     //(DW-5a) - calculate variable "c"
                                 //(DW-5b) - adjust variable "c" - January, February and year 2000
  if ((rtc_mnt < 3) && (rtc_year == 2000)) cd_c = cd_c - 1;
// -------------- formula implementation: part 1 ----------------------------
  cd_help1 = ((26 * cd_m) - 2) / 10;  //(DW-C1)
  cd_help2 = cd_y / 4;           //(DW-C2)
  cd_help3 = cd_c / 4;           //(DW-C3)
// -------------- formula implementation: part 2 ----------------------------
  cd_w_w2 = (cd_d + cd_help1 + cd_y + cd_help2 + cd_help3 - 2 * cd_c) % 7;  //(DW-C4a)
  if (cd_w_w2 < 0) cd_w_w2 = 7 + cd_w_w2;                                   //(DW-C4b)

  rtc_wday = cd_w_w2;            //(DW-5)
}
// ---------------------------------------------------------------------
// ---------------------------------------------------------------------
```

At the beginning (DW-1x) we declare a large number of local variables for the calculation; the first four and the last one corresponding to the variables described with the equation.

In step (DW-2) we calculate the variable "d". In steps (DW-3x) we calculate the variable "m" - based on definitions we did earlier. Based exactly on the same definitions we calculate variables "y" and "c" in steps (DW-4x) and (DW-5x).

Then we start with the formula calculation. First, we calculate a partial result for our formula. In step (DW-C1) we replace first part-calculation with the help-variable called cd_help1 (part highlighted in green):

w = (d + (2,6 x m - 0,2) + y + (y / 4) + (c / 4) - 2 x c) mod 7
cd_help1 = 2,6 x m - 0,2

After this calculation we can say:

w = (d + cd_help1 + y + (y / 4) + (c / 4) - 2 x c) mod 7

In step (DW-C2) we calculate the next small part and store the partial result to variable cd_help2 (in red):

w = (d + cd_help1 + y + (y / 4) + (c / 4) - 2 x c) mod 7
cd_help2 = y / 4

After this step we can simplify the equation a little more:

w = (d + cd_help1 + y + cd_help2 + (c / 4) - 2 x c) mod 7

The last partial result will be stored in variable cd_help3 (in black) - step (DW-C3):

cd_help3 = y / 4

And after last simplification, our formula looks like this:

w = (d + cd_help1 + y + cd_help2 + cd_help3 - 2 x c) mod 7

This formula is then calculated in steps (DW-C4x).

We are done. The day of the week is obtained. In the last step (DW-C5) we put the calculated value to the final destination - variable rtc_wday.

5.5.8 • AT30TSE754

In this chapter, we will look at the function i2c_temp_1(). This takes care of the AT30TSE754-screen of our application. Just to refresh our memory, the main temperature sensor screen looks like this:

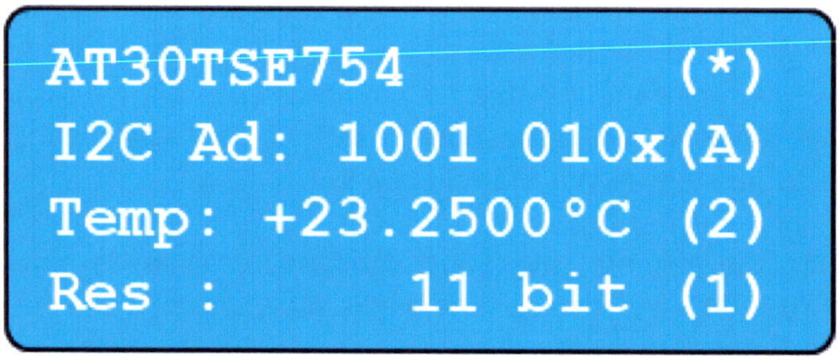

We can leave (by pressing "star"), change the I²C address of the sensor to be used manually (by pressing "A"), switch between 2 or 4 decimal places shown (by pressing "2"), and change the resolution: 9 to 12 bits - by pressing "1".

This piece of firmware can be seen here:

```
// ---------------------------------------------------------------------
// ---------------------------------------------------------------------
// ---- I2C Temperature meassurement / AT30TSE754
// ---------------------------------------------------------------------
// ---------------------------------------------------------------------
void i2c_temp_1()
{
   gv_format = 0;

   lcd.clear();
   lcd.setCursor(0,0);
   lcd.print("AT30TSE754        (*)");
   lcd.setCursor(0,1);
   lcd.print("I2C Ad:           (A)");
   lcd.setCursor(0,2);
   lcd.print("Temp:             (2)");
   lcd.setCursor(0,3);
   lcd.print("Res :         bit (1)");

   while(active_key != 0xFF) read_kbd();
   while(active_key != 0x0E)
   {
      Wire.beginTransmission(i2c_add);
      Wire.write(0x00);
      i2c_answer = Wire.endTransmission(1);
      if (i2c_answer == 0)
      {
        lcd.setCursor(0,2);
        lcd.print("Temp: ");
        lcd.setCursor(17,2);
        lcd.print("(2)");
        lcd.setCursor(0,3);
        lcd.print("Res :     ");
        lcd.setCursor(13,3);
        lcd.print("bit (1)");
        Wire.requestFrom(i2c_add, 2, 1);    //I2C address / 2 bytes // stop
        v_temp_msb = 0xFF;
        v_temp_lsb = 0xFF;
        v_temp_msb =  Wire.read();
        v_temp_lsb =  Wire.read();
        w_temp_ub(6,2,0);
//      ---------------------------------------------------------------
//      --- configuration register: resolution -------------------------
//      ---------------------------------------------------------------
        read_t_config_reg();
        if (active_key == 0x01)
```

```
        {
          t_change_res();
          read_t_config_reg();
          while(active_key != 0xFF) read_kbd();
        }
        lcd.setCursor(10,3);
        temp_res = temp_res + 9;
        w_print_dec1_nlz(temp_res);
      }
      else
      {
        lcd.setCursor(0,2);
        lcd.print("No response          ");
        lcd.setCursor(0,3);
        lcd.print("from Sensor          ");
      }
      w_i2c_add(8,1);
//    -----------------------------------------------------------------
//    --- read the keypad --------------------------------------------
//    -----------------------------------------------------------------
      read_kbd();
      delay(200);
//    -----------------------------------------------------------------
//    --- change used I2C address ------------------------------------
//    -----------------------------------------------------------------
      if (active_key == 0x0A)
      {
        i2c_t_change_add();
        while(active_key != 0xFF) read_kbd();
      }
//    -----------------------------------------------------------------
//    --- 2 / 4 decimal places ---------------------------------------
//    -----------------------------------------------------------------
      if (active_key == 0x02)
      {
        gv_format++;
        if (gv_format == 2) gv_format = 0;
        while(active_key != 0xFF) read_kbd();
      }
    }
    gv_refresh = 1;
}
// ------------------------------------------------------------------
```

As this is a pure LCD-focus function, and we have already seen them before, we can skip a detailed description here.

5.5.8.1 • Changing the I²C address of the temperature sensor

What is interesting is the option to adjust the I²C address for communication with this temperature sensor. As we know, the AT30TSE754 can be accessed through 8 different I²C addresses. In the firmware, the current address is kept in variable i2c_add. When we want to change the address manually from the menu, we can call the following function:

```
// ----------------------------------------------------------------------
// ----------------------------------------------------------------------
// --- Change the last 3 bits of used I2C address for temp sensors ----
// ----------------------------------------------------------------------
// ----------------------------------------------------------------------
void i2c_t_change_add(void)
{
  i2c_add++;                                        //(CA-1)
  if (bitRead(i2c_add,3) == 0) i2c_add = 0b01001000;    //(CA-2) 111->000
}
// ----------------------------------------------------------------------
// ----------------------------------------------------------------------
```

We just increase the content of the variable i2c_add (CA-1), and once we reach an "address overflow", put the address to the lowest possible (CA-2).

5.5.8.2 • Search I²C temperature sensor

The firmware can find a connected I²C temperature sensor automatically by looking up the I²C addresses from 1001 000x to 1001 111x.

In the software we just try to "ping" a sensor on a specific address. If there is no reaction, we increment the address and try again by looking up all 8 available addresses starting from 1001 000x. If we have more than one sensor connected the "lowest" address will be the winner.

Function find_i2c_temp() executes the search:

```
// -----------------------------------------------------------------
void find_i2c_temp()
{
   i2c_add = 0b01001000;                     //(ST-1) we start with lowest i2c address

   while(1)                                  //(ST-2) end-less loop starts here
   {
      Wire.beginTransmission(i2c_add);       //(ST-3) ping the sensor
      Wire.write(0x00);                      //(ST-4) write dummy value
      i2c_answer = Wire.endTransmission(1);  //(ST-5) get tge result of our ping
      if (i2c_answer == 0) return;           //(ST-6) leave, if there was an answer
```

```
        i2c_add++;                                  //(ST-7) increment i2c address
        if (bitRead(i2c_add,3) == 0)                //(ST-8) address overflow?
        {
          i2c_add = 0b01001000;                     //(ST-9) re-set i2c address to the lowest
          return;                                   //(ST-10) leave the search, nothig found
        }
    }
}
// -------------------------------------------------------------------
// -------------------------------------------------------------------
```

We will start with the address 1001 000x (in "Arduino-Language" it's 01001000b). The initialisation of the I²C address is performed in step (ST-1). The search itself is made in a kind of endless loop (ST-2). "Kind of" because the en-less loop ends, once there's an answer from a sensor, or we looked up all available addresses.To see if there is a device on the tested I²C address, we can execute a "dummy communication" by opening the I²C connection on the current address (ST-3) and sending byte 00h to the device through this address (ST-4). We then close the communication and receive the result (ST-5).

If the result is 00h -, it means ACK is on the bus for address and our 00h send which means there is a device on this address willing to communicate with us. Therefore we just leave the function (ST-6) and the successfully tested address stays in variable i2c_add.

If the communication was unsuccessful, we increment the I²C address (ST-7) and check that all 8 possibilities have been tried(ST-8). If there was no sensor found on the bus, reset the I²C address to the default (the lowest one) (ST-9) and leave the function (ST-10).

The function itself does not provide any information about the fruitfulness of the search - The firmware does not use this information.

Our "dummy communication" just writes the value 00h to the Pointer Register, setting the pointer to the temperature register (the default value of the pointer after power-up).

5.5.8.3 • Configuration register of the I²C temperature sensor

The last piece of functionality we will look at in the context of the AT30TSE754 is the communication with the configuration register of the sensor.

Function read_t_config_reg() will fetch the current configuration of the sensor. This is used for example to display the corresponding screen configuration on LCD.

```
// -------------------------------------------------------------------
// -------------------------------------------------------------------
// AT30TSE754 - read configuration register
// -------------------------------------------------------------------
// -------------------------------------------------------------------
void read_t_config_reg()
{
  Wire.beginTransmission(i2c_add);    //(TCR-1) open i2c communication
  Wire.write(0x01);                   //(TCR-2) set pointer to the config.reg.
  Wire.endTransmission(1);            //(TCR-3) finish i2c comm.
  Wire.requestFrom(i2c_add, 1, 1);    //(TCR-4) open i2c for read: I2C address / 1 byte // stop
  v_config_msb = Wire.read();         //(TCR-5) read config.reg.
// -------------------------------------------------------------------
  //(TCR-6) "calculate" the resolution based on info from config.reg.:
  temp_res = 2 * bitRead(v_config_msb,6) + bitRead(v_config_msb,5);
}
// -------------------------------------------------------------------
// -------------------------------------------------------------------
```

When we want to read the configuration register, we have to first set the point register to the address of the configuration register (this is 01h). This happens in steps (TCR-1) to (TCR-3), where we write the 01h to the sensor.

(TCR-4) then opens the I²C communication again, but this time for reading, and indicating that we intend to read one byte and close the communication once the byte has been received. At this moment everything is prepared, and we can fetch the configuration byte (TCR-5).

It is important to mention that the configuration register contains 2 bytes. We are only interested in MSB (the upper byte) which is sent first. Therefore it is enough to read only one byte and cut the communication after this byte has been received.

In the last command of the function we "calculate" the resolution for internal use in the firmware based on bits 14 and 13 of the configuration register. This corresponds to bits 6 and 5 of the MSB of the register. The resolution is defined like this:

Bits 14:13 MSB bits 6:5	**Resolution**
00	9-bits (default after power-up)
01	10-bits
10	11-bits
11	12-bits

Let's take a look at the communication the other way around using an example of function t_change_res(). This changes the measurement resolution and will update the configuration register.

```
// --------------------------------------------------------------------
// --------------------------------------------------------------------
// AT30TSE754 - update configuration register
// --------------------------------------------------------------------
// --------------------------------------------------------------------
void t_change_res()
{
  temp_res++;                            //(TCU-1) increase the resolution
  if (temp_res > 3) temp_res = 0x00;     //(TCU-2) overflow - set back to 00
  v_config_msb = temp_res * 32;          //(TCU-3) calculate the new value for config. reg.
                                         //        all other config bits are eq zero
  Wire.beginTransmission(i2c_add);       //(TCU-4) open i2c comm.
  Wire.write(0x01);                      //(TCU-5) send 01h - the address of config.reg.
  Wire.write(v_config_msb);              //(TCU-6) send the configuration byte
  Wire.endTransmission(1);               //(TCU-7) finish i2c communication
}
// --------------------------------------------------------------------
```

The first 3 steps are just about increasing - let's say improving the "handling" of the measurement resolution. Every call will sort of rotate the resolution like this: 9 -> 10 -> 11 ->12 -> 9 -> 10 -> ...

Step (TCU-4) starts the I^2C communication with the temperature sensor. In step (TCU-5) we are sending the chip address of the configuration register, followed by the new configuration (TCU-6). The last step of the function is finishing I^2C communication. Now the new configuration word has been stored in the temperature sensor chip.

5.5.9 • HYT939

It is time to continue with the next sensor, the HYT939. It is a humidity and temperature sensor. The functionality of the temperature measurement is used as a "fall-back" by the application in case there is no AT30TSE754 connected.

There are two important parts of the communication with the sensor - a triggering of the measurement and retrieval of results.

The first function will trigger the measurement itself and is called hyt939_start():

```
// ----------------------------------------------------------------------
// ----------------------------------------------------------------------
byte hyt939_start()
{
   Wire.beginTransmission(0b00101000);     //(H1-1) I2C Address = 0101 000x = 50h
   return(Wire.endTransmission(1));        //(H1-2)
}
// ----------------------------------------------------------------------
// ----------------------------------------------------------------------
```

The trigger is a very simple piece of code. We just need to start I²C communication in write mode (H1-1) and then stop the communication without sending any data (H1-2). This is the trigger to initiate measurement of humidity and temperature.

The next important section is the retrieval of measurement results. This is in firmware commonly implemented with the calculation of humidity and temperature based on retrieved data.

```
// ----------------------------------------------------------------------
// ----------------------------------------------------------------------
void hyt939_read()
{
// ---------------------------------------------------------------------
// -- Read the Humidity and the Temperature -------------------------
// ---------------------------------------------------------------------
   Wire.requestFrom(0b00101000, 4, 1);    //(H2-1) I2C address / 4 bytes // stop
   v_h939_cap_msb =  Wire.read();         //(H2-2) read humidity / MSB
   v_h939_cap_lsb =  Wire.read();         //(H2-3) read humidity / LSB
   v_h939_t_msb =  Wire.read();           //(H2-4) read temperature / MSB
   v_h939_t_lsb =  Wire.read();           //(H2-5) read temperature / LSB
// ---------------------------------------------------------------------
// -- Calculate the Humidity -----------------------------------------
// ---------------------------------------------------------------------
   v_h939_cap_msb = v_h939_cap_msb & 0b00111111;
   v_h939_c_raw = v_h939_cap_msb * 256 + v_h939_cap_lsb;

   h939_rf = (float)((float)v_h939_c_raw / 16383 ) * 100;
   h939_rf_new = (float)h939_rf * 10;

   if(h939_rf_new != h939_rf_old) lv_c2++;
   else lv_c2 = 0;
   if(lv_c2 == 3)
   {
      h939_rf_result = h939_rf;
      h939_rf_old = h939_rf_new;
      lv_c2 = 0;
```

```
    }
    if (h939_rf_result == 0)
    {
      h939_rf_result = h939_rf;
      h939_rf_old = (float)h939_rf * 10;
    }
// -----------------------------------------------------------------
// -- Calculate the Temperature ------------------------------------
// -----------------------------------------------------------------
    v_h939_t_lsb = v_h939_t_lsb & 0b11111100;
    v_h939_t_raw = (v_h939_t_msb * 64) + (v_h939_t_lsb / 4);

    h939_temp_long = 165 * (long)v_h939_t_raw;

    h939_temp = (float)((float)h939_temp_long/16383) - 40;
    h939_t_new = (float)h939_temp * 10;
    if(h939_t_new != h939_t_old) lv_c3++;
    else lv_c3 = 0;
    if(lv_c3 == 3)
    {
       h939_temp_result = h939_temp;
       h939_t_old = h939_t_new;
       lv_c3 = 0;
    }
    if (h939_temp_result == 0)
    {
      h939_temp_result = h939_temp;
      h939_t_old = (float)h939_temp * 10;
    }
}
// -----------------------------------------------------------------
// -----------------------------------------------------------------
```

As we can see in the first part of the function, we start I²C communication with the chip in read mode (H2-1) and then consequently read 4 bytes. That's it. The first byte obtained (H2-2) is the MSB byte of the measured humidity. The next byte (H2-3) is the LSB byte of the 16-bit humidity register, and this is followed by MSB(H2-4) and finally LSB of the temperature register (H2-5). With this step, the communication itself is finished and in the following two blocks we calculate, based on information shown earlier, the relative humidity and temperature.

As we can see, in the calculation is an "anti-flashing effect" is included. This means, we first accept the measurement when the result is the same three times in a row. The reason is to stabilise the information provided on the LCD. It will happen quite often, that the two following measurements will differ "a bit", and if we immediately show the current result, the display may become "jumpy".

5.5.10 • Keyboard

As we know, the keyboard is driven by a PCF8574A chip. The whole communication with the microcontroller is therefore done by the I²C bus. The matrix-connected keyboard is processed by the GPIO chip, where 4 ports are used as outputs to the matrix and the other 4 ports as inputs from the matrix.

The whole, let's call it "keyboard driver" can be grouped into three parts:

1. I²C communication with host.
2. The Main driver examining the pressed / idle keys.
3. The special part of the driver for RTC set-up allows retrieval of 2-digit numbers from the keyboard.

I will skip the "special part" (point #3) from the description - it doesn't make sense and is just a piece of code... It can however be found in the coding for download.

We can now start with I²C communication - this is probably the easiest part of the keyboard driver routines.

5.5.10.1 • I²C communication routine

We only have one communication routine which takes care of writing to and reading from the PCF8574A. As you remember, we are using a matrix keyboard with 4 rows and 4 columns. Columns are used as "input" to the keyboard matrix and are connected to ports P4 - P7. Rows are used as "outputs" from the keyboard and are connected to P0 - P3. Therefore we need to be able to send some data to the PCF8574A chip and also read some data.

Our routine is called get_col() and can read which button is pressed in a specific column.

```
// -----------------------------------------------------------------
// -----------------------------------------------------------------
byte get_col(byte in_col)                    //(K-1) get active button in a column
{
   Wire.beginTransmission(0b00111111);       //(K-2) start write to PCF8574AN -> 0111 111x
   Wire.write(in_col);                       //(K-3) write required byte
   Wire.endTransmission(1);                  //(K-4) finish write phase
   Wire.requestFrom(0b00111111, 1, 1);       //(K-5) request 1 byte: I2C address / 1 byte
// stop
   return(Wire.read());                      //(K-6) get the requested byte
}
// -----------------------------------------------------------------
// -----------------------------------------------------------------
```

We can see that there is only one import variable: in_col. Here we put the code of the column we want to test.

Steps (K-2) to (K-4) will write the requested byte to the PCF8574A (by our hardware used I²C address is - let's say - the highest one for this kind of chips: 0111 111xb). We always write a logical one to the P0 - P3, which are used as inputs.

In steps (K-5) and (K-6) we receive the value from the GPIO.

For example - if we want to read the first column (containing buttons 1, 4, 7, and *) we will send to GPIO this byte: 0111 1111b. With this byte, we will put P7 to zero and then test if the zero is on some of the "outputs" P0 - P3.

For example, if "1" is pressed, the situation can be described with the following picture:

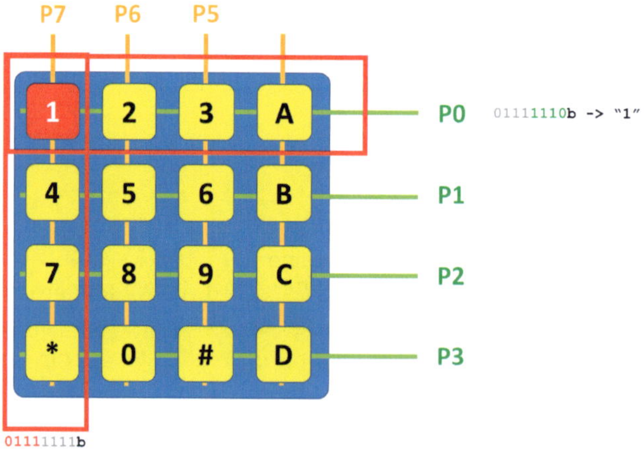

We will send out the byte 0111 1111b (below the picture) and we will read back the byte 0111 1110b (on the right side). The zero from P7 is "taken over" to P0 by pressing the "1".

If nothing has been pressed, P0 - P3 will be inactive (logical one) and we will read back the same byte we sent: 0111 1111b.

In case button 4 has been pressed, it will look like this:

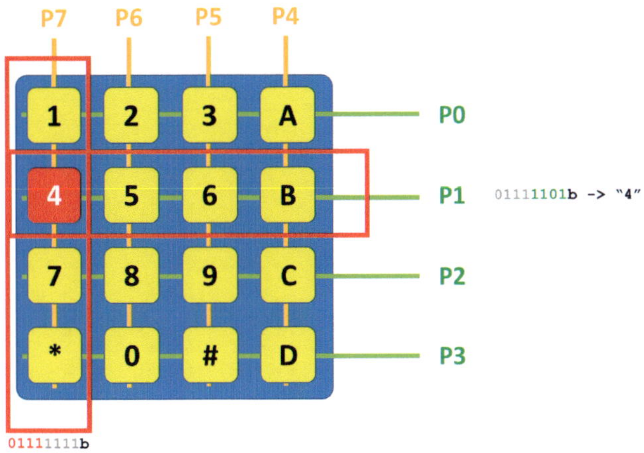

This means the logical zero from P7 is "taken over" to P1 by button "4" - we will read back 0111 1101b.

And so on. If a button outside the column tested is pressed, we will not find it out in this column test.

If for example button "9" has been pressed, it will be found out during the test of column P5:

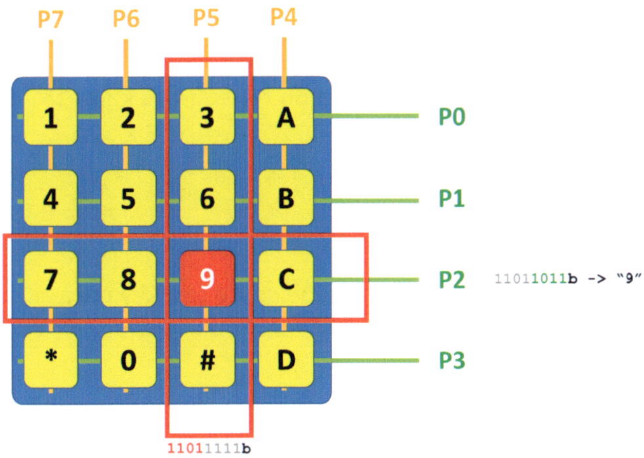

In this situation column "P5" is being tested by sending out: 1101 1111b. If button "9" is pressed, the zero from P5 will be "taken over" to P2 and will read: 1101 1011b.

And so on...

If we press two buttons in the same column, say 9 and 3 - we will jump to the following situation:

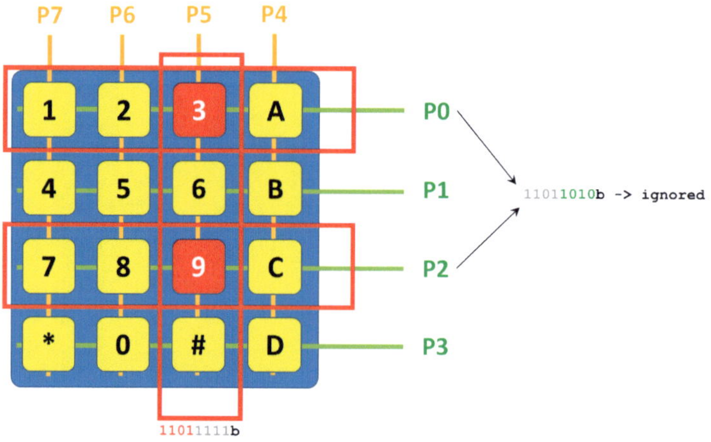

There will be more than one zero in the output: 1101 1010b, meaning, buttons on P0 and P2 are pushed.

Current firmware does not support simultaneous active buttons.

5.5.10.2 • Main keyboard driver

In the meantime, we know the logic behind the keyboard driver and therefore can walk through the code quite easily. The main function to read the keyboard is read_kbd() and sets two global variables:

- active_key
- act_key_ascii

Variable active_key is just the assignment of a hex code to a key pressed. act_key_ascii will contain the ASCII code of the pressed key - based on the labels on the keys.

We can summarise the assignment of these two codes in the following table:

key label	column	row	active_key	act_key_ ascii	character
0	P6	P3	00h	48d = 30h	0
1	P7	P0	01h	49d = 31h	1
2	P6	P0	02h	50d = 32h	2
3	P5	P0	03h	51d = 33h	3
4	P7	P1	04h	52d = 34h	4
5	P6	P1	05h	53d = 35h	5
6	P5	P1	06h	54d = 36h	6
7	P7	P2	07h	55d = 37h	7
8	P6	P2	08h	56d = 38h	8
9	P5	P2	09h	57d = 39h	9
A	P4	P0	0Ah	54d = 41h	A
B	P4	P1	0Bh	55d = 42h	B
C	P4	P2	0Ch	56d = 43h	C
D	P4	P3	0Dh	57d = 44h	D
*	P7	P3	0Eh	42d = 2Ah	*
#	P5	P3	0Fh	35d = 23h	#
Nothing active	--	--	FFh	FFh	n/a

We can see the corresponding function here:

```
// ---------------------------------------------------------------------
void read_kbd()
{
//Part A - read the keyboard
   active_key = 0xFF;                    //default - no key is active
   in_kbd_7 = get_col(0b01111111);
   pcf8574_send(in_kbd_7);
   in_kbd_6 = get_col(0b10111111);
   pcf8574_send(in_kbd_6);
   in_kbd_5 = get_col(0b11011111);
   pcf8574_send(in_kbd_5);
   in_kbd_4 = get_col(0b11101111);
   pcf8574_send(in_kbd_4);
   get_col(0b11111111);
   pcf8574_send(0xFF);
```

```
//Part B - analyze
   switch(in_kbd_7)
     {
      case 0b01111110:
         active_key = 0x01;          //key 1
         break;
      case 0b01111101:
         active_key = 0x04;          //key 4
         break;
      case 0b01111011:
         active_key = 0x07;          //key 7
         break;
      case 0b01110111:
         active_key = 0x0E;          //key *
         break;
     }

   switch(in_kbd_6)
     {
      case 0b10111110:
         active_key = 0x02;          //key 2
         break;
      case 0b10111101:
         active_key = 0x05;          //key 5
         break;
      case 0b10111011:
         active_key = 0x08;          //key 8
         break;
      case 0b10110111:
         active_key = 0x00;          //key 0
         break;
     }

   switch(in_kbd_5)
     {
      case 0b11011110:
         active_key = 0x03;          //key 3
         break;
      case 0b11011101:
         active_key = 0x06;          //key 6
         break;
      case 0b11011011:
         active_key = 0x09;          //key 9
         break;
      case 0b11010111:
         active_key = 0x0F;          //key #
```

```
            break;
        }

    switch(in_kbd_4)
        {
         case 0b11101110:
            active_key = 0x0A;          //key A
            break;
         case 0b11101101:
            active_key = 0x0B;          //key B
            break;
         case 0b11101011:
            active_key = 0x0C;          //key C
            break;
         case 0b11100111:
            active_key = 0x0D;          //key D
            break;
        }

//Part C - calculate ASCII code
    act_key_ascii = 0xFF;
    if (active_key != 0xFF)
        {
         act_key_ascii = active_key + 48;
         if (active_key > 0x09) act_key_ascii = active_key + 55;
        }
    if (act_key_ascii == 'E') act_key_ascii = '*';
    if (act_key_ascii == 'F') act_key_ascii = '#';
}
// ------------------------------------------------------------------
// ------------------------------------------------------------------
```

Very briefly, in Part A, single columns are the results stored to help variables in_kbd_7 (for column P7) to in_kbd_4 (for column P4).

In Part B we analyse the information captured in Part A and set up the result in the variable active_key.

Part C calculates the ASCII value of the button pressed in case there is a recognised active button.

And that's it. I hope you enjoyed the book and can find some help and inspiration through it.

Thank you.
Miroslav Cina

• Index